Let
Their
Voices Be Heard

*Quotations from life stories related to physical
activity, food and eating, and body image*

Betty Holmes
Suzanne Pelican
Fred Vanden Heede

Let Their Voices Be Heard

Betty Holmes, MS, RD

Suzanne Pelican, MS, RD

Fred Vanden Heede, MA

Copyright © 2005 by

Discovery Association Publishing House

Library of Congress Control Number 2005925219

Holmes, Betty; Pelican, Suzanne; Vanden Heede, Fred

Let Their Voices Be Heard / Betty Holmes, Suzanne Pelican, Fred Vanden Heede.

p. cm.

Includes index.

ISBN 1-931967-07-5

1. Agriculture and Food Systems. 2. Food and Eating. 3. Body Image.
4. Nutrition Education. 5. Physical Activity. 6. Holmes, Betty. Pelican, Suzanne. Vanden Heede, Fred.

Acknowledgements

We gratefully acknowledge the many contributions of our narrative team members: Linda Melcher, Martha Raidl, Mary Kay Wardlaw, and Barbara Wheeler helped collect and interpret interviewees' life stories; Julie Harker, Shelley Hill, and Barbara Wheeler arranged for the individual interviews and focus groups; graduate students Frank Blakely helped collect life stories and Marc Schure carried on with interpretation after Frank completed his degree; and Kim Puls transcribed most of the audiotapes and coordinated the overall transcription process. We offer special thanks to Sylvia Moore for her staunch support of this aspect of the WIN the Rockies project. We extend sincerest thanks to David Buchanan and Sandra Shepherd for their tireless encouragement and insightful guidance with all aspects of this project. Keith Armstrong has provided invaluable advice and support in relation to editing and publication. We would also like to thank Carolyn Law for her dedication and expertise with editing and developing the index for the book. And all of us involved in this project are deeply indebted to the study participants who shared so much of themselves and their lives with the hope of helping others.

Funding for WIN the Rockies is from the U.S. Department of Agriculture's Initiative for Future Agriculture and Food Systems (IFAFS) Competitive Grants Program, award #0004499.

"I think life is beautiful . . . but it is not that simple . . . . We all have to weave our own way and . . . find how to be comfortable with ourselves and others."

Female, early 60's

"I feel that the body is an intricate system and something that no human being understands completely. So, it's really quite a marvel."

Male in his 50's

"If you don't keep your body healthy, you're not going to live long, and if you want to enjoy life and live life and feel good about yourself . . . , your healthy habits are going to carry on longer than anything else."

Male in his 40's

Table of Contents

Chapter One - Physical Activity   1

Table of Contents

Physical Activity (continued)

Individual Traits and Experiences Associated with Physical Activity

Other Factors Related to a Person's Physical Activity Level or Abilities

---

Summary quotation on physical activity

"As we get older, the importance of trying to maintain . . . physical conditioning is probably a basic health insurance." *Male in his 30's*

Table of Contents

Table of Contents

Food and Eating (continued)

Summary quotations on food and eating

What is the first thing that comes to mind when you think about food and eating?

"Always joy."   *Male in his 70's*

"Enjoyment."   *Female in her 60's*

"I think food is just a whole lot of guilt."   *Female, early 40's*

Table of Contents

Chapter Three - Body Image   145

Table of Contents

Body Image (continued)

Summary quotation on body image

"The general lifestyle which we grew up in taught us to take care of our bodies and to have respect for them . . . , to think of our bodies as a precious commodity."

Male in his 50's

Table of Contents

Chapter Four - Connections
Physical Activity ✳ Food and Eating ✳ Body Image   **221**

Connections

Summary quotation on connections

"You can eat almost any food as long as you learn how to eat the right quantities of food . . . and get some physical activity with it. . . . And as long as you're healthy, it really doesn't matter . . . how other people think of you. It's a matter of how you feel about yourself." *Male in his 30's*

Foreword

Opening doors. *Let Their Voices Be Heard* opens doors, as the editors say, letting in breaths of fresh air and shining shafts of bright light on the joys and worries of being human. It invites the reader into the thoughts of these generous souls who have shared a vital part of their lives with us—how they understand the role of diet, physical activity, and body image in life's journey. It presents deeply personal reflections on the relationship between one's sense of identity and one's flesh-and-blood physical presence. The participants share their inner thoughts, sometimes bemused, sometimes bewildered, on the apparently fickle bond between mind and body, between brute corporal appetites and profound longings to be the more ideal person of one's dreams and aspirations. They offer observations on the tensions between how one sees oneself and how others see us and on living with external and internalized norms of behavior and appearance, how we should eat, how we should look, and how we should spend our time.

The community members who have been interviewed here tell us their stories, stories of tragedy and triumphs, sometimes great, sometimes small. Their stories dramatically illustrate the human need to interpret and incorporate the twists and turns of life's fortunes into a personal history, a personal narrative with a past, present, and future. Unlike academic theories about the causes of obesity concocted in the modern social sciences, the narrative form is essential for making moral sense of our actions, conveying the traits of character involved (courageous, cowardly, generous, honest), and putting events into a context that displays an underlying thematic unity that we call a meaningful life. They vividly demonstrate how we must work to make sense of the relationship between the events that befall us and the choices that we have made over time, realizing their emotional significance and appreciating the full range of motivations that move us in certain directions. Their stories show how the meanings that we attach to events can lead to growth and change, especially to changes in the way that we feel about ourselves, feelings that often become physically apparent. As these stories so richly relate, our lives gain continuity, coherence, and integrity by actively weaving the threads together into a sense of who we are, who we have become, and who we might still want to be.

The stories of the WIN the Rockies participants are told against a backdrop of human values, sometimes clear and transparent, more often implicit and only dimly perceived. These values connect our daily joys and struggles to the larger meanings that make it possible for us to keep plugging away and doing the best we can day after day. In revealing the connection between everyday decisions and enduring human values, *Let Their Voices Be Heard* deepens our understanding of what it is to live a human life. We hear ourselves in these voices, we see our own yearnings in a new light, we gain a deeper appreciation of the different ways that others cope and find happiness.

How are we to make sense of the pursuit and preservation of personal health? Is being healthy our highest priority and chief source of happiness, as many public polls have found? How does it fit with our other projects, plans, and interests? *Let Their Voices Be Heard* draws us into the conversation. We can agree, we can argue with the respondents, we can ask our spouse, our friends, and family members what they think: 'Is that your experience?' 'Is that what it is like for you?' As many of the participants here suggest, perhaps good health is not the most important goal in life, but simply a vehicle, neither necessary nor sufficient, which can either help or hinder us in realizing the things that really matter to us, things such as feeling a sense of accomplishment, having deep intimate interpersonal relationships, and experiencing a sense of enjoyment from life. This is a book of daily meditations. We can pick it up, turn to any page, and mull over a few passages until something strikes us. The words spark an insight, triggering thoughts for further contemplation, 'Is that the way I feel? I have never thought about it this way before, but wow, now it seems so obvious.' In seeing how others have wrestled with the issue, I can understand my experience more fully, less blindly, perhaps by picturing more clearly how I think about these things in a slightly different way. *Let Their Voices Be Heard* makes us more self-aware and lets us find a way forward through the experiences of others.

We now seem to be in the midst of an "epidemic" of obesity that is as troubling as it is difficult to comprehend. It is one price we pay for living in such a highly individualistic culture that it is almost impossible to escape the finger pointing and pangs of self-doubt: "Am I to blame?" "It is my fault, isn't it?" "Why am I so weak?" (or "Why can't that fatso just shut his mouth and show some self-respect?"). One of the great contributions of *Let Their Voices Be Heard* is that it allows us to see that we are not alone, and if many people are struggling with the same problem, then perhaps there is something more to the picture than the sum of individual failings.

The sociologist C. Wright Mills once wrote that the goal of research is to illuminate and thereby transform "personal troubles" into the "public issues" of the day. There can be little question that the food industry's marketing departments have learned how to cleverly exploit deeply embedded cultural values and turn them on their head. It was a psychologist working for McDonald's who found that consumers thought that buying two servings was excessive and immoderate, but if the same amount of food was repackaged as a single serving, then people could be lulled into believing that they were being prudent as well as getting a better buy for their money. And so, as food prices have dropped over the last 30 years, portion sizes and the calories they contain have grown. Yet, as *Let Their Voices Be Heard* shows so clearly, we still tell ourselves that we should clean our plate, as it would be a shame to let good food go to waste. We do value being productive and not being wasteful; the WIN the Rockies participants help us to reconsider how not eating everything or spending time exercising (instead of doing something useful) can be consistent with the values we truly cherish. In making these personal reflections public knowledge, this book provides an opportunity for thinking beyond individual responses and blaming oneself to consider the cultural milieu that fosters unhealthy behaviors. In so doing, it asks us to contemplate what we can do to contribute to making this a more humane and decent world.

Let Their Voices Be Heard also eloquently demonstrates the power of others on our feelings and behaviors, documenting childhood memories that still resonate decades later. It reminds us how we can be both so cruel to one another – with rude stares and careless comments – and so incredibly supportive and caring. It portrays the many ways that we may find our own happiness bound up with the happiness and well-being of others, and the sacrifices so many people make to care for their family, friends, and neighbors.

Finally, in giving voice to real community members, this book celebrates individual differences and makes clear that there are no cookie-cutter recipes for finding the way, and the time and the energy, to take care of our bodies. It presents many, many strategies—a wealth of ideas and ways of thinking about health, diet, feelings of self-worth, activities, and zest for life—and invites us to go through the doors of our own choosing. *Let Their Voices Be Heard* never glosses over the contradictions and complexities of trying to live a human life; the people are portrayed as they are, in all of their paradoxical glory, no simplified stereotypes to better living. Their voices ring true.

It was a pleasure to hear the voices of these good people. I feel like I have made some new friends. Take a look. You may find yourself here too.

David R. Buchanan
University of Massachusetts, Amherst
September 2004

Introduction

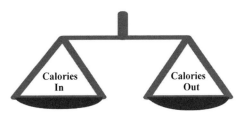

While the chemistry and physics of the above relationship are simple and straightforward, the "hows" and "whys" of body weight balance encompass an array of factors: availability of food choices, cultural and familial traditions and influences, emotions and moods, family and other demands and stresses, feelings of self-worth and competence (or lack thereof), financial resources, gender, genetics, health status, neighborhood safety, opportunities to be physically active, personal preferences, physical abilities, societal pressures, and values, to name just a few. This book reflects the complexities and interactions of these factors in the life experiences of everyday people.

How this collection of quotations came about

A network called WIN Wyoming. In 1998, recognizing the complicated nature of body weight issues in contemporary society, a group of educators and health professionals at the University of Wyoming and throughout the state convened and formed a network dedicated to a health-focused rather than a weight-focused approach to well-being. Two aspects of this multidisciplinary network called Wellness IN Wyoming (WIN Wyoming) distinguish it from other health promotion efforts. First, it has championed the concept that to be beneficial, lifestyles must be enjoyable as well as healthful. That is because in the long term, most people will not stick with health-promoting habits they don't enjoy. In contrast, optimal well-being requires long-term – ideally lifelong – healthy lifestyles. Second, since its inception, WIN Wyoming has embraced the idea that helping people achieve a healthy lifestyle and its many benefits, including healthy weight, requires attention to physical activity, food and eating, and body image. Although physical activity and food and eating are universally accepted as cornerstones of weight-related health programs, considerable controversy surrounds the issue of whether body image needs to be included as an essential dimension in these efforts, and if so, how that should be done. At the same time, research demonstrates that how people feel about their bodies can profoundly influence their eating and their level of physical activity.

The importance of body image. Many people are consumed with negative thoughts about their bodies, and, interestingly, the level of their dissatisfaction often has little to do with their actual size or shape. For example, several individuals who are quoted in this book told us they have always been dissatisfied with their bodies, but they also said that when they looked at pictures of themselves at a younger age, they were amazed by how thin they were, or how muscular they were, or how great they looked. Nevertheless, without exception, these individuals told us that at the time, they were completely dissatisfied with their bodies. One woman said, "I think I've always seen myself as obese. I look back, and I see my pictures and I think, 'Wow, I was so thin!' But if I think about what I thought at the time, I thought I was fat." We wonder what amazing accomplishments could be achieved by individuals if the time and energy devoted to "body bashing" were spent differently – say, on living a healthier life, or even more basically, on efforts to become a better parent, sibling, son or daughter, friend, or just a more decent human being.

A project called WIN the Rockies. WIN Wyoming, now a network of over 100 individuals representing approximately 60 agencies and organizations in 17 states and Australia, was the genesis for Wellness IN the Rockies (WIN the Rockies), a three-state community-based research, intervention, and outreach project in Wyoming, Montana, and Idaho. The project's mission has been to assist communities in educating people to value health, respect body size differences, enjoy the benefits of self-acceptance, enjoy physically active living, and enjoy healthful and pleasurable eating. Funded by the U.S. Department of Agriculture, WIN the Rockies has conducted research and carried out intervention programs in six communities, two in each state: Preston and American Falls, Idaho; Lewistown and Miles City, Montana; and Powell and Torrington, Wyoming.

A key research component of WIN the Rockies has been the collection of life stories (or narratives) from adults in three of the project's communities where WIN the Rockies programs were first introduced (Preston, Idaho; Lewistown, Montana; and Powell, Wyoming). Our team's overall purpose in gathering these life stories was to elicit individuals' experiences related to physical activity, food and eating, and body image to illustrate the challenges they have faced, the successes they have achieved, and the insights they have gained. (We were not disappointed!) Our goal has been for these narratives to inform and guide educational efforts to help make such efforts more meaningful and relevant. We want these narratives and the challenges, successes, and insights they reflect to help other people make lasting changes to improve their own health as well as the health of their families, their communities, and the nation as a whole.

Gathering the life stories
A group of ten WIN the Rockies team members helped collect these life stories via individual interviews and focus groups. With guidance from two qualitative research consultants, we led this research team in developing a series of questions and procedures that we used in practice sessions. We then revised the questions and procedures accordingly. Our philosophy was one of trying to "open doors" through which interviewees could choose to enter (or not) in order to share relevant life experiences and perspectives. Interviewees were recruited using a variety of methods, including newspaper and radio announcements,

promotion through community-based groups and classes, and referrals from other individuals and through other community networks. Ultimately, life stories in the areas of physical activity, food and eating, and body image were gathered from 103 adults—57 women and 46 men.

The individuals who shared life stories represented a broad spectrum. The youngest was 17 years old and the oldest was 87. They ranged in height and body size from very short to very tall and from slender to very large. To give some idea of the variation among these individuals' stories, there was . . . a man whose failures in physical education as a youth negatively shaped his lifelong activity attitudes and behaviors. . . a woman whose supportive coach helped her at an early age develop a love for being active . . . a middle-aged man who enjoyed trying different cuisines . . . a grandmother who would rather play with her grandkids than eat . . . a man who loathed fat people . . . and a young mother who wanted her daughter to accept children with different body sizes and shapes. These are just a few of the people whose stories we hope can help others in their journey toward healthy, enjoyable lifestyles in health-supporting environments.

The interviews and focus groups – over 55 hours of conversation – were recorded and then transcribed. The result was nearly 2,300 pages of transcripts. From the transcripts, the research team highlighted approximately 2,000 quotations that were then grouped into 146 thematic categories (see Appendix). These categories form the organizational structure of this book. Some quotations appear more than once because their content fits within more than one category. As you explore this book, keep in mind several other points. First, this project was approved by the committees at the University of Wyoming, Montana State University, and University of Idaho that review all research involving human subjects at their respective institutions. Second, all individuals who participated in the interviews and focus groups signed informed consent documents. Third, the ages of the individuals cited at the end of quotations are approximate. Sometimes individuals stated their exact age somewhere in the interview or focus group; otherwise, the team member conducting the interview or focus group estimated the person's age. Fourth, brackets indicate words added or changed for clarity or to help ensure the person's anonymity.

About the authors
To provide a sense of our roles in this narrative effort and the events leading to it, we offer a short summary about each of us. Betty has co-led WIN Wyoming since its beginning and has served as the regional coordinator for WIN the Rockies. In 1998, she developed a presentation called "Size It Up!" that focuses on physical activity, food and eating, and body image and that incorporates personal experiences – hers as well as those shared by other people who have responded to her presentation. Since 1998, she has delivered versions of this presentation to over 6,000 individuals in the United States and Australia, ranging from preschool children to health professionals. During one of these presentations, at a regional public health conference in Denver in late 2002,

Betty described the narrative research component of WIN the Rockies and shared a number of quotations. The response from dietary and mental health counselors, in particular, was very positive, and a number of these professionals encouraged her to compile the quotations into a book that could be used by counselors and their clients. The counselors felt that reading and identifying quotations that reflect their clients' views, situations, and/or experiences would facilitate the counseling process and increase the likelihood that issues and obstacles would be addressed successfully.

When Suzanne was hired as a food and nutrition specialist with University of Wyoming Cooperative Extension Service in the Department of Family and Consumer Sciences in mid-1997, she brought a strong interest in helping people become healthier regardless of their size or shape. She also brought a long-standing desire to work collectively with colleagues to achieve a broader, more substantive goal than could be attained by individuals working alone. With support and encouragement from Betty and other colleagues and friends, including Linda Melcher and Sylvia Moore, Suzanne organized what was to become WIN Wyoming, which she continues to coordinate. She co-wrote the grant proposal for WIN the Rockies and has served as the project's co-principal investigator.

Although Fred has long appreciated the roles that quantitative research can fulfill, he strongly believes that qualitative inquiry is essential to fully understand human experience. When he heard Betty's "Size It Up!" presentation for the first time in early 2000, he was struck by the stories that Betty had incorporated into her presentation as well as the experiences people shared with her afterwards. He saw the need to tie the experiences Betty talked about to an emerging body of literature related to the value of narratives, a specific type of qualitative inquiry. As the lead grant writer for WIN the Rockies, Fred did just that. He incorporated into the proposal a research component to gather narratives related to physical activity, food and eating, and body image.

How might this book be used?
David Buchanan has analyzed how the scientific model and the humanistic model link theory and practice in nutrition education.[1] He questions the extent to which the scientific model is adequate and appropriate for understanding human behavior. Science seeks to predict and control outcomes, but humans possess free will. By contrast, the goal of the humanistic model is "to gain clarity, not to claim certainty" (page 151). In the humanistic model, practitioners use theory as a stimulus for dialogue about the role of eating habits in living the kind of life that community members feel is more valuable. Our hope is that the quotations in this book will, indeed, stimulate dialogue among professionals involved in health care and health promotion, between professional counselors and their clients, and among everyday people who use this book on their own to connect – through words and emotions – with individuals like themselves.

As you peruse this book, it may be helpful to do what our participants did: reflect on your life experiences in the areas of physical activity, food and eating, and body image. For example, what experiences have you had in these areas throughout your life? How have these experiences shaped you? Do you have hurdles you need to overcome to embrace healthy eating, an active lifestyle, and respect for your body and other people's bodies? How can you best overcome these hurdles? The quotations in this book may help spark some insights into and understanding of your own attitudes and behaviors. This book's non-directive approach of simply presenting quotations under thematic headings allows you to use the book in a wide variety of ways and settings, some of which we almost certainly have not foreseen.

But what are some specific uses that we do foresee? Counselors and/or clients may want to use the thematic Table of Contents to find quotations that can "break the ice" in initiating a dialogue about subjects that may be difficult to broach. The Index may prove helpful in locating quotations related to topics and issues not readily apparent within the Table of Contents. Quotations that concretely describe specific problems, circumstances, or solutions can be used by counselors and their clients or by people reading on their own who want to see how other individuals in comparable situations have framed or resolved a particular set of issues. There can be a great deal of solace as well as progress toward a life that is healthier and more enjoyable when people recognize they are not alone in facing a particular challenge or when they find a way forward through someone else's experiences. We wish readers all the best on their journey.

---

[1] D. Buchanan, Two models for defining the relationship between theory and practice in nutrition education: Is the scientific method meeting our needs? *Journal of Nutrition Education and Behavior*, 2004;36:146-154.

Chapter One

PHYSICAL ACTIVITY

*Participate in activities for the joy of
feeling your body move.*

Guiding principle from Wellness IN the Rockies

Physical Activity - Definition

1 "Physical activity means maintaining an active and healthy lifestyle that allows you to do the types of activities that are important to you . . . so that on a day-to-day basis you feel healthy and strong and awake and alert." *Male, early 40's*

2 "Physical activity is . . . doing things at your own level. . . . Somebody may be a rock climber or some may be just an afternoon walk, so *anything* being physical, any movement." *Female, late 20's*

3 "There are so many different aspects . . . about physical activity. I mean . . . leisure to one person is work to another. And physical activity to one person depending on what they do, may be not doing anything to another. To me, going for a walk with my kids is physical activity. But for someone else who is very athletic, they may have to work up a sweat." *Male in his 30's*

4 "Just making it to the kitchen and to the bathroom is good enough for me."
Female, late 40's (suffers from degenerative disease)

5 "I get tired. Chasing cows. Chasing kids. . . . I don't do a lot because I'm lazy." *Female in her 30's*

6 "[When I hear the term physical activity, the first thing that comes to mind for me is] pressure to try and exercise . . . . For me, physical activity [is] just trying to survive the day." *Female, mid 40's*

Typical definitions of physical activity

7 "not being a couch potato" *Male, mid 70's*

8 "anything that makes your body build a heart [rate] or exert energy"
Female in her 30's

9 "moving your body from one place to another" *Female, 50ish*

Humorous sidenote
One of the interview questions asked about physical activity in the broadest sense. This person indicated she did not think housework or vacuuming qualified as physical activity. And why not?

10 "Because I don't do it often enough. Vacuuming once every couple of months doesn't qualify, does it?" *Female in her 30's*

---

11 "I have . . . little kids, so a lot of my time goes to them. And of course in [this state] when it's wintertime you're not out going as much. . . . You are kind of limited in this part of the country. . . . I think I'm pretty active; I run around with the kids a lot. We play in the house. . . . With summer coming, I usually officiate soccer, play softball, and of course in the winter we play volleyball. And then, with the kids, we kind of go through swim lessons and gymnastics, and I get in the pool with them and stuff like that. . . . But right now, I have to admit I haven't been as physically active as I would like to be." *Male in his 30's*

12 "I'm so active in my free time . . . that I will go back to work to rest. All my vacation time is used in competitive events. . . . Honestly, I can never remember not being physically active. I started working when I was eight, nine years old with a paper route. So this has been my whole life. I played football all the way through college. And I coached and have competed my whole life. It's who I am. I enjoy it. . . . I've hunted and I've done a lot of outdoor activities since coming to the West. . . . That's who I am. . . . It is. I just thrive on it. I really do." *Male, almost 50*

13 "And some people do [physical activity] really early in the morning and I would rather stay up late at night." *Female, mid 40's*

14 "[To add variety, to my stair walking routine, I started walking up 14 stairs, down 14, up 13, down 13, up 12, down 12, etc.] If I'm concentrating on the stairs, I'm not concentrating on the time. That's what I decided, and my son gets so hung up on the time [that] he's having a hard time with it. So I thought maybe that [would] give us something else to look at." *Female in her 30's*

15 "[My children] think that to exercise you have to go to a bodybuilding establishment, but I feel that we can create our own. And the exercises I do are pretty reasonable. They don't cost very much." *Male in his 50's*

16 "[My physical activity] would be sporadic. . . . I don't know if I want a routine. I kind of like being independent." *Female, early 60's*

17 "I don't really do a whole lot of physical activity. . . . Help cook, help shovel the sidewalk and we got a few birds and stuff . . . I gotta take care of, and . . . in the summertime . . . grass to cut and weed-eat and work on my garden and stuff like that, and that's about all [the physical activity] I get. Take out the trash."
Male in his 40's

18 "I have a daughter who could work out 24 hours a day and be totally happy. . . . I've never really enjoyed exercise per se." *Female, mid to late 40's*

Quotations on preferences for certain types of physical activity

19 "I wouldn't jog for anything in the world. . . . Walking is fine. . . . I've never seen a jogger with a smile on his face, and I'm dead serious. . . . I enjoy walking." *Female in her 60's*

20 "So, [daily treadmill walking] is what I have done and it really has helped an awful lot. . . . I just feel this has just been a real godsend to me. It just has really helped me a lot. The climate is good inside the house and it's really level, and besides, you have something to hang on to." *Female, 50ish*

21 "[Tae Bo] is a combination of karate movements and exercise. . . . You do some punches, you do some legwork. . . . There's a lot of variety. . . . To me, the dance [videos] look great, but again that takes coordination and that is just not in my brain. . . . Because I guess the biggest part for me is the variety you get. . . . You know I could never do the push-ups. . . . Climb the rope, absolutely forget it! I mean I hung myself trying to do it. I mean all the standard conceptions you have of exercise, . . . it doesn't apply [to Tae Bo]. And it's not regimented either." *Female, early 40's*

22 "I dislike running. I mean as far as staying in shape, I'll go out and play basketball . . . . I run up and down a court, but just to run . . . I've never liked it. . . . Let me dribble a basketball or run with a football, but if I have to run just to run, I dislike it, period." *Male in his 20's*

23 "I think that dancing is a wonderful exercise, and I have a real strong feeling about the fact that they don't teach dancing in schools and you can dance all your life. . . . I've danced ever since I was five years old probably. That's the way we grew up. We went to the country dances and I didn't realize it was exercise, but I do now. I love to dance." *Female in her 50's*

24 "I play [golf] three times a week and I play two-and-a-half hours for 18 holes, on foot. I had the world's land speed record for actual playing 18 holes with a score that's suitable for 36 holes. . . . It doesn't sound like much when you figure it's only four-and-a-half miles a round for 18 holes, but we stop off and hit something with a stick every now and again. It's kind of satisfying."
Male, 70ish

25 "I remember coming upon Jack LaLanne on TV one time. I thought he was just a pretty neat character. . . . He was probably the original [exercise] guru. . . . It just kind of got to be a routine. It was just kind of a fun thing to do. He did it a little easier than some of this bump and go they do now. . . . I guess that was probably my first real routine of exercise." *Female, 50ish*

26 "In the summers . . . I love to walk and I'll get up early in the morning and go walk for an hour. . . . I have a treadmill, but I really don't enjoy walking on it nearly as much as I do outside. It's just too boring." *Female, mid 40's*

27 "[Due to cancer treatments], breathing is very difficult for me now and I get real frustrated in the winter because I can't even get outside when it is cold. . . . Real hot weather I can't handle, wind I can't handle. Trying to walk doesn't work. . . . So I sit at home and eat more and get fatter." *Female, mid to late 60's*

28 "Right now, [I've] been sitting around all winter. It's been a heck of a bad winter. [I] haven't done very much, but I've got a lot of jobs coming and I know that I'll be right back to [my desired weight] if I keep at it, if the joints don't wear out completely before the weight drops off." *Male, 60ish*

29 "I check on my mother every day, . . . and it's almost impossible to walk from work to her house and then eat and walk back to work in an hour's period of time. I make it faster on the bike, but . . . because of the snow on the roads, I had to stay at work." *Male, mid 50's*

30 "I got a dog so I walk probably two miles a day. . . . Because with the wind blowing today, it was probably about a mile. . . . Boy, it just was not pleasant out there. . . . Well, I have to admit that I would probably not walk at all during the winter if it wasn't for the dog." *Male, 70ish*

31 "Last fall, . . . I did start to ride my bicycle to work . . . and I found that to be enjoyable. But when winter set in, it started to get bitter cold, and [riding my bike] wasn't too much of an option." *Male, mid 50's*

32 "I kind of hibernate in the wintertime. . . . I have for years." *Male, mid 50's*

33 "[My physical activities are] very seasonal. And we have a short [summer] season. . . . You can do a lot of things in the summer, and the wintertime, you become very housebound." *Female in her 60's*

34 "It seems like the colder it gets, the less I want to go outside, and it's just easier to stay home and be warm." *Female, mid 20's*

35 "Where you live and the weather and things like that contribute so much to [being physically active] because I'm an outside person, and when we have six months of cold weather, I don't have a desire to go outside." *Female, 40ish*

36 "About the only thing I really do in the winter is shovel snow and I have a machine that does a lot of that." *Male, mid 50's*

6

37 "I still try to jog three days a week. But as I've gotten older . . . there's always things interrupting it. . . . I'm busier now than I ever have been in the past. . . . Just age and time . . . are the things that are deterrents now I guess."

Male in his 30's

38 "I would like to be more active. . . . So I was walking at work, but even taking that half hour away from my family, from my . . . teenagers and my husband, *really* bothers me. I *don't like* it." *Female, 40ish*

39 "I do like physical activity . . . but it's just I think we get caught up in our own little world that we're always too busy. We say, 'Well, we're gonna do it,' but we never get to it. It's like, 'Let's put it off until tomorrow.' Then you put it off tomorrow." *Female, early 30's*

40 "When you get out [of college] there's all these other people wanting things from you at work, your husband, and you're trying to juggle this and it's like, 'When am I going to find time for *myself*?' " *Female, late 40's*

41 "I, like everybody probably, [have] gone through periods when I didn't do much . . . physical activity—taken a demanding job . . . and I got bigger than I wanted to be and didn't feel as good as I wanted to feel." *Male in his 50's*

42 "When you were younger, . . . you didn't *think* about [physical activity], you just *did* it. . . . As we change in our lives, physical activity, as taking time out for ourselves, becomes more difficult to schedule." *Female, late 40's*

43 "I would like to be more active, but I also have other people in my life. I have my family, my kids and my wife. . . . It's more important to me to spend time with them than to go run." *Male in his 30's*

44 "It's harder to make time for [physical activity]. I'm not as active as I used to be. . . . I think . . . you get in the routine of life and you get married and you have kids and you get busy taking care of them." *Female in her 20's*

45 "I have so much stuff going on and I know I should do [exercise] and I really want to. I get so tired. I come home and it's like the last thing I want to do is go to the gym. I'm . . . in the [health] profession. I know all the benefits of [physical activity]." *Female, mid 30's*

46 "I feel like I don't get enough [physical activity] and I'd like to do more, but with the time restraints of . . . [two jobs and the National Guard] and taking care of my family, I'm pretty busy. So, I do what I can when the time's available."

Male, early 50's

47 "[My present level of physical activity] is all right. I'm proud of where I'm at, at this point, because [the doctors] kept telling me I wasn't gonna be able to [walk – that I would be in a wheelchair by now]. So I'm proud of [myself], but oh, there's so many things that I'd love to do, and I just can't." *Female, late 40's*

48 "[I] got a [serious back injury]. . . . I think the hardest part was when everybody said I can't do, I can't do, I can't do, I can't do, and I said to myself, 'Well, what can I do?' And that made the difference. I started doing things that I *could* do. And I can do a lot more things than they said I could." *Female, 40ish*

49 "My problem is [my disability]. . . . And to be right frank, I'd *love* to get a job. I'm sick and tired of sitting on my ass. . . . There's gotta be more to life than to just getting [*starts to cry*] out of bed and sittin' on your . . . ass. Excuse me, I'm sorry. . . . The best coach that I have is my mom and we go to [the local fitness center] about three or four times a week. And I *like* it." *Female, early 30's*

50 "I have a real hard time just getting my groceries in the house from my car. . . . [And] when I get home with the groceries, I have to go rest for an hour or two before I can put away my groceries. . . . When I was a kid we walked a long ways to school, . . . at least a mile and a half . . . and now I feel fortunate to get to this room." *Female, mid to late 60's*

51 "The granddaughters were playing soccer, and the parents were invited to join in. . . . Well, I love doing stuff like that. . . . I went out and played one quarter. . . . I went down with the tackling of the ball . . . and I ended up in the . . . emergency room because my knee was twisted in. So it's a trick knee now, but it's not unbearable. . . . I have to be careful. I'm [over 60]. I'm not gonna play soccer anymore." *Female, early 60's*

52 "I was born with a dislocated hip and . . . for about a year I was in a body cast and then I had a brace . . . . At about seven I think the brace came off, . . . [and] my mom said I never went anywhere without running after that. . . . Then all of a sudden you got it off and you experience freedom for the first time. Yeah, that's when I just loved to run." *Male, early 40's*

53 "We lived on a ranch and I went out and worked; of course, I had the allergies and the asthma so I could only do [chores] kind of in bits . . . [so] I could breathe." *Female, mid to late 40's*

54 "Last winter I used to get up early in the morning. I would go and exercise and lift weights. And I felt good then. . . . I caught a cold or something, and it got so it was hard for me to go in . . .'cause I just didn't feel good. . . . And then it broke my routine and then I stopped." *Male in his 30's*

55 "In retrospect, having overdone [competitive athletics] . . . has caused the problems that I have today. . . . Now I have rheumatoid arthritis, and every night . . . I'm quaffing down inflammatory this or whatever, so I can walk the next day. . . . And all of the issues that I have with [my] knees . . . are [responsible for me] not being able to exercise enough now to keep my weight down. . . . I miss that . . . intense competition that I enjoyed as a youth, . . . but the by-product of that has been [that I am generally] unhealthy as an adult. Catch-22." *Male, mid 30's*

56 "My mother noticed I had some talent as an acrobat. And so she took me to dancing school. . . . And I loved it. . . . And it has helped me have some ability and grace throughout my life. But when I was 12, I contracted rheumatic fever and I was in bed flat for three months." *Female, early 60's*

57 "At this point in my life I'm fighting three diseases now, and just to get up out of the bed in the morning is an awful lot of pain. . . . As the day goes on you have to force yourself to go. If you didn't, you'd become totally petrified. . . . But when you do this all day long, . . . you're exhausted and you don't feel like going for a walk or helping with the dishes or anything else. You just want to kind of curl up and forget about it. . . . I put on a hundred pounds laying in a bed the last two and a half years. . . . And I was a big guy anyway, but now I've got so many problems I can't seem to do anything to get it off." *Male in his 60's*

58 "I had a pretty severe [car] accident. . . . And since then, it's pretty much slowed me down. I used to do a lot. I mean, I was a little heavy before then, but I probably gained 125 pounds since then. . . . I'm slowly getting back into the walking but nothing like I did before." *Male in his 40's*

59 "I would still like to be able to do all the things I could 40 years ago. . . . I don't run no more at all. . . . And I still try to keep in some kind of shape to where I can do those things, especially with grandkids. But unfortunately the joints aren't allowing it to happen." *Male, 60ish*

60 "I was in the [military and I was] . . . severely injured. . . . Walking became a chore . . . because of the problems with this knee. Over a period of 20 years, . . . I developed arthritis in it. . . . There was a period in there I was almost afraid to move. Doggone it, if you want to go A to B, you better drive it because you're not going to be able to walk. Now I've gained quite a bit of weight."

Male in his 70's

61 "Well, my physical activity is quite limited anymore because I have become inflicted [sic] with rheumatoid arthritis, and it just gradually beat away on my ability to do things." *Male, 70's to 80's*

62 "Right now, I don't like [physical activity] 'cause it hurts. . . . It's kind of like you *gotta* do it in order to keep yourself healthy as you get older. And it's like there's a difference between wanting to and knowing you *have* to do it. It's easy to have bad habits. It's hard to make good habits." *Female, late 40's*

63 "I would like to play sports at a drop of a hat, anytime I wanted to. . . . Where I didn't have such a gut . . . and I would be able to maneuver better both in sports and also just [getting] around." *Male, early 30's*

64 "Getting out and walking around is sort of painful for me now . . . . And I think to myself, 'Gee, if I'd been more active I wouldn't be like this now. . . .' I've spent quite a few years just sitting at home doing nothing. I look back now and I think, 'What a waste.' " *Male, early 30's*

65 "The first few days [of walking along the beach] were pretty rough because I'm not in good physical condition. . . . But it gets better, and I know it's good for me. . . . Most people walk all the time, but for me it's kind of a big deal to walk a lot. . . . It'd be better if I did it every day, but I don't." *Male, late 30's*

66 "When I was at college, . . . I really liked to run. It was so fun to run. But now I'm heavier. I'm so big up top that when I try running, it jogs at different times than the rest of me. So I can't run anymore." *Female, mid 40's*

67 "But as I've gotten older, things don't work as well as they once did. And so it's not as enjoyable. I can't just jog and enjoy it for the most part because there is always an ache or pain." *Male in his 30's*

68 "[Physical activity] used to be a lot more enjoyable when I would get out and walk. . . . For one thing, I could get around a whole lot better than I do now. There wasn't discomfort to be concerned about." *Female, 50ish*

69 "We walked a mile to school a lot of the time. And a mile home. I loved to walk. I was younger and things didn't hurt so much. . . . I have arthritis, so walking now hurts, but I still try to do it as much as I can." *Female, mid 70's*

70 "By the time we are done with [the physical training for my job], my knees are hurting so bad that I'm on Advil for a week or two. . . . The negative is the pain afterwards, but that's life. Everybody has pain and stuff. . . . It's just a few more aches you have to deal with." *Male in his 40's*

71 "If I kick up that [physical] activity level, I know I'm going to be taking fists full of [pain] pills. So I don't know. . . . I would love to do more." *Male, mid 30's*

10

72 "Well, [inactivity] kind of sneaked up on me. . . . You sit with your feet up and you do that for a while and, gee, it feels so good, you want to do it some more." *Female in her 60's*

73 "And that's probably one of the toughest things to find, good activities that you can enjoy. Especially when you get heavier. . . . If you get heavier and older at the same time, you're saying to yourself, 'I don't know if I want to do [physical activities]. I don't want to have to go through what it takes to get there anymore.' " *Male in his 40's*

74 "My husband is on his feet all day. . . . I sit at my desk eight hours. . . . His day is more balanced, mine is more sedentary. And then I get home and I'm less [active] than I was at work. I think mine is more mental [work], where his is more physical, . . . but we have different kinds of exhaustion when we get home." *Female in her 30's*

75 "At the top of the steps I'm winded. Or going from my car to my office—if I'm late, which I normally am, [I'm] really walking at a clip getting there. . . . Just speeding myself up that much more was *exhausting*. You get to the office and hope that you don't have to answer the phone or talk to anybody for a couple of minutes so that you can regain and get your breath again." *Female in her 30's*

76 "You set up one of those mental templates where, 'Hmmm, if I do that I will get breathless and I don't want to do that,' and so . . . [physical activity] becomes an *avoidance* thing." *Female, 60ish*

77 "My physical activity—I don't know, . . . I seem to have created my life around just doing my usual thing. It's not like one day I was a great athlete and the next day I wasn't. It's not like I lost anything, so I don't notice any great change. . . . I do know that when I was employed full time, I had trouble with being exhausted, but I also hated the job." *Male, late 30's*

78 "I'm getting older. It's like,'What happened? I did this just yesterday; I was able to *do* these things, and now it's like . . . *damn*, I hate 40.' It's kind of like, 'Where did I go?' " *Female in her 40's*

79 "Sitting behind a desk can [make you lazy]. Your mind is constantly going, . . . and so you're a zombie in your brain. . . . And you find yourself just getting lazy." *Female, 40ish*

80 "When I was a kid, I thought [physical activity] was really enjoyable. And
. . . in college I gained the Freshman 15, so [physical activity] became really
uncomfortable. I couldn't hardly walk or run around . . . because I was
out of breath." *Female in her 20's*

81 "I probably enjoy [physical activity] less [now] because I'm not in as good as
shape, and so it makes me realize how bad a shape I'm in. And it makes me
tired more because I have to work harder." *Female in her 30's*

82 "We had another child [last year] . . . . I was too tired from not sleeping at
night to get up early in the morning and go [work out]. Or at least that was my
excuse." *Male in his 30's*

83 "I like [physical activity] when I do it, but now that my body is bigger I feel
like it's a burden to try to do." *Female, mid 40's*

84 "I like to see the countryside and that's why I enjoy the four-wheeler. . . . We
do some hiking there, but I don't do an awful lot of hiking. Because of my
weight, it's probably slowed me down . . . some." *Male in his 40's*

85 "If I don't keep a handle on [my weight] and it gets away from me a little bit,
it's just going to be a lot more uncomfortable just to plain walk and get around."
Female, 50ish

86 "Most of my work has been desk work [and] it's a challenge. . . . There's a
different kind of fatigue that comes from sitting behind a desk, but it's still
fatigue. So to get up after work and try and do something, . . . it's a struggle."
Female, 40ish

Memorable quotation

87 "We used to have to run a mile in PE class. . . . [We] had to do it in
less than 15 minutes. And even when . . . I was skinny as a rail, I
couldn't do it. And obviously when I got fat, then I couldn't do it in an
hour and a half." *Male, late 30's*

---

88 "[While loading over two tons of coal], I thought, 'You better slow down here, you're going to have a stroke or a heart attack or something' because I'd fill those gunny sacks too full of coal and then it was more than I could do to lift it and I was in a hurry and trying to do a lot of things in a short period of time. . . . I just thought, [I've] got to lose a little weight, . . . and I think that's the whole problem. I'm probably packing more weight than I should. . . . I got up on my mother's roof. . . . I got concerned about the depth of the snow on her roof and I went around the outside perimeter about three feet back from the eaves. . . . I decided if I had to shovel that whole roof off with a shovel then I was going to be dead. And so I went and I got a little small snow blower and just took it up on the roof and took the snow off with that. . . . And there was more than one time [we] took dead bodies off of roofs from heart attacks [in this county]. . . . Old men getting up on roofs to get snow off roofs and having heart attacks and dying." *Male, mid 50's*

89 "You're always taking a risk of blowing a knee or ankle when you're playing basketball, and the older that you get the harder it is for those things to mend or recover, and I think maybe it's fun, but there are other ways to keep in shape. . . . But I keep thinking, gee, it would be fun to play basketball after I turn 60, just to say that I did." *Male, almost 60*

90 "The weather [recently] was yucky-poo. . . . And then I'll tell you what, if I fall down—that's the end-gate for me. If it gets slippery and snowy and that sort of thing, I hide out until it gets okay and then I love [going outside]. . . . I love to ice fish. Yeah, I love to do that, but I don't do that anymore. . . . I fell down on the ice and I went, 'Okay, that's enough. I'm done.' " *Female, late 40's*
(suffers from degenerative disease)

91 "Up here our hands are tied pretty much in the winter because . . . I don't care much for the ice. I don't want to reinjure [myself]." *Male in his 70's*

92 "I kind of outgrew the basketball because there's too much danger of getting injured." *Male, almost 60*

93 "I'm not that active, I guess, in the winter. I have this terrible fear of falling, and one of us down is enough!" *Female, 70ish (cares for housebound husband)*

94 "Since November, you haven't been able to walk here because there's too much snow. The sidewalk isn't cleaned off freely and that's what I'm afraid of —falling down. . . . I haven't done any [physical activity] since November."
Female in her 70's

13

95 "When I was about six years old, I remember my mother signing me up for tap dance lessons. After about three months, I remember so clearly, the dance teacher came over to my mother and she said, 'You've wasted *my* time and *your* money long enough. She is so clumsy you might as well not bring her back.' . . . At the time I was trying to learn to ride a bike and I didn't have good large-motor skills, and riding a bike was really hard, so that reinforced the fact that I'm this . . . clumsy child and so I just went into a mode of not doing *anything* that reinforced that image to myself or anyone else. And it became an absolute conscious effort to avoid physical activity situations." *Female, 60ish*

96 "[One of my junior high teachers was] used to working with athletes, and when [he didn't] have . . . athletes to work with, this gentleman had *no* patience and that definitely formed my opinions of myself. . . . Some people are athletic; . . . some of us aren't. I didn't get those genes." *Female, early 40's*

97 "I think . . . [in the] earlier part of my life . . . I related [physical activity] with being *good* at it, with being *athletic*. And I just did not get a single gene of coordination in my whole entire body. And . . . that's very hard when you're not athletic to think that's the only thing that there is [to physical activity]."

Female, early 40's

98 "I never could participate in sports. . . . In PE, I was horrible. I used to fail physical education class because I wouldn't go." *Male, late 30's*

99 "[My current level of physical activity is] horrible. I really would like to increase that, but I'm just not disciplined to do it. . . . I don't know if it's one of those things that if I try and fail, then I don't know how I would respond to that. . . . I'm a bit of a perfectionist. So for me . . . if I can't do it well, I don't want to do it at all." *Female, mid to late 40's*

100 "[When] you would play baseball . . . or basketball and when you're next to last always chosen because you're uncoordinated, it definitely shapes your opinion for physical activities. . . . I remember coming up with tons of excuses why my mom had to write me a note because I hated PE." *Female, 40ish*

101 "[I tried] this Cindy Crawford workout and it's like, 'Yeah, *right!* You know, *in my dreams* I'll ever be able to be athletic like that.' " *Female, early 40's*

102 "When I was growing up, I was quite clumsy and very uncoordinated, and I did not like to play sports, and I hated PE because I could not do what the rest of the kids did, and do it well. So as I got older, I just accepted myself for what I could do, and it is much better now." *Female in her 50's*

103 "I can kind of remember as a little kid I was heavier. They didn't call you obese in those days. They called you chunky or husky. I didn't get tall and thin. I was more short and round. . . . It was tough to try and keep up with some of my friends [who] were taller and thinner—as far as day-to-day kid things. . . . I had one friend, he liked to set you up for a fall. A lot of times [he'd] say ,'Oh yeah, you can do it, you can do it,' . . . only to see you fail miserably and [he'd] have something to torment you about." *Male, mid 50's*

104 "[When I was in my 20's] I was very thin. I would go to exercise class and people would say, 'What are *you* doing here?' . . . And part of the reason I thought at that point was, 'So I don't look like you.' . . . I wanted to stay physically fit. I wanted to be able to do that and through jealousies I think they made me feel bad." *Female, mid to late 40's*

105 "In high school, . . . I took auto mechanics. . . . The class I graduated with was quite cliquey and you had the athletes and you had all the good-looking girls . . . and if you weren't an athlete, . . . as far as they were concerned you were a scuz bag. I thought that I wanted to be an athlete at one time, tried out for teams, and I would make the team but never ever had the opportunity to play and still put forth all the effort to be a part of the team but never got the reward of some playing time. . . . The ones that did get to play treated the ones that never did play differently. And I think that had a little bit of negative aspect on me too."
Male, mid 50's

106 "I came from a country school and didn't know how to play [basketball when I went to high school], and I remember them all laughing when I started to run down the full length of the court instead of the half court, and . . . I never have cared for sports." *Female, mid 70's*

Overcoming negative perceptions of physical activity

107 "When I was about six years old, I remember my mother signing me up for tap dance lessons. After about three months, I remember so clearly, the dance teacher came over to my mother and she said, 'You've wasted *my* time and *your* money long enough. She is so clumsy you might as well not bring her back.' . . . So that reinforced the fact that I'm this . . . clumsy child and so I just went into a mode of not doing *anything* that reinforced that image to myself or anyone else. And it became an absolute conscious effort to avoid physical activity situations. When I got to be in [middle school] and they said, 'Come on and play softball,' I ran so fast in the other direction. I made up excuses ten feet high. . . . And it took me until way into my adulthood to go, 'Wait a minute, I'm the master of my fate here.'"
Female, 60ish

108 "If I can exercise alone then I'm a lot happier. . . . I think I'm embarrassed to do things with people in case I can't do it or I can't keep up; then it makes [me] feel inferior and I'm not into that either. . . . Fat guys don't look good in shorts anyway." *Male in his 40's*

109 "The negative aspect [with physical activity] for me . . . is the *group*. . . . The loudest voice that's inside of you is people's perception. . . . I'd rather go home and [exercise] on my own than to be embarrassed, or *perceived* to be embarrassed in front of a group." *Female, early 40's*

110 "I used to lift weights. . . . [My high school friends and I] pushed each other. . . . But we were intimidated by each other, and I guess that's part of . . . exercise. . . . It is intimidating to do . . . with other people." *Male in his 40's*

111 "When I exercise, sometimes this *stupid* belly flops. . . . And I quit exercising. . . . That's why I don't like to go to a gym where there's a lot of skinny ladies. . . . I mean, when you're 300 pounds plus and you look at somebody . . . who looks skinny, . . . it's really frustrating." *Female, early 30's*

112 "My wife's tried several times to get me to do aerobics with her. . . . I just can't do that. In fact I feel foolish doing stuff like that. Maybe it's not a guy thing. . . . I can't just look at a wall and exercise." *Male in his 40's*

113 "I think one experience . . . in the negative category would be when you can't perform physically the same as others. So, for me that led to . . . , 'You know, I don't really care, I ain't gonna go out and play basketball with my friends anymore. I'm just gonna loaf around, watch TV.' " *Male, early 20's*

114 "This is a lot of woman to be carrying around . . . and [I] try hard to hide it from the skinny people that I can't breathe. . . . Today . . . I was carrying some stuff up . . . a long flight of stairs and when I got to the top I was trying to regulate my breathing so [my friend] wouldn't know I was winded walking upstairs. Stupid. . . . And she's my best friend." *Female, late 20's*

115 "When I went to the college gym and I was around all the little hard-body girls who looked like little supermodels out of magazines, . . . I always was comparing myself to them, and I didn't feel as good when I worked out because I didn't see myself looking like them." *Female, mid 20's*

116 "I used to, when I was younger, [go to the gym] and play basketball. But now that I'm older, I don't need to go in there and have them young fellows push me around. I'd look out of place." *Male, 70ish*

16

117 "A year ago my wife and kids gave me a year's subscription to the gym and I'd go up there in the mornings and . . . it was like a rat in a cage. You're on the treadmills—I just didn't get a lot of pleasure out of it. To me that was just too boring . . . . To me it's just kind of staring at a wall. . . . I just didn't like it. . . . It . . . just wasn't that fun." *Male in his 50's*

118 "[I won't walk on my own], I think, because I get bored. There isn't anybody to talk to. . . . And I can only deal with my own company for so many hours a day! . . . So . . . I think a lot of it's boredom. . . . And I tried to swim, . . . and I get bored. . . . You can't listen to music while you're doing it. You certainly can't sing while you're doing it, and pretty soon I'm just going slower and slower and thinking it's time to get out of here. My mind is too busy to be [swimming laps]. . . . I went to [a circuit gym], . . . and I enjoyed that 'cause [there] was music. And I didn't run in place, I usually danced. And then it's interspersed with weights and then aerobic, and then weights, and then aerobic. But it got boring, too. I was doing good at that and had lost some weight and was stronger, but I just—I got bored." *Female, early 40's*

119 "I think [walking is] boring. . . . That's just a waste of time. . . . It's terrible! . . . I don't like to be alone. . . . I hate walking. It's absolutely so boring. I don't have time for it." *Female in her 50's*

120 "[Physical activity is] something I *should* do but that I *don't want* to do. . . . When I think of physical activity, it's usually *have to* exercise. I haven't found anything I love to do yet." *Female, mid 40's*

121 "I've never been an exercise person. To go and do aerobics or things like that— I've never enjoyed that. . . . I have a daughter who could work out 24 hours a day and be totally happy. . . . I've never really enjoyed exercise."

Female, mid to late 40's

122 "[Physical activity] was always a chore and a bore. I don't ever remember anybody ever doing [it] just for the fun of exercising." *Female in her 30's*

123 "Exercising on the treadmill . . . just seems so *redundant*. . . . It's just a half an hour that you spend . . . wasting time." *Female, 40ish*

Humorous sidenote

124 "Laps in the pool would bother me. I guess that's why I like the reservoir. There's still things to see, things to do. . . . Plus if you stop, it gets cold." *Male in his 40's*

---

125 "[I could never sustain physical activities in the past.] I wanted to get skinnier. . . . I didn't see results after a month or so, and so it . . . didn't encourage me to keep going." *Female in her 30's*

126 "My [grown] daughter . . . watches me do these various [attempts at routine physical activity] . . . and then when it doesn't work [for losing weight], that's good for her because then she doesn't have to mess with it." *Female in her 30's*

127 "If I do [physical activity] because I [want to] lose weight and I don't lose weight, then I would feel like I have failed. If I would do it so that I could become physically fit—to the dogs with the other part—I think I could feel much better about that. But I don't know that I'm at that point."

Female, mid to late 40's

Humorous sidenote

During one focus group discussion, an overwhelmingly active woman spoke rapidly and at length about how much she does and how she needs to be busy all the time. After she finished, one of the other members of the focus group asked,

128 "Can I just tie a rope around you and let you drag me around?"

---

129 "If somebody wants me to come to work, I can set a schedule and come to work, but if it is up to me to get up [and] do my yoga and run my laps . . . it's like, 'Mmm, I can do it tomorrow.' . . . So . . . I just need someone to crack a whip. Get busy boy! Whack!" *Male, mid 50's*

130 "I like dancing. My husband doesn't. So we don't do that anymore. . . . It's a crying shame because that's one of the most pleasant ways to exercise there is." *Female in her 60's*

131 "And I'm hoping to go back to water aerobics, but it's hard at a quarter to six at night to want to go do something else. . . . Some of [the ladies] are nice and some of them are meaner than mean." *Female, early 40's*

132 "I would appreciate it if I had more support from my husband because he feels like his job gives him enough physical activity. If he would participate with me it would make it even more enjoyable." *Female in her 30's*

133 "I could never get my husband to watch my babies for me to go do [physical activities] and so I think [that's when physical activity] started being a negative connotation. And then I gained more weight. I see everybody on TV and they keep talking about [daily physical activity] and it's like, 'Easy for you to say, try living my life for a while.' " *Female, mid 30's*

134 "[My friend and I] meet at the park [to walk] 'cause . . . we don't like walking on the roads 'cause people drive like idiots. They drive way too fast and we don't really want to get crushed." *Female, early 40's*

135 "I realize now that at my ripe old age of [over 50] if I'd have left the god damn car parked at the curb or in the garage and did a lot of things with bicycle or walking [I'd be better off.] Vehicles make people lazy." *Male, mid 50's*

136 "When I was younger, . . . my thing was to get out of this, . . . get out of doing that. If I could drive somewhere, yeah I'd drive. . . . Looking back now, heck, that would be the only one thing I'd change in my entire life . . . because, [as] I look back on it now, I wasted a lot of years." *Male, early 30's*

137 "My mom went to . . . Czechoslovakia . . . and she said they walk everywhere. . . . We hop in the car every time we turn around." *Male, early 40's*

138 "The [military] service requires that you do [physical activity] for another purpose [other than enjoyment]. And you know, I did what I had to do. And the way I thought about it at the time was . . . I'm going to be in the best shape. I'm going to be the baddest son-of-a-gun that walks the face of the earth so that if something does happen to me at least it won't be for lack of me trying. But I don't know, after a traumatic injury your mind doesn't fall in sync with your body. Your mind says, 'Well, god, you used to be able to do dah-dah-dah or whatever.' And then to go from [elite physical condition] to not being able to do anything, it messes with your head. It affects your feeling of worth, and you really don't know how to deal with it." *Male, 40ish*

139 "My first husband was a real jerk, and he helped get my kids taken away and so I got depressed, and so I quit doing stuff. I was like that for a long time. I finally looked at myself and said, 'I've got to get off my gosh damn ass and *do* something,' and so I'm slowly getting back into [physical activity]."

Female, early 30's

140 "I was doing much better [with my regular walking program] and then last year I got some bad . . . information about my son, and so I quit exercising. I quit walking. I quit doing everything." *Female, early 40's*

141 "I know I listen to those people who exercise and I think, 'I'm gonna exercise,' and I turn on the TV and . . . it's like, 'I'll do it tomorrow.' With me, I'm an all or nothing type of person, big time. And if I fail, then I just say, 'To hell with all of it.' " *Female, late 20's*

142 "I collect disability, and I just can't sit around and do nothing all the time, so I figure I'd go down [to the food bank] helping the people that need food. . . . I can get in front of that TV and . . . just give me that remote control."

Male in his 40's

143 "When I got in my mid 30's I started getting some medical problems, kinda got negative about doing different things, depressed and stuff. And then I started getting out of shape from not doing nothing and then I kinda got [like I am] now." *Male in his 40's*

Thoughts about the focus group

144 "I thought it was just fascinating to listen to everybody's different point of view and to realize, 'Hey, I was thinking really close-minded about something like that and I should try to be more open-minded and try to experience the kinds of things that they feel and how they think.' "

Female, late 20's

---

145 "I've done [a walking program] off and on for a long time. But I go in spurts. And I'll do really good sometimes for a year and then fall off and not do anything. But the one thing I know is that I can't go, or won't go, walk by myself. So I've got to know that someone's going to be waiting there for me, so that I will go. . . . 'Oh, well I better go. [My friend is] going to be waiting on me.' And if I don't have that impetus, I won't get up and go. . . . And there have been several times I've gotten there and she hasn't been there, and even though I'm there, I won't walk. I'm *there* and I won't do it. I sit and read my book and I go home." *Female, early 40's*

146 "My husband, when he was alive, we used to walk every night. And it was just being able to walk with somebody and talk. . . . To me that was the best part. I mean we could walk several miles . . . [and we'd] just visit and catch up on the day. And I enjoyed that. . . . I would like to say that I really hated exercise, but if I have someone to do it with, then it's okay. But to go out and do it yourself, I just am not one to do it by myself." *Female, late 60's to early 70's*

147 "And I like [the local workout facility] because there's all different kinds of people that go there, like all different ages, versus when I used to work out at the college. . . . The people there were a lot younger than me . . . so they could do a lot more than I could. . . . There's tons of different ages [where I go now]. Tons of different people at different levels in their physical fitness, and I don't feel like I'm compared to anybody." *Female, mid 20's*

148 "We [do water aerobics] about half an hour and then we play for a little while, just do what we want to do, swim, talk mostly, which when you're alone, the talking means a lot . . . because I lost my husband, . . . and it wasn't until after I'd lost him that I knew I had to start getting out and doing something. So I started water aerobics." *Female, mid 70's*

149 "I like to feel . . . strong, and . . . [a] guy that has an office down the hall from my office . . . works out a lot more than I do, but he's always kind of . . . checking in, 'You been working out?' . . . I like people being able to . . . notice that you are trying to stay in shape." *Male, early 40's*

150 "I like our group [at the local gym] because I like the support that you get from having someone else. Of course, I can go to the gym alone, and it doesn't bother me, but I like that support group that says, 'Oh, how much weight did you put on [when you lifted] today?' . . . It makes you do a little more and I like that." *Female, mid 60's*

21

151 "We used to belong to a health club, . . . my girlfriend and I. . . . We had the best time. Every morning, five days a week we went. . . . And we felt really wonderful. And you do. And I miss it. . . . And [my friend and I] always got into something, . . . trying to lose weight and keep it off. But . . . I need a partner to do it with." *Female, late 60's to early 70's*

152 "When I think of walking, I don't think of it as being exercise. I think of it as getting to go visit with somebody." *Female, early 40's*

153 "I don't like exercise, and I guess if I can have company that's okay. . . . I don't like to be alone, . . . [so] I think it is the company, . . . having people with me. . . . Now I go up to [the local gym] and there [are] people there, and I enjoy that a lot better than if I just do something by myself." *Female in her 50's*

154 "[Walking with friends is important] for the accountability of doing it. . . . The good thing about walking with friends, you don't even think of the time factor 'cause you're so busy talking that it goes fast." *Female, mid 30's*

155 "For years . . . I had some friends I walked with, and I'd leave the house, and I knew just what time to leave and pick them up. We just made a loop. . . . Walking with friends was. . . a good thing because I always knew that somebody was out there waiting for me, and it gave me that little extra push to get out of bed and get out and going because somebody else was out there. I didn't want to let them down." *Female, 50ish*

156 "[Our aquatics group] laughs so hard we almost drown. . . . We have a real fun group. And *that* makes it fun." *Female, early 40's*

157 "Walking [with my co-worker] is good because then we can visit as we're walking. . . . And so that social time is a valuable . . . part of that exercise. It makes it easier to do it. I have never been one that could use the video exercise tapes. And I think part of that is . . . the motivation. You have somebody else to be accountable to with . . . walking." *Female, late 40's*

Humorous sidenote
When was the last time you were physically active? Can you tell me about the experience?

158 "Physically active . . . oh, I got up this morning."

Female, mid to late 40's

---

159 "A positive experience that I've had with physical activity is being on the swim team.... Practices ... would be extremely difficult, and all of us knew that we were there to finish the workout together.... It kinda brought us together.... That was the basis of what the swim team is about ... [that sense of] unity and just accomplishing something together or working hard for the same goal." *Female, early 20's*

160 "If you're going to do [sports], you better give it 110 percent. If you're going to make the commitment, then you owe it to your teammates or to yourself ... to see it through to the end.... So that's what you did, ... gave your all, ... did the best you could. I didn't feel like I ... had to be a superstar or anything, but you had to make sure you gave as much as you had." *Male, 30ish*

161 "Probably the best lessons on commitment came from ... sports, ... that commitment not only to yourself, to improve, but ... the commitment to the team effort. I think those lessons probably would have been hard to learn in any other environment. And those are the ones that I still carry today, for whatever team I might involve myself in, whether that would be work-group team or a sports team; those lessons came from the sports activities." *Male, 30's to 40's*

162 "I used to fail physical education class because I wouldn't go, but bowling was fun and there's some exercise involved. Obviously not very much, it's a fat guy's sport or game. And I had a little team to go with. We had a team. The school provided a bus.... It was very fun." *Male, late 30's*

163 "[I] play volleyball with my friends ... because [of the] companionship."
Female, 30's to 40's

Humorous sidenote
Please think back to the last time you were physically active and tell me about it.

164 "Now, this stays out of the bedroom, right?" *Female, late 40's*

---

165 "I'll be real honest with you, I'm a recovered drug addict and alcoholic and been clean for [several] years, and the physical activity highs are far greater than any high I've ever had from any drug I've ever done. And I love it. . . . You get addicted to that feeling somewhat. I think you run, and the endorphins kick in, and you feel like you're floating. After that you don't really care; you could run forever it seems like and you stop for a while, and [the endorphins] are still kind of kicked in for at least 15, 20 minutes after that, and you just feel refreshed, and . . . your body . . . has got a good workout and your mind [as well]."

Male, early 40's

166 "It's not just the mere exercise that I enjoy. . . . I love to be physically active. I love to play I guess. . . . I truly do value play. And I think that a lot of adults forget what it means to play. And it doesn't mean that you have to be a kid to play. I mean everybody plays. You know, we all as adults have time for recreation. And what recreation is, is play." *Male in his 30's*

167 "I've always enjoyed being physically active. . . . I've always enjoyed being outside. I love that. I love doing all kinds of physical things. I like even playing with all of the grandchildren, even though they laugh because I can't run anymore. . . . They're trying to outdo me a little bit in soccer, but we have fun in doing it. And volleyball, we love that. . . . The grandchildren haven't gotten me on a snowboard yet." *Female, mid 60's*

168 "I've always liked to walk. . . . I'm from [another country] and they didn't have cars. . . . So it don't bother me to walk. I like to walk." *Female in her 70's*

169 "I enjoy doing stuff. . . . I remember being little, and . . . I always looked forward to Saturday to get out and go snowmobiling. . . . But I remember that was the driving force in the week to get to Saturday. . . . That's what I looked forward to." *Male in his 20's*

170 "An 89-year-old lady . . . leads our water aerobics. We have lots of fun. . . . [We do it] three times a week. . . . In the water, you don't feel the weight. And you can keep going. It just gives you a little pep, a boost for the day."

Female, mid 70's

171 Reactions after recently starting physical activity program: "Well, at first it was total exhaustion. Now it's actually invigorating. It gives me energy. . . . I certainly never thought I would get to almost enjoying it. I never expected to do that. I just figured I'd trudge along and we'd set our goals. . . . I just didn't ever think I would enjoy it." *Female in her 30's*

172 "I liked the farm work. . . . Back in those days, I remember when I can first remember things, putting up loose hay where it wasn't baled, and you'd go out there with pitchforks, and I just loved it. I would work all day long, and I looked forward to the next day. . . . I would get out there and sweat and work in the field, and shoot, late in the day, we would quit and go and play baseball somewhere. It was a great life." *Male, almost 60*

173 "I do more [physical activity] now, just because I don't have to show up and get my name checked off on a roll. . . . I enjoy it now 'cause it's my own choice. I choose to do it." *Male in his 20's (played college football)*

174 "I love to walk and so I try to walk three or four times a week. . . . It is very invigorating to me. . . . It is a pleasant experience. . . . I love to walk. . . . It's my prayer time." *Female in her 50's*

175 "I enjoy physical activity as opposed to mental activity. It's much more fulfilling than sitting in an office all day. So when I do get the opportunity to do it, I really usually enjoy it." *Female in her 40's*

176 "Evenings and in good weather [my wife and I] walk as often as possible. . . . Those are really very enjoyable times because we talk with each other. . . . We're buddies and partners." *Male in his 70's*

177 "[Walking] is *very* pleasant. In fact, it's something I look forward to. My husband tells me if I don't walk every day I am really a grouch, and I probably am because that's kinda my release time." *Female in her 50's*

178 "And then I started running with [my sister] . . . probably because I saw the change in her, not only physically but also I know that it made her happy and emotionally it made her focus." *Female in her 20's*

179 "It's a treat for me to get to go out and do something. . . . 'Yeah, I'll go mow the lawn. You stay in here and watch the [kids]. . . .' That's great. . . . I enjoy being able to go out and have some physical activity." *Female, late 30's*

Fun family activity shared by participant

180 "One of the fun things we do [at family camp] is . . . called marshmallow wars. . . . You take half-inch PVC pipe . . . and miniature marshmallows fit in there really good, and [you] use them as a blow gun. . . . One team has to attack the other team and it's a blast. And you have to wear goggles because you will get welts from [the marshmallows]. It's good for the whole family. . . . I'm [over 50] years old and I enjoy running in the woods." *Male, early 50's*

181 "I never really was into . . . exercise much when I was a little kid, . . . but
what really changed my viewpoint . . . was when I started going to the gym. I
. . . found that you get more endurance, and you feel stronger, and you
feel better. . . . You don't feel tired all the time." *Male, early 20's*

182 "I work in accounting, so if the numbers just won't equal . . . I just get up
and walk away from it. . . . And I'm fortunate that I work next to a park, so we
can get up and go walk around the block. . . . And it's just amazing how you get
up and move and get away from it and come back and it's like, 'Oh, well duh,
there's a mistake.' " *Female, early 40's*

183 "[I started to work out] just to feel better about myself and have more
energy . . . and it's amazing how much energy I have now. I don't feel tired all
the time or groggy. . . . I actually go to school and . . . babysit . . . and
. . . work a full-time job. [Before, I] noticed like by the end of the day that I was
always lagging, and I was tired, and I was yawning, and . . . I just didn't feel
good." *Female, mid 20's*

184 "I [feel] better, . . . more awake, more energetic, . . . when I [do] something
[physically active] each day, . . . something besides sitting at a desk."
Female, 40ish

185 "If I get a workout lunch hour, it seems like nothing really bothers me in the
afternoon. I just kind of feel like I'm a lot more relaxed and just a lot more
patient and have good energy just to carry on through the rest of the day. . . .
The days I don't do that I kind of feel a lot more drained. Energy-wise I just
don't have near the amount energy I usually have." *Male, early 40's*

186 "I can be *dog* tired when I come home, but once I start doing all those
chores and picking up and vacuuming and doing dishes and running the laundry
upstairs and downstairs, . . . and all of a sudden I just kind of get a second wind
of energy. . . . Nobody wants to do chores around their house, but I feel like I get
kind of a burst of energy." *Female, mid 20's*

187 "And if I can stay in relatively good condition, then I have a whole lot more
energy for work and church and all the other things I do. [I] feel better about
myself mentally, [and] physically [I] have the stamina to do what [I] want to do."
Male in his 50's

188 "When I finish [walking on the treadmill], I just physically feel better. Boy,
I feel like I could get up and really get something done, where I might have been
dragging before I started. It energizes me." *Female, 50ish*

189 "The last time I had any physical activity . . . was the Tae Bo tapes. . . . [When you do the tapes, you have a] very uncoordinated feeling, that's for sure. You do . . . , trust me. I close all the curtains because no one is going to see this. And my husband and I do it together, and it's like, 'Don't look at me' . . . but you're moving all the parts of your body and it's balancing, it's stretching, . . . it's really excellent, and they'll do it in stages where you can go up to the advanced and that may never happen because I think you need to be 20 to do some of that stuff. . . . It was good. I enjoyed it. . . . I don't mind sweating. I like the perspiration, I mean dripping—and that sounds disgusting—but I like the dripping. You know, horrible dripping all over. My hair is disgusting, everything is dripping and you finish up and you think, 'Oh my lord that was the worst thing I've ever done,' and then you shower and get ready for work and you feel good." *Female, late 40's*

190 "In between the resistance machines, [the facility has] these boards that have springs in them and they have stair steppers and you can get on those and you can jump up and down. And I notice that if I skip those and I just use the resistance machines, I don't hardly sweat at all . . . , but if I get on the treadmill or I use the springboard, I really work up a sweat. . . . It's probably disgusting, but I associate me sweating with me getting a better workout." *Female, mid 20's*

191 "I liked the farm work. . . . I would get out there and sweat and work in the field, and shoot . . . . It was a great life." *Male, almost 60*

192 "We put up a fair amount of hay, but I always put up . . . hay in small bales for one reason—because I thought my boys and I needed to see the joys and benefits of some hard, physical labor. . . . And that's one of the opportunities you have is to go out there and work hard together and sweat together and it's a [rite of passage]." *Male, early 40's*

Initial response to topic of physical activity

When I say the term 'physical activity,' what comes to mind for you?

193 "Sweating." *Female in her 20's*

---

194 "There's nothing easy about [fitness]. If you're wanting to stay physically fit, you have to commit to it. It doesn't just happen without you paying a price. We've kind of developed in our society to where we want things the easy way. That's one thing about physical fitness—it doesn't come easy." *Male, early 40's*

195 "My parents really knew how to work. I don't really work as hard as they did, but I still believe that a person needs to do things that keep the muscles toned, the muscles in shape . . . so that if [you] get into a situation where [you] have to do something strenuous, [you're] able to do it. And that takes some daily activity of exercise." *Male in his 50's*

196 "It probably took me two years to get out of shape. And it's probably gonna take me a couple years to get back in shape. . . . I've been doing [my aerobic workout] . . . for about two months. And I didn't get this out of shape . . . in two months and it's gonna take longer to get back in." *Male in his 60's*

197 "I would like to go back to when I was walking and doing [circuit training], how I was feeling then. Because even though I wasn't measurably skinnier, I was in better shape. I had more physical strength. . . . And so I wish I was back just even where I was a year and a half ago. Well, I don't know if I've got what it takes to get back there." *Female, early 40's*

198 "Maybe I'm silly—I'm almost 60 years old—to worry about lifting weights. I don't need any muscle, I guess, but I'd just like to be a little stronger and I think the aerobic part is the most important for me at this time." *Male, almost 60*

199 "I've made a strong effort . . . to haul hay with the family and . . . we do it the old way, by hand. And I've enjoyed that because it's helped me build up my shoulder strength. . . . And it's given me a little bit more self-esteem to know that I do have the strength . . . to take care of what needs to be taken care of."
Male, early 50's

200 "I go to [the local fitness center]. I love it. . . . [Other people] sit and look at me like, 'Gol, what are you doing here?' I need to be here. I told the lady that owns it, 'I don't need to lose the weight; I want to tone up.' " *Female, early 30's*

201 "I still want to keep working out and getting . . . toned . . . ; I don't want to . . . have huge muscles or . . . be super, super skinny. . . . Being toned . . . is just my main focus." *Female, mid 20's*

202 "As [I] get older I begin to appreciate that . . . exercise is key to keeping your range of motion. . . functional." *Male in his 50's*

28

203 "I was never the smart kid in school. I was—not smart. So my out was physical education. I was good at PE. I was like the *only* girl in the fourth-grade class that got the physical fitness [award], so to me, 'Oh, this is something I'm good at, so I'm gonna do this.' " *Female, late 20's*

204 "I was a varsity running back, and we won state championships in track, and I participated in a lot of sports. . . . I was successful in sports. . . . And I think that had a lot to do with it. You know, partly because I was naturally athletic. People who are not naturally athletic may not have the same opinion about physical activity that I do. . . . I loved PE classes when I was a kid."

Male in his 30's

205 "I have always been able to do things physically as compared to people I've known where it's very difficult. So that does make it more pleasurable. I can imagine that if I were excessively overweight or felt uncoordinated that it would be very frustrating. And I've not had that kind of an experience."

Female, late 40's

206 "When I was in high school, being physically active and athletically active, it was a . . . part of gaining confidence in myself . . . [and] having some self-confidence. . . . Sports was an important part of [my] self-concept as a kid. It was one of those things I could do and do fairly well and so you get some benefit out of that and don't worry about yourself." *Male in his 50's*

207 "When I was in fifth grade, I was a big kid compared to my classmates. I grew fast. It was kind of interesting. . . . I was a fast maturer. I was big. I was muscular and I was strong. . . . So it was good for me. . . . I was good at sports in junior high because I was big—bigger than other kids. . . . So that definitely influenced the way I perceive myself. And I felt good about my body image."

Male in his 30's

208 "I suppose it's the size and shape of my body that allowed me to be as athletic as I was. My athletic experiences are some that I really enjoy and treasure and I'm glad I was able to do those things." *Male, almost 60*

One woman's message to youth on athletic abilities
209 "If I can speak to children, . . . just to have an awareness that everyone is different, and everyone's talents lie in different areas. And being athletic . . . [is only] one of those talents. . . . So [children need] that awareness that people are different." *Female, early 40's*

210 "I think running marathons is very mental, more than even physical . . . , but *accomplishing* it, running across the finish line, you just feel amazing even though you walk like you're pregnant. . . . You feel really good when you accomplish something like that. . . . And one thing that I did realize is . . . I'm capable of more than I thought I was." *Female in her 20's*

211 "When I just go down and jog on the treadmill, . . . I don't get much satisfaction out of it. But where I go and help out for a day on the family farm or ranch, . . . at the end of the day I still have the aches and pains, but I feel like I accomplished something for the day, instead of just running and getting nowhere." *Male in his 30's*

212 "[Basic training for the military] was really, really hard, but I was really proud of myself too when I got it all done. That's probably the thing that I can think of that made me kind of enjoy [physical activity] now. You know, there's some purpose to it, instead of making me miserable." *Female, mid 30's*

213 "Seems like [when] we get enough physical activity, it makes us too tired to do the routine of exercises. . . . But when you got 20,000 bales sitting out there in the field and the sooner you get them stacked the better the feed's going to be, so you did it from dawn 'til dusk and piled them again in your sleep that night."
Male, 40's to 50's

214 "That . . . regimented kind of physical activity, I'd rather have my physical activity actually accomplishing something . . . sheet rocking, carpentry, . . . stacking hay bales, that kind of work as opposed to going to the gym and pumping iron. . . . I think that is why the [exercise] machine is sitting there inactive." *Male, mid 50's*

215 "Thinking of yard work in the summer, . . . your heart's going the same rate as if you're over walking on the treadmill or something. You're perspiring. You have the same sore muscles and so you start to recognize, 'Boy, this really isn't much different than walking on the treadmill.' . . . And I'm getting something *done* too. . . . It's such an accomplishment." *Female, 40ish*

216 "I try to stay physically active now. I walk about two miles a day. I'm a crossing guard for the school and that gets me up in the morning and gets me over there in the afternoon and I walk rather than take my car." *Male, mid 70's*

217 "[In college,] I would walk to the store every night and then walk back . . . but it accomplished something. . . . I bought a magazine or a drink or something to eat. . . . I just can't exercise to just exercise. I don't know if I'm bored or . . . I detest physical labor." *Male, late 30's*

30

218 "When I go up and do the cardio part [at the fitness gym], then I take a book with me. A lot of people don't, but see there again, I just feel like I can't waste time. I've got to be doing something while I'm doing that. I was *taught* that. . . . My mom taught me that you don't just sit." *Female, mid 60's*

219 "Farm work is a lot of exercise, . . . [but] I never think of it as exercise; it's work." *Female, mid to late 70's*

220 "I never put myself first. I never have. It has always been family or the house has got to be cleaned or the floor has to be scrubbed and the dinner has to be cooked or whatever. But as far as putting myself first, I never have."

Female, mid to late 60's

221 "[Reading a book while walking is] kind of a reward in a sense. . . . I think, 'Oh, you know I'd really like to read this. Well, what can I do while I'm doing that?' " *Female, mid to late 40's*

222 "I don't have a riding mower. I have a pushing mower and I enjoy doing that. I always have. That takes a couple of hours most every weekend."

Male, almost 60

223 "In the fall we take out hunters for elk and deer or antelope and sometimes we walk with some of them and that has a purpose 'cause you are hunting."

Female, mid to late 70's

Insightful response on work ethic and physical activity

224 "I wonder, though, if [thinking that physical activity has to have a purpose] doesn't have to do with the work ethic that comes from childhood, because . . . if there's purpose behind what I am doing, then there is a reason to go out and do it and I will enjoy it more. But just to walk around the block or jog around the block, . . . it's a waste of time. . . . But I think some of that . . . lies in the [fact that the] only value that we . . . [give] is when we produce something, instead of edifying ourselves with doing something just for ourselves. I learned that when I kinda worked through, it's okay because I really enjoy going up and spending an hour at [the local gym], even though I didn't produce something while I was doing it, but it was a good thing to do for *me* and that was okay, even though there wasn't some *thing* coming out of it, or the floor wasn't cleaner, . . . I didn't go shopping for it or I didn't throw hay for it [but] . . . it was okay because it was for me." *Female, late 30's*

225 "When you go to the doctor's office and you fill out that family history, that can be pretty much a good indicator that you better start changing. . . . The doctors usually roll their eyes at me. . . . I mean, mother's side of the family—high blood pressure, diabetes, heart problems, you name it, [it's] pretty much there. On my father's side, three different types of cancers, cholesterol problems. . . . I've lost both my parents and I'm [only in my 40's]. Siblings are starting to run into serious health problems, but definitely [I've gained an] . . . awareness . . . of [mortality]. But it's a little bit different when the seriousness of health hits your siblings." *Female, early 40's*

226 "I'm basically healthy. My lungs are good, my heart's good . . . . They're sluggish because I don't get any physical activity. I'm almost at the threshold of an unhealthy body. . . . I look at my mother and she is a complete . . . prisoner in her body. . . . I can foresee if I do not do something at some point in the near future, I'm going to be that [prisoner] also." *Female, mid to late 40's*

227 "I got hurt quite badly five years ago and the doctor had told me that if I needed to bend over and stuff like this, I had to do some exercises and I would have to do them until I ended up in the nursing home. And I thought, 'Ahh, this is really a pain.' But I did them for quite awhile and then I quit. Well, all of a sudden one day I realized my back was stiff and I couldn't bend over like I was doing before, and so I'm back doing the exercises again, and I know he's right. I have to do them for the rest of my life." *Female in her 50's*

228 "I've always kind of struggled with weight, and . . . I know the heavier I get the harder it's going to be and the more it's going to hurt. . . . It's like, man, do I want to be laid up? Or do I want to get out and move?" *Female, 50ish*

229 "I got my knees injured [at work] and I just kept thinking, 'Man, this shouldn't happen,' and then . . . you're laying in the hospital after surgery and just wishing that you could have done something different. . . . Since it has been a few years and you're still feeling the pain from it, you think maybe if you had been in better shape, maybe it wouldn't have happened." *Male in his 40's*

230 "[I lift] weights. [I got started with] a group at the [local] hospital. . . . I had high blood pressure, and . . . I've always been heavier than I should be. . . . I didn't know I had . . . high blood pressure. . . . I just sat eight hours a day with the typewriter." *Female, mid 60's*

231 "I have started in the last month making sure I go a mile and a half a day, seven days a week. . . . And the reason I'm getting active again is my blood pressure has . . . increased." *Male in his 60's*

32

232 "I understand that it's good before surgery to have your muscle structure pretty sound. It actually might heal faster, so I've been doing a lot of work on shoulders and upper body." *Male, almost 60*

233 "All of us [in the pedometer walking program] have tried to get 10,000 [daily] steps. . . . We're not gonna be on a magazine [cover]. . . . I mean, . . . that isn't our goal. Our goal is to be healthy." *Female, mid 60's*

234 "I would rather spend my money signing up for gym or going rock climbing or skiing or something like that. . . . I don't go to the doctor much [because] I hardly ever get sick. . . . I'm grateful for the benefits of being physically fit, and you don't have to be thin to be fit." *Female, late 20's*

235 "I've always enjoyed doing physical things. . . . I just think you lose out . . . in lifestyle in general if [you're] not exercising and doing things that cause you to be able to enjoy life." *Male in his 50's*

236 "Getting out and walking around is sort of painful for me now. . . . And I think to myself, 'Gee, if I'd been more active I wouldn't be like this now, or it wouldn't be hurting like it is now.' " *Male, early 30's*

237 "Exercise can be beneficial as far as your overall health, . . . your heart, your lungs, the workings of the body, as well as the emotional aspect of endorphins, pain control, all of those kind of things. Intellectually, I know that, [but I'm still fairly inactive]." *Female, mid to late 40's*

238 "I certainly appreciate just . . . having the opportunity to . . . be physically active. . . . I feel like it does more for me now because when I was eighteen I didn't care what my blood pressure or cholesterol was. Now I certainly do and I know how physical activity helps both." *Male, 30's to 40's*

239 "One thing I notice is when I was physically active all the time I slept so much better." *Male, 70's to 80's*

240 "[I went] through drug and alcohol addiction. . . . I treated my body [terribly] all those years. . . . That really drove home to me . . . that I needed to get physically fit again [and] stay fit. . . . I . . . know it sure helps protect you from a lot of things." *Male, early 40's*

241 "With exercise, there's many things that it can help overcome physically, emotionally, and mentally. It's a good tool to use to balance your life."
Female in her 30's

242 "Nobody wants to get old. . . . I'm not going to get old gracefully. . . . I see people who give up their physical activity at an early age and then they are never able to enjoy the things which are available to us. So I'm not going to go down without fighting. . . . I think I enjoy [physical activity] more now than I did 20 years ago. . . . You can start looking around you and see those who . . . have just given up—let themselves physically go—and [you] say, 'No, I don't think that's what I want.' . . . When my wife and I reach the golden years, [I want to] be physically fit so we can enjoy our lives. I see too many people that once they reach a certain age, their whole social life . . . is based around their doctor appointments, and that's sad. I'm not a big proponent of drugs to change the way you feel or . . . dull things. If I got a pain, it's probably there for a reason, and I don't need to take some kind of a substance to reduce that or hide it. And so I think you're better off to stay [physically fit]." *Male, early 40's*

243 "Just having kids, you want to be around to see them when they're older. You want to be there when they are graduating. When they have a career going or [are] going into the military, you want to be there to see that. You'd be a little ashamed if you weren't there . . . just because you didn't get out and be physically active. . . . I mean you have a child, you see two things, you see yourself and you see your own tombstone." *Male, early 30's*

244 "I . . . [run] because I can see direct benefits. I also think I do it because I believe there are long-term benefits that I may not realize now because I'm younger, but when I get older I'll start to see some of the benefits of having been more physically active. . . . Of course, young is a relative term." *Male in his 50's*

245 "My one grandfather lived a long life. He died at 79, but he lived a full life. . . . He was real content with his life. He was real happy with it. . . . Had another grandfather, and I never really thought about it until now, so this is kind of neat, but he made it to 63. He was not so careful about his health. And he had quite a few health problems due to not being physically active, so I had a real juxtaposition. It really made me think." *Male, early 30's*

246 "The wife and I wish now [during] the cold months [that] we didn't have to get up and drive to an exercise place. It is a controlled exercise program which we know our bodies have to have, that otherwise we'll be laying on the couch and, 'Okay, I'm just laying here waiting to die.' That's not going to happen to us. Not if we have any control over it." *Male in his 70's*

247 "I can be depressed or down, especially since my husband died, and a couple of times I've talked myself into just getting up and going out and going for a walk. And I do that, and I come back, and I have a whole different outlook. I'm fine! I've lost the depression, or loneliness, or whatever it is. . . . Just get off the couch and get outside and get out the door." *Female in her 60's*

248 "I was a single mother for about eight years. . . . The stress was really high, and I think that's when I really began to realize how much I needed to vent stress. And so I would take off running in the morning, and my best girlfriend lived next door, and she would watch my [kids]. . . . But I needed an outlet with all the stress and that's what running did for me." *Female, late 40's*

249 "When I swam in college, it was simply to get out of my dorm room and away from my roommates. So it was an outlet to get away from a bad situation. . . . And I swam a hundred lengths every night, by myself. Whereas now when I'm doing [walking], I'm doing it with a friend; I have somebody to talk to. It's an emotional outlet that does more for me because I can talk and share my feelings. And then [the stress is all gone]. It just goes away." *Female, early 40's*

250 "Right now I'm overweight because I've been three months without any activity because of the surgery. . . . It's made me more irritable because I don't have a way to let my steam out." *Male, early 50's*

251 "I really struggle with depression, and when I get to that point I'm like a homebody. . . . I don't like to communicate. I just want to be by myself. . . . When I exercise, . . . that has helped me improve that. It's mostly in my head, just the thoughts I have, and when I clear those with the help of exercise, that helps a lot." *Female in her 30's*

252 "From my profession . . . you [sat] in the office and talked to people, and you got a lot of mental stress. . . . One thing that I could do [to] relieve pressure and stress . . . was a good fly-fishing pond that I could get out on and just sit there and catch and release those big trout. It would take your mind clean away from the stressful activities that I was doing on a daily basis, and I would come back and have a good night's rest. So physical activity, doing something that you like, relieves a lot of mental stress." *Male, 70ish*

253 "I go out and walk a lot. . . . My husband was gone working, and we had just moved into town off of the farm. I had never lived in town in my whole life. And he was gone all day and I had to get out. I didn't know anybody or anything. And I just had to get out and walk. It was a release for [me]."

Female in her 60's

254 "When you work, you're normally putting a lot of your energy into there, and you're concentrating on getting the job done. And sometimes you've got a . . . [deadline], . . . so you get a little bit wrapped up in it and get a little bit of anxiety built up in you, frustration sometimes if things don't work out right. And a good way to release that frustration is to go play a good friendly game of ball or tennis or something. Something that will take your mind off of what you're frustrated about." *Male, early 50's*

255 "I've got weights at home, so. . . I bring them upstairs. Then they're always there and I see them and use them, . . . so that has helped. And then I have a Stairmaster at home too, so . . . I don't have any excuse not to work out–the stuff is right there. . . . [What] I tell myself consciously is you can not use it and not work out and feel crappy and growly or you can exercise and . . . then feel good the rest of the day. So I mean I know that's the options." *Male, early 40's*

256 "In wintertime, cabin fever comes on me very quickly and this winter here with the snow and ice it has been devastating. [My wife and I] get out as often as possible to relieve the pressure, not only the . . . [relief] of the exercise but the . . . [relief] of the mind being able to communicate with people when you're out." *Male in his 70's*

257 "I've grown to appreciate [physical activity] more, not only for what it does for the body but kind of what it does for the sense of well-being. You just have more peace." *Male, early 30's*

258 "I like to speed walk, and . . . after I'm done I just feel great. It starts my day off really good. I get like that walker's high 'cause I'm not getting runner's high." *Female, mid 30's*

259 "[I was going through] a personally difficult time as a single parent and a lot of emotional struggles, and so the exercise was . . . a release." *Male, almost 50*

260 "With the stress we have on our lives, you have to find a way of getting rid of it. . . . Whether it's going for a walk, or swimming laps, . . . you *have* to do *something*. You can't just ignore it, 'cause it will eat you." *Female, early 40's*

Summary quotation on stress release and physical activity
261 "When I first get started walking, it's fun and everything, but as [I] keep going, [I] get over this threshold. . . . You just feel like you have no cares in the world. It really releases all that stress you've had." *Female, mid 30's*

---

262 "My family moved around a lot, so being accepted was part of being successful at athletics. And then I'm sure that is probably why I strived so hard for that and worked hard at it. . . . In the small towns . . . athletics was pretty much the key . . . [as] a way to gain acceptance when we moved around so many times." *Male, almost 50*

263 "I felt better about myself [when I was more physically active]. My self-esteem was quite a bit better. . . . I guess it's one of those things that feeds on itself. You do a little bit of it and you feel better so you do more of it. . . . And in retrospective [sic] of that, I've sort of lost interest in physical activity, and it's almost the opposite way. The less I do, the less I want to do." *Male in his 40's*

264 "When I was in junior high . . . all the other kids thought that because I was heavy that I couldn't participate in these activities, but in . . . volleyball and softball, I *creamed* all those skinny girls. And it made me feel really good about myself." *Female, late 20's*

265 "Sports was an important part of [my] self-concept as a kid. It was one of those things I could do and do fairly well, and so you get some benefit out of that and don't worry about yourself." *Male in his 50's*

266 "Through high school I had made a commitment to [lifting] weights and . . . I always wanted to appear tough and in control, and so once you develop that early, that stays with you. Once you feel at an early age that you're kind of somewhat dominant . . . you maintain that degree of persona throughout your life." *Male, early 40's*

267 "When [I] got into . . . organized sports, it was a whole different world than playing backyard bronco. . . . Sometimes [negative experiences] just make you want to fight a little harder and gain a little bit more ground, and maybe . . . you didn't win, but if you finished, you had some self-respect." *Male in his 50's*

268 "When I am physically active . . . it helps me emotionally. . . . I think it even helps me with my confidence. . . . Even though I can't fit into the jeans that I fit into when I was running marathons, if I'm physically active, I feel a lot better about myself." *Female in her 20's*

269 "It seems like when you are physically fit you feel good about it, and you feel good about yourself." *Male in his 40's*

270 "I started working out on a daily basis. . . . It's just boosted my self-esteem, and I feel so much better about myself." *Female, mid 20's*

Physical Activity - Motivator: Appearance

271 "I know [if I stay physically active] that my pants will zip up easier and I will just feel better. And I want to be ready for summer and to wear my shorts."
Female, 30's to 40's

272 "I'm probably in the best shape I've been . . . since I was a teenager. . . . I'm getting old and I'm not married. . . . You try to stay in the best shape you can because opportunities are dwindling." *Male in his 30's*

273 "I notice there's a difference [if I'm not working out], not so much my weight, but you can tell the clothes are tighter because things are floppier."
Female, late 40's

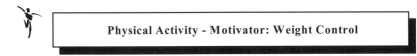

Physical Activity - Motivator: Weight Control

274 "I had a mother that was constantly trying to lose weight, and we figured this out together: that it's not going on those silly diets. . . . We found that walking was the key to keeping us healthy and it was easy and fun."
Female, mid 30's

275 "I'm one of the guys that [has] no physical control relative to eating things. So I have to fill in the other side of the equation, which is I just have to get enough exercise so I stay in weight and feel good about myself." *Male in his 50's*

276 "[There was] a period [of] time there where . . . , without fail, I was gonna be [at the gym] for my hour and nothing would stop me. Then I think I realized that this was just not reasonable. And I didn't have the outcome that I thought I would have, losing the 20 or 30 pounds I was hoping to lose." *Female, 40ish*

277 "I would say in my . . . 30's I was in fair shape . . . , and because of the running . . . I really stopped exercising . . . completely, 'cause it just hurt. And then I ballooned up [in weight]. . . . And I said I'm going to put this [weight] down and I really stuck to it for seven, eight years, . . . where it was just strenuous exercise and I lost it all. . . . But it took a lot of work." *Male, almost 50*

278 "To be honest, a lot of [encouraging physical activity for my kids is] not wanting to see them get overweight, because you miss out on a few things [when you're overweight]." *Male, early 30's*

279 "[I started going to the gym] 'cause I'm starting to gain the Freshman 15, as they would call it." *Female, early 20's*

280 "I like to hunt and go fishing, . . . but to go lift weights or run [on] a treadmill, . . . I don't particularly care for that. . . . I would walk all day in the hills if I was hunting . . . but to just go out and do it to be doing it, . . . it's been a real struggle for me. That's probably why I'm like I am." *Male in his 60's*

281 "When I go running, . . . it's just me and that fresh morning air. Even when it's 17 below. I know that sounds crazy, but I've learned how to run in temperatures that cold and I enjoy that peace." *Female, late 40's*

282 "[I like] fishing and snowmobiling and outdoor things. . . . It defines who I am. . . . That's why I go to work in the morning and work all week, so [I] have money to do those kind of things." *Male in his 20's*

283 "I was . . . a ranch kid. We piled bales, built fence, played football. Almost everything you did was hard, physical activity. . . . [If] you go outside and find something to do in the fresh air and work up some activity, it just makes you feel good. " *Male, 40's to 50's*

284 "We did end up getting a bike stroller that you could hook to your bike so we could put our daughter in it and go for bike rides. . . . It was always nice just to get outside and get away from the house." *Female in her 20's*

285 "My parents were outdoorsy people, so we would just spend a lot of time outside just fishing or doing property improvements [or] walking. . . . I think it's somewhat passed down to my kids. We try to go outside as much as possible . . . and try and do outside activities rather than watching TV or playing on the computer. Except for when it's so darn cold." *Female in her 20's*

286 "[When I walk with my brother-in-law], we look to see if there's any rabbits or road runners or tracks of the coyotes. . . . That's what makes walking fun. Because even if you walk the same road a hundred times, there's still something new." *Female in her 60's*

287 "I would rather do the outside work and not do the inside work. I like physical activity more than I do pencil pushing." *Male, mid 70's*

288 "If I do [go outside], then I get more exercise. But I like to read, so I get stuck in the house." *Female, mid 40's*

289 "[My daughter and I] play softball . . . together. . . , and . . . just being outside in the sun, . . . you're, 'Oh, summer's rolling around,' and . . . all the smells and senses and sensations you have when that season rolls around."
Female, 40ish

290 "I worked out this morning . . . and I always feel good when I do it. It makes my day better too. But I think you really have to take time. You have to say that you have to do this because it's easy to say, 'I don't have time.' But I just have to take the time so I feel better during the day." *Female, 30's to 40's*

291 "After a few laps [of running], . . . you're breathing hard and you get tired. To me it's not a fun thing. I feel good afterwards. That's maybe what I'm going for while I'm doing it, but I don't enjoy it." *Male in his 20's*

292 "The truth of the matter is . . . I don't enjoy running . . . while I'm doing it. I enjoy the benefits of running. . . . But most runs . . . when I finish, I am tired, and, 'Ah gosh, I'm glad I got through that one.' . . . I get a runner's high but it's after I run. I've never been one of those people that thought they had a runner's high when they run. Big fat guys are like that. I mean, the more you have to carry around, the worse it is." *Male in his 50's*

293 "It's a pain to get on [the treadmill] and do it, but when I get off, I feel so good, I'm glad I did. . . . I feel good that I've [walked on the treadmill]. When I finish, I just physically feel better." *Female, 50ish*

294 "As far as going to the gym, I don't actually look forward to it. I know when I go I feel better afterward." *Female, early 20's*

295 "It takes me a little bit to get started [with physical activity], to motivate myself, but once I do that, I feel a whole lot better after I've got it done."

Female in her 30's

296 "I like to speed walk, and . . . after I'm done I just feel great. It starts my day off really good." *Female, mid 30's*

297 "When you're doing [Tae Bo], it's like, *'This sucks,'* but you get the benefits later." *Female, late 40's*

Selected quotation on physical activity in schools
298 "You go to your high school and there's selected jocks, but that's only two percent. What are the rest of the kids going to do for physical activity? So . . . personally, I'd like to see . . . activities that were more broad and . . . to get more physical activity [in the schools]." *Male, 70ish*

---

299 "[Walking with friends is important] for the accountability of doing it. But you just had me trigger a thought. When I would walk by myself, back in my high school days, I think it was better for me 'cause then I didn't have the stress of thinking of all the stuff we talked about. Like sometimes we do get into some pretty big issues when we're talking and walking. So probably to get a real good high out of walking, I need to do it by myself." *Female, mid 30's*

300 "I used to have a friend that ran [with me], and between sprained ankles and injuries and age, he doesn't run anymore, so I run by myself. . . . [My] dogs would always be chasing him." *Male in his 50's*

301 "I enjoy [physical activity differently now]. I would say in the past, . . . I would have probably just gone out there and walked. Now I can walk, but it's a lot more a time to think, a time to kind of reflect." *Female, mid to late 40's*

302 "I enjoy [physical activity] . . . just because it's a break from the regular day. It's some time to just focus on me and to work on something to improve myself." *Female in her 30's*

303 "There are exercise places that you can go and dance with the ladies to music and I don't like that much. [I like activities] more on my own."

Female, mid 40's

304 "When I swam in college, it was simply to get out of my dorm room and away from my roommates. So it was an outlet to get away from a bad situation. And I did it alone. And I swam a hundred lengths every night—by myself."

Female, early 40's

305 "We first moved here to take care of my husband's parents. They were ailing and sick and failing, and so when we got here we needed to take care of them. When they got better . . . we needed to get away. When they were fine, when they weren't needing us, we went out to [the local resort], . . . just going out to have a little bit of free time and to swim." *Female, early 60's*

Key quotation on physical activity and solitude

306 "When I go running, I use it just to clear my head. It is my time to think, and there's no phones, no kids; I don't have to worry about homework. It's just me and that fresh morning air. . . . Sometimes I just let my mind wander. . . . Sometimes I may have a serious issue in my life that I need to sort out without anybody around, and so I work through it." *Female, late 40's*

---

307 "I think I got to get my body to go with my brain, because I know the benefits [of physical activity]. I also know that's why I should [do it]. I also know what will happen if I don't, and so I think it's a matter of doing it. . . . You know my mind is there. My will is probably half there, three-quarters there, and my body is just apparently waiting for me to do it." *Male, early 30's*

308 "I really don't like exercise. . . . And . . . as I got older, . . . we were still on the farm, [and] . . . the doctors . . . would say, 'Well, you have to exercise,' and finally I just decided that I did get my exercise [working]. But now that I am older, I don't like to exercise. So it is hard for me to even be nice about having to go to exercise." *Female in her 50's*

309 "I've always loved . . . pushing myself physically. I like to think that I'm some sort of athlete. I can't say as I'm a real good athlete, but it's a major focus for me to try to stay fit and more of a challenge as I age, which it is for all of us."
Male, early 40's

310 "I really enjoy walking if I plan to, . . . [but] if I get to the far end of the ranch somewhere, and the pickup won't start, and I have to walk home, when I get home I am just fuming." *Female, mid to late 70's*

311 "I think [the military] probably shaped [my attitude toward physical activity] for the negative and that would be going back to [physical training] tests. It's something I dreaded. I mean, I would do it and do it well, but I hated that part of . . . having to force yourself to prepare for it." *Male, mid 50's*

312 "Physical exercise has always required conscious effort and thought. It's *never ever* in my *whole life* been something that came just naturally or that I just did. It's been something that's had to be consciously pursued." *Female, 60ish*

313 "I think that . . . a person makes [physical activity] what they want to. If it's a drudgery, then they make it that way." *Female, mid 60's*

314 "I don't want to make it sound like [physical activity] is better than taking time to relax. I think both have their time and place. . . . [If] I'm not doing [physical activity] instead of something else . . . that needs to be done . . . then it's very fulfilling." *Female, 40ish*

315 "I was going to have surgery here maybe on the shoulder, and that came from a softball injury, throwing the ball too hard. . . . I said that's kind of my philosophy, that when they bury me, there's not a whole lot left. I would just soon wear it out." *Male, almost 60*

316 "I like the attitude, the mind-set to get in there and just say, 'Hey, [physical activity] is a matter of what you choose, and it doesn't matter if you're seven years old or 50 years old.' " *Male, 30's to 40's*

317 *When you were jogging on your trampoline, how did you feel at the time you were doing it?* "[I thought], this is taking too long." *Female in her 30's*

318 "Physical activity . . . has always more been participating in things with my family. . . . I don't think about [needing] to go out and run two miles every day. [Physical activity] is just a part of life. It's nothing I really worry about."
Female in her 40's

319 "Now [physical activity] seems to be more work. Back [when I was younger], it was fun. . . . But now it seems to be you have to force yourself to schedule a time to go do something." *Female, 40ish*

320 "I have a [relative] and she is *so* exercise crazy, and she's skinny, but she spends a whole lot of time exercising and I think it's a big waste of time to do that much." *Female, mid 40's*

321 "[Physical activity in my life is] positive in the fact that it's good for me, but it's negative in the fact that I feel like I have to do it." *Female, late 20's*

322 "I stay away from pain. . . . [It's] just my attitude of, if I'm going to die, I'm going to die happy, so . . . [I don't] do anything that I don't want to do."
Female in her 30's

323 "I know that [my current level of physical activity is] not nearly enough. But I'm comfortable with it. I'm one of these people—I like to watch TV. . . . I know I should be doing more, but I'm comfortable with what I'm doing."
Female in her 60's

324 "[Physical activity is] stuff I don't do a lot of. . . . It's one of those things that I have good intentions of doing, and see myself doing, and it's so easy not to do it." *Female in her 30's*

Physical activity and financial struggles
325 "It's amazing when you're financially just beaten down, . . . financially struggling, it's amazing how you can let other things [like physical activity] go." *Male, early 30's*

43

326 "I think I always do like the birthday thing. . . . You start out and you think, 'Oh, you know here comes another year, I need to do something,' and then I kind of start-start and fizzle-fizzle." *Female, mid to late 40's*

327 "Coyotes . . . always take the easy path, and so . . . they get trapped. If they took the hard path, . . . they'd be around a while. Well . . . life is the same way. . . . You could take the easy path and not . . . exercise and eat a lot and [that] gets you into trouble. . . . But . . . you've gotta have . . . willpower."

Male, early 60's

328 "[Walking] feels good to do it. One problem I have is I'm not a very disciplined person. And so if something else comes in the way . . . I can easily abandon [walking]. I mean, it takes time, it takes commitment. I have a reasonably busy life. . . . I can put [walking] off where I don't put off other things." *Female, mid to late 40's*

329 "My dad goes to the gym four times a week. . . . He doesn't like it, but he does it because he's a hiker and . . . he's a mountain climber. . . . And I just can't bring myself to do . . . physical activity just to be exercising, like my dad does, like my sister does. She's an incredible athlete and to maintain her perfect physical condition she works at it. . . . She goes to the gym six days a week to stay in condition. And it's hard to believe that we're even related because she's an incredible natural athlete and I'm not. . . . She's like my mother, who is a very disciplined person." *Male, late 30's*

330 "And as awareness is out there to high cholesterol, heart disease, all these things, as this awareness goes up, I think there is more pressure to be fit. Why would you want to have high cholesterol when you can do [physical activity] and lower it? But doing that's just not so easy." *Female in her 30's*

331 "When I was smaller, . . . I was doing factory work, and it was heavy work. . . . And two kids later . . . [I] had a job behind a desk. . . . And now it's just trying to get motivated to get back [to being physically active]. And getting the motivation is just like, 'Forget it.'. . . I got lazy." *Female in her 40's*

332 "I'm not very disciplined. I couldn't make myself go out and walk up and down the roads. . . . I'd rather be doing something else, so I started water aerobics." *Female, mid 70's*

333 "[Before] . . . I started doing the two jobs, I was doing aquatics three nights a week and . . . working out with free weights or machines. . . . I was very regimented, and . . . I have to again learn to get it back." *Female, early 40's*

334 "It's a pain to get on [the treadmill] and do it, but when I get off I feel so good, I'm glad I did. It takes discipline to do it. I've found it really takes discipline to get on it. It's just getting started that's kind of tough. Once you do that first little bit and get into it, it's fine." *Female, 50ish*

335 "You know it's [easier] to sit down and smoke a cigarette and drink a cup of coffee than it is to go over and get on the [exercise machine]." *Male, mid 50's*

336 "There's a lot to do [as far as physical activity], it's just you got to put your mind to it and keep on doing it. It's back to the old couch potato thing."
Male, mid 50's

337 "There's nothing easy about [fitness]. If you're wanting to stay physically fit, you have to commit to it. It doesn't just happen without you paying a price."
Male, early 40's

338 "I think you really have to take time [to be physically active.] You have to say that you have to do this, because it's easy to say, 'I don't have time.' "
Female, 30's to 40's

339 "[My current level of physical activity] is horrible. I really would like to increase that, but I'm just not disciplined to do it. I can make every excuse."
Female, mid to late 40's

340 "[My current level of physical activity] is poor. I could probably improve greatly. . . . I know I need to improve. . . . I don't know how dedicated I am."
Male in his 40's

341 "[Physical activity is] stuff I don't do a lot of. . . . It's one of those things that I have good intentions of doing, and see myself doing, and it's so easy not to do it." *Female in her 30's*

Summary quotation on physical activity and discipline

342 "I do try to get exercise because I think that's the only way you're going to stay healthy. . . . I just think we have to always work hard to stay healthy. I think that's an ongoing thing. It's something we need to always work at. Anything worth having is worth working at." *Female, 50ish*

Side-by-side comparison of two single mothers

343 "I started this job, and I have
. . . kids, and I'm a single mom,
. . . and I keep reading all these
articles in . . . magazines— *'you
have to make [physical activity] a
priority,'* and I'm like, my kids are
a priority, my job is a priority,
school is a priority, National
Guard is a priority—well, exercise
really gets pushed down there. . . .
I know I should do [exercise] and
I really want to. I get so tired. I
come home and it's like the last
thing I want to do is go to the
gym." *Female, mid 30's*

344 "I go running in the morning.
. . . I'm doing my master's and
working full time. And when you
have kids and homework, you can
overload, and my running helps
me organize the schedule that I
have." *Female, late 40's*

*[Note: She found a way to run
when her children were younger
by having her best friend watch
her kids for her.]*

345 "I felt positive about physical activity when I was swimming and doing
those things. I felt better about myself. My self-esteem was quite a bit better.
Plus it was easier to breathe and it was easier to do lots of things. I guess it's
one of those things that feeds on itself. You do a little bit of it, and you feel
better, so you do more of it, and you feel better. And in retrospective [sic] of
that, I've sort of lost interest in physical activity, and it's almost the opposite
way. The less I do, the less I want to do." *Male in his 40's*

346 "I sit too much. I know that. I love to read and sew, and as a result I don't
get out and moving enough, and I'm feeling it physically. I realize the muscle
strength is not there, [but] recognizing that you need to do something about it is
one thing; doing it is another." *Female, late 40's*

347 "I've been trying to get my program going again. I'm one of those that I
walked and walked and walked every day and then missed a few days and went
on to something else, just didn't even look back. And so I think I'm really
missing that, but yet I'm not. I'm *still* not making the time." *Female in her 30's*

348 "I've never been athletic. I'm too much of a klutz. . . . But . . . it's learning
to prioritize, that [physical activity] is just as important as getting up and earning
your keep every day. And . . . I'm still struggling with . . . making [physical
activity] as much of a priority as anything else. . . . [Physical activity] needs to
become a habit, otherwise you lose that habit, . . . and . . . once you get out of
that habit, it's horrible to try to get back." *Female, early 40's*

349 "At my house, . . . when we were old enough to work, we had to go find a job. And so in our house growing up, work was more important than the physical [activity]. . . . And I think that's what I still play in my head today is I first have to take care of my family and my job and if I have time to do . . . physical activity, that's great. But these other things are much, much higher on the priority list." *Female in her 30's*

350 "I'm always making sure that I'm building . . . [physical activity] into my day. . . . And seeing the accomplishments, . . . that's worth it. I used to just hate it . . . because I really didn't see the point behind it. . . . It was funner to watch TV than to go outside for a walk or do something like that." *Male, early 20's*

351 "We lived on a farm. You did farm work. You took care of the family, and you were last. I still do it now—you take care of this and this and this and you're last." *Female, late 40's*

Another focus group member responded: "You have to make time for yourself. . . . Even if you have to take care of all these other people, you still have to take care of yourself, so you can take care of them." *Female, 30's to 40's*

352 "I still have a . . . [child] at home, so by the time I get home from work and fix supper and pick up the house, it's dark. . . . And, unfortunately, I'm not one that really likes to get up any earlier than I have to [because] sleep is a priority." *Female in her 40's*

353 "I guess maybe I'm getting to the age . . . [that] I'm starting to be a little sedentary. . . . When I come home from work, I'm ready to just be done. . . . It's probably a gradual change. . . . I got a lot of things going in my life and [physical activity] is not on the priority list. And I'm probably not in as good as physical shape as a guy ought to be." *Male, mid 50's*

354 "I've always been involved in sports. It's always been important to me. Now as an adult, you get a job, and you get busy, and it's one of the things that kind of falls off your priority list." *Male in his 30's*

355 "I think I get busy and I've got . . . kids . . . at home, and there are also grandkids, so you just tend to separate your time and fit everything in, and so your priorities are different." *Male in his 40's*

356 "To me, physical activity is important. Like I don't see taking a half an hour and running as different than doing my housework. . . . Physical activity is just part of life. . . . I see it as . . . part of daily everything." *Female, 40ish*

47

357 "In high school, I was pretty active. . . . I mean, I always did sports—volleyball, basketball. We horseback rode and we fished and camped and did all those things. . . . I never seemed to have to think about it. You were just automatically busy." *Female, mid 30's*

358 "Being on the farm, . . . we had to work hard; everybody did, so you didn't feel that you were picked on. . . . If [kids today] had to deal with what I had to do, I'm sure that they would have felt abused. Everybody had to [work hard] because that was the means of how we made a living." *Female, late 60's*

359 "Running that mile in junior high, I will always remember . . . being the last one across the line. That wasn't the most positive experience. . . . I felt like I was the last one across the line and pretty far behind. I wasn't as fast as the other runners, but I didn't give up, so I guess that's a good thing." *Female in her 20's*

360 "My view of how I think my body ought to be is pretty heavily motivated by participating in sports a bunch as a kid. 'Cause you kind of have a sense of . . . how much you want to weigh, and how much body fat you ought to have, and how far you ought to be able to run." *Male in his 50's*

361 "I had a hideous gym coach . . . once. . . . He was not a nice fellow. He hated fat people. He thought it was purely self-inflicted even though it turns out I actually had a . . . thyroid disorder. . . . He really hated fat people. And that was when I quit going to PE class all together. . . . He was too hard on people and . . . I couldn't do it. I couldn't compete in anything. Going somewhere and failing every day, that's not fun. . . . And so I would get Fs, and then you have to deal with getting Fs, and parents don't like seeing the Fs, and school counselors don't like seeing Fs. And so I just decided to quit going, which didn't fix the F thing, but at least I wasn't getting an F and being miserable." *Male, late 30's*

362 "I can certainly remember kids that resisted [PE in school]. . . . Because I was part of the girls' athletic program, my physical education period was with kids who were out [doing] the same things, so we didn't have those [kids] with us that couldn't stand it. That would be my frustration. If you're playing a sport and you've got people that just don't put their heart into it, it's like, '*What fun is this?*'. . . the frustration with those that . . . could care less." *Female, late 40's*

363 "I would say that I enjoy [physical activity] more now than I used to because I think so often that in elementary and junior and high school you're *forced* to be in gym class, and that sometimes there's a negative view about gym classes; . . . 'We have to run our laps today,' or whatever." *Female, early 20's*

364 "When I was younger I enjoyed [physical activity]. I think now that I appreciate it more. Back then, I . . . took it for granted, especially coming through high school and into college, that's kind of what you lived and breathed, . . . and from my point of view . . . I really didn't appreciate the big picture of it 'cause it was highly competitive, and that's what I lived on." *Male, 30's to 40's*

365 "I came from a very little high school, so I got a chance to play ball. I wasn't a good athlete, but I got in shape playing ball anyway. I think that we should have intramural sports and everybody ought to get the chance to play."
Male, mid 70's

366 "When I was growing up, I had a growth disease in my knees. In PE when I was a kid, it was this forced thing and the PE teacher was like . . . , 'You go out and you run and it doesn't matter what is wrong with your knees, you just go do it,' . . . [so PE] was a forced painful thing as a child. . . . I remember enjoying going out . . . and playing, . . . but when it came to physical exercise and PE, it was not a pleasant experience." *Female, late 30's*

367 "In junior high and high school when I was active in sports, I did a lot of the conditioning work and the weight lifting and the running just because I knew that I *had* to, to be in that sport. And I didn't *dis*-enjoy it, but . . . yeah, I didn't really want to be there." *Female, mid 20's*

368 "[I] would have given anything when I was a kid to have had more of the physical education on conditioning. . . . Just because of size, I made the football team. And that was a rude awakening to go from just kind of being big to trying to be big and in shape. . . . [I wish] they had physical education teachers rather than coaches who are pretending." *Male, 70ish*

369 "Having the [PE] class requirement makes you do things that you might not. . . . So the stamina that's built up, I recognize it, but maintaining it is another story. . . . I have friends that continue to jog or whatever all through their adult lives, [but] I have never had that desire. . . . I have to have some kind of outside motivation." *Female, late 40's*

370 "After your sophomore year [in high school], they don't make you do PE anymore. . . . The last time I've been active was sophomore year in high school because we [had] PE. . . . I'd have to say my physical activity dropped off and I still [ate] everything." *Male, early 30's*

49

371 "I was a varsity running back, and we won state championships in track, and I participated in a lot of sports. . . . I was successful in sports. . . . People who are not naturally athletic may not have the same opinion about physical activity that I do." *Male in his 30's*

372 "I never could . . . do the . . . chin-ups that we used to have to do to test your physical [abilities]. Climb the rope, absolutely forget it! I mean I hung myself trying to do it." *Female, early 40's*

373 "I . . . really intensely disliked PE in high school and was very uncoordinated in everything I did." *Female, 50ish*

374 "I was raised on a farm [when I was a child], and it was wartime and no hired hands, and so I was probably *very* active in chores and stuff."

Female, late 60's

375 "We walked a mile to school a lot of the time. And a mile home. I loved to walk. I was younger and things didn't hurt so much." *Female, mid 70's*

376 "[When I was a kid], we didn't have Nintendo games and that kind of stuff. We created our active fun." *Male, early 40's*

377 "When I was growing up, I was quite clumsy and very uncoordinated, and I did not like to play sports, and I hated PE because I could not do what the rest of the kids did and do it well. So as I got older, I just accepted myself for what I could do, and it is much better now." *Female in her 50's*

Reflection on PE uniforms and showers

378 "I hated [PE gym classes]! Our so-called uniform was a one-piece bloomer outfit. That, and taking showers—I hated that! And I never was good enough to be on a so-called team, so I spent most of my time sitting on the bench. There was nothing exciting about gym—period! . . . Gym class was probably 30 minutes 'cause you had to undress and dress. By the time you got there, [gym time] was maybe 30 minutes, [but] I doubt it. And then you had to go back, take a shower, and dress up again." *Female, 70ish*

379 "That muscle ache you feel after you work out feels good. . . . Sore muscles don't bother me. . . . Maybe there's something mental or emotional there, too, that makes you feel good about yourself, that you're doing something to take care of yourself." *Male, almost 60*

380 "The best feeling . . . is having sore muscles the next day. I *love* sore muscles! Then I know that I worked hard." *Female, 30's to 40's*

381 "[I like sore muscles] because it's like, oh, they're awake now. I do have muscles. They haven't all turned to flab." *Female, late 40's*

382 "[My high school coach's exercises] were just killers. He would make us do really strenuous ab exercises and really hard exercises that stretched our quads and really got the muscles burning in there. And after practice, I hated those days . . . because . . . they were just too much for me. They just really pushed muscles that didn't want to be pushed." *Female, mid 20's*

383 "I haven't been active for nine months. I just had a baby a little while back, so I haven't done any activity—went bowling this weekend and I woke up the next day and said, 'Oh, my butt muscles are sore. I haven't used these in I don't know how long!' I just couldn't walk. . . . Yeah. Oh yeah! Those butt muscles, like, ooh, I don't remember those." *Female, late 20's to early 30's*

384 "Even though I have aches and pains and stuff, I just ignore them because I want to play [volleyball]. I don't tell my husband because then he says, 'If you're gonna gripe you can't play.' So he doesn't know about the aches and pains that I have. He doesn't know that my knee hurts constantly and my back hurts all the time, because I'm going to go play volleyball anyway, whether he likes it or not." *Female, 30's to 40's*

385 "I almost go to extreme. . . . Like I just taught ten PE classes today, I ran with my track team, . . . and then I just taught an aerobics class. . . . I am so Type A. I have to keep moving. . . . I can't slow down. It drives me crazy. . . . It's just like I have to accomplish so many things in a day, and if I don't, then I don't feel like I've been successful today." *Female, late 20's*

386 "I have a daughter who could work out 24 hours a day and be totally happy." *Female, mid to late 40's*

387 "A lot of times, what we do in our youth, we pay for when we're older. . . . Maybe instead of going to the five yard line, we figure we can push a little bit harder and get to the goal line and then by doing so you pull your hamstring. . . . As you get older, it's going to affect your walking when you're 60 years old. But we don't think of things like that when we're young." *Male, early 50's*

388 "About a week and half ago, we had a snow storm here and I moved a lot of snow, from seven in the morning 'til it got dark, for myself and a couple of my neighbors and [a relative] . . . because he's too lazy sometimes to get out and do it. . . . I went to bed that night [and] . . . I started having some real pains . . . and I thought, 'Boy, am I having a heart attack?' . . . I went over to see [the doctor] and he said, 'No, it's just overexertion.' " *Male, 60ish*

389 "I screwed up my ankle stepping off a pickup. . . . It was a busy time of the year as it is now, [and I] did not take off work, . . . continued to do my job. . . . Eleven years later I'm still fighting ankle problems." *Male, 30's to 40's*

390 "I never did like being last picked or never getting picked at all [for sport games]. . . . It did lower my self-esteem in some ways because it made me feel like I wasn't good. . . . So I think over the years of not being picked it kind of lowered my self-esteem, which has affected some of my other activities in life."
Male, early 30's

391 "In retrospect, having overdone [competitive athletics] . . . has caused the problems that I have today. . . . Now I have rheumatoid arthritis, and every night after volleyball, I'm quaffing down inflammatory this or whatever, so I can walk the next day." *Male, mid 30's*

392 "I had rheumatic fever when I was a youngster and was told I'd never run again. . . . And so I became a runner and that was what I was, a track star. I enjoyed it. The only negative part, I . . . wore out the joints. So I have bad knees, bad ankles, and [my] feet hurt. . . . So . . . I wish I hadn't done all I had . . . because I'm paying for it." *Male, 60ish*

393 "Because of my weight, I've broken both my ankles playing volleyball, so I can't do that anymore." *Female, late 20's*

394 "I can sure attribute a lot of the knee stuff that I've got going on today [to] playing hurt. Shouldn't have been on it, went out and got hurt more."
Male, 30's to 40's

395 "We put up a fair amount of hay, but I always put up . . . hay in small bales for one reason—because I thought my boys and I needed to see the joys and benefits of some hard, physical labor. . . . It goes beyond just physical [activity] because there's a little degree of bonding that goes along with working together, and that's one of the opportunities you have to go out there and work hard together." *Male, early 40's*

396 "For a long time I thought [physical activity] had to be something that was an exercise that I went up to [the local gym] and worked out, or I went out and ran, or I walked for three or four miles. And it was real freeing for me to realize that in carrying my one-year-old around and vacuuming the house I am getting . . . physical exercise. . . . I . . . still get physical activity that benefits my body."
Female, late 30's

397 "When I was younger, I wouldn't really care one way or the other [about being physically active]. I see a little bit of it in my kids and I try to kick them outside more and want them to get out. They listen to me about as well as I listened to my father at the time. . . . To be honest, a lot of [encouraging physical activity for my kids is] not wanting to see them get overweight because you miss out on a few things [when you're overweight]." *Male, early 30's*

398 "I . . . have trouble getting myself in gear. If I didn't have my wife, I probably wouldn't be doing as much as I do. She is more inclined to exercise than I am, and so I go with her." *Male, early 80's*

399 "We've always been kind of more poor or on a lower income side . . . and when I was between second and third grade my dad decided he would go off to [find work in another state], and when he left I guess . . . I didn't do a lot. I missed my dad. So I kind of gained a little bit of weight there and kind of held it ever since." *Male, early 30's*

400 "I'm trying very hard not to have my kids be overweight, trying to have them enjoy physical activity, which is why I'm really glad my son enjoys swimming. . . . And I'm trying to do all these swim meets, . . . not so he will compete and go on and become an Olympic swimmer, but so that maybe by the time he gets to be an adult, he will have an activity that he really just enjoys going and doing." *Female, early 40's*

401 "Mostly my [physical activity] motivator now is my son. . . . I feel that if I'm going to expect him to [be physically active] then I need to be an example. . . . I have really tried to make my attitude positive again for my son ."
Female in her 30's

402 "I have never ever reflected on the positive aspects of exercise, how I got started, . . . and [when I] went back as far as [I] did [how I used to rabbit hunt with my Dad], I think that surprised myself. . . . So I guess it kind of goes back, boy, how our parents, or we as parents, really lay something on our kids at the very core of the things they do sometimes without even realizing how it influences them." *Female, 50ish*

403 "I have . . . kids and I think just picking them up all the time and helping them and trying to keep up with [them keeps me active], . . . [but] if we did walks just as a family, they wouldn't be fast enough for me. I know you're supposed to enjoy the moment, but it's like, 'Well, I want to go get a good walk by myself,' but I just wasn't able to do that with the kids." *Female, mid 30's*

404 "I'm an only child, . . . but my mother married a man with . . . children and so there was obviously some real adjustment there. And I think to get out of the chaos or whatever, I did go to my own room or go to things that didn't include physical activity." *Female, mid to late 40's*

405 "I wish that my parents would have seen that we did more [physical activity] as a family. I mean we worked, but . . . we didn't do things like they're stressing now. . . . I have grandchildren and I see that they're swimming, playing soccer, doing gymnastics, . . . kickball, . . . all kinds of things." *Female, mid 60's*

406 "My husband *really* enjoys TV. . . , especially since he's so physically active . . . . That's . . . where we are if we want to spend time with him. And I'm not going to tell him to turn off the TV, 'cause he's an adult." *Female, 40ish*

407 "I will always be physically active. . . . I think I had positive role models. My mother and father were both active." *Female, early 60's*

408 "I would like to be more active, but I also have other people in my life. I have my family, my kids and my wife. . . . It's more important to me to spend time with them than to go run." *Male in his 30's*

409 "[My husband's brothers' girlfriends] are *really, really* tiny and my mother-in-law always drops hints like, 'Well when are you going to start working out?' "
Female, mid 20's

410 "Some days [physical activity for me is] getting up off of the couch . . . [and] chasing the kids." *Female in her 40's*

411 "I hate seeing kids sitting in front of a computer or video game. I just think parents are copping out." *Female, late 20's*

412 "I am so Type A. I have to keep moving. People are like, 'How do you keep going?' and I'm like, 'If I stop I'm going to keel over.' . . . I'm not like my family, . . . and it's hard 'cause my family . . . —they aren't as active as I am and it drives them crazy that I'm this way." *Female, late 20's*

413 "Sometimes I've been called 'Mr. Cautious.' I think that makes a difference . . . in how a person's body might continue to function during life. Because a lot of people's knees are worn out after high school football. . . . I did consider quite a few things that some of my friends did to be foolhardy because I was more of a cautious person; I wouldn't do some of those things and [didn't] have some of the accidents or some of the doctor bills that they [had]."

Male in his 50's

414 "About ten years ago . . . I worked 14-16 hours a day. I put in landscaping—hard work. So I wouldn't stop. . . . I told you, I come from an age span that loves to work." *Male, late 50's*

415 "My daughter is a teenager and . . . we . . . play softball . . . together. And I'm a . . . manager kind of person, a leader, so I always organize the team and do the coaching. And I find I'm fulfilled in that, being able to use my skills. And then of course I love to win." *Female, 40ish*

416 "I will always be physically active. . . . My daughter . . . says I'm a show-off. And maybe that's part of it, . . . being in the public eye. . . . I always thought I was an introvert. I was, you know, shy. In fact, I do have some shy moments, but I like to be out doing stuff." *Female, early 60's*

417 "I . . . lost a friend this winter [who was] 60 years old. [He] went mountain lion hunting, and everybody can have their own opinion, but knowing him and his personality, I think he probably overdone it when those hounds were chasing that lion. But if it had been me now, I don't give a damn how many mountain lions are on that mountain or if I get one today or not. It ain't worth going out here and running and putting the stress on my heart and lungs until I have a heart attack, which happened to him." *Male, 70ish*

Feeling of "being in shape"

418 "Being in sports and being physically active and competitive, you've seen how you can feel . . . and you've always kind of strived to be that way after you've been in good shape. . . . Then when you quit your physical activity, it's so easy . . . not to do anything and become heavy. . . . It takes work to keep your body healthy." *Male, early 60's*

419 "I'm a competitive person. When I'm in competition, I'm willing to exert a lot more than just standing on a treadmill running. . . . You don't really recognize that you're exercising when you're in competition. . . . It's enjoyable because you are focusing on a game. You are playing a sport. You are trying to win, or . . . you are just trying to play good. And so you don't think as much about the exercise. I would much rather do that than stand on a treadmill and look at the wall and run." *Male in his 30's*

420 "If you look at athletics, when you first start out it's win, win, win by any cause, run over who you have to, [hurt] who you have to hurt to win, and it doesn't take you very long to understand that's not the reason you're doing it. . . . [You do it] to participate. . . . Everybody . . . can't compete at the same level as somebody else, but they can compete at their own level and gain valuable benefits from it." *Male in his 50's*

421 "My friend has got one of those new hydraulic splitting mauls, and [he] went to town on the hydraulic splitting maul, and I went to town chopping wood [by hand] to see who could chop more wood, and I had a whole pile of wood around me before [he had] six stumps split. . . . I like doing stuff like that; I kind of push myself." *Male, early 40's*

422 "I was good at sprinting, so I really liked to sprint. . . . It was more of a rush to me to race against somebody because I always wanted to beat them. . . . It was that feeling of excitement . . . when you want to race or when you know that you did really, really good." *Female, mid 20's*

423 "[My friend and I] went hunting last year, and he told me I about killed him because he was trying to hike with me and we were going up a mountain and I just kept going and . . . he said that he tried to keep up with me and he just kept looking at me thinking, 'He'll slow down, he'll slow down, he'll stop, he's got to catch his breath sooner or later.' And I didn't, and I pushed all the way to the top before I stopped. . . . It's kind of a challenge to me." *Male, early 40's*

424 "I prided myself in being the fastest person on the [basketball] team, and . . . we had to race each other one time to determine who was the fastest on our team, . . . and I got matched up against the fastest kid, and I smoked him, so . . . it was fun for me because everyone else saw that I could run that fast." *Male, early 40's*

425 "I've always been very competitive. . . . When I was in my 30's, I loved to play basketball against young kids . . . and still be able to beat them. . . . As silly as it may sound, I'd like to go over and play basketball one more time after I'm 60, just to say that I did, and see if I can beat anybody." *Male, almost 60*

426 "Sometimes [playing a sport] gets more competitive than . . . I think it should, . . . and it gets a little complicated . . . because [someone's] skill level isn't any better than anybody else, but that person wants to tell everybody else how to play or what to do and direct and instruct the whole time, and it just gets frustrating." *Male, 30ish*

427 "I [wanted] to be on the varsity wrestling team extremely bad. So there were some commitments I had to make at the time. A lot of it had to do with weight reduction because [only] certain slots [were open] on the team. You did whatever you had to do to make the weight. And quite often a lot of the things that you did weren't healthy . . . 'cause a lot of it was just starvation. . . . Your physical well-being suffered a little bit at that time." *Male, early 40's*

428 "I have a hunting partner, . . . and he's ten years older than me, and . . . [sometimes] you need to admit that somebody might have more stamina than you. . . . I hate to act like I'm the unfit one and . . . his level of commitment to physical activity was a push for me. Everything is competitive in life. Especially amongst guys, buddies." *Male, early 40's*

429 "I know when I was in basketball, the training you would do before you got to actually play, . . . I remember that being very physically exhausting. And I wasn't as athletic as some of the other girls in high school. I don't do well when there's competition involved. So maybe that's why I picked walking as my sport, because you don't have to compete." *Female, mid 30's*

430 "I started watching on TV professional basketball, professional football, those type of things. And that led me into the physical activity. It made me want to compete . . . and do those things. And then once that started, it's just kind of been a lifelong process, wanting to keep physically active." *Male in his 30's*

431 "Whoever is competitive [says], 'Okay, I'm gonna beat this person. I'm gonna get up every morning, . . . so they better keep up with me.' I mean, you just want to outdo the next person." *Female, late 20's to early 30's*

One perspective on competition and high school sports

432 "In high school . . . you did [sports] more to fit in with the group. . . . That camaraderie was nice, but I can also remember times . . . the competition just about was overwhelming, even at that point where it felt like, 'Man, that's a lot of pressure to put on people.' That competition piece, it is stressful, and I guess there is good and bad with the competition." *Male, 30ish*

433 "Fifty-five [was a tough birthday]. I think it's just in my head: . . . 'Am I over the hill?' But then I talk to other people, . . . retired people, and they . . . look good, . . . and they tell me what they do. So I get on this guilt trip that I should start taking better care [of myself]. . . . I can't just give up, . . . especially with my grandkid now." *Male, mid 50's*

434 "I kind of look at [physical activity] as the difference between age groups, 'cause physical activity for a certain age group is aggressive. . . . When you get older you have to decrease the physical activity just to fit. . . . Believe it or not, I used to run. I can't do it anymore because of the shin splints that I would get . . . and I had a lot of back and neck pain, so I have to drop down to walking. As you get older, your body just won't take it." *Female, late 40's*

435 "One thing that is very important in life is always to have something that you can look forward to. I think that if you can't look forward to anything, then your life is about over. There's got to be something out there. Like now, I've taken up golf. I think you can play golf as long as you can walk, can't you?"
Male, almost 60

436 "[My husband and I] used to go fishing and hiking, and we used to chop wood. . . . Now I read and write, things like that. . . . Both of our lives were set on curiosity. . . . And we used to not go without a camera, but we've gotten old now, and there's not as many pictures to take, I guess." *Female, 70ish*

437 "I think . . . you get in the routine of life, and you get married, and you have kids, and you get busy taking care of them. . . . But since [my husband and I] had our [child], we haven't been able to do quite as much as we would have liked [as far as physical activity]." *Female in her 20's*

438 "This past weekend we went down to my parents' place . . . and we had to remove Russian olive trees. . . . Well, two, three years ago, I wouldn't have any problem with that. I was literally exhausted. My muscles could not pick up anything anymore after a couple hours of that. And it got so frustrating. I hate the fact that I can't do what I used to be able to do two, three years ago. And I'm like, I'm [in my 20's]. Oh my goodness!" *Female, early 20's*

439 "When you get a few years on you, when you stop and look at things seriously that you're going to get slower, you better get all the life you can now because . . . [when] you're 80 years old you can see how people slow down. So I want to enjoy my physical activity as much as I can and enjoy life as much as I can. . . . Enjoy life so you've got some memories that you did make the best of your life." *Male, 70ish*

440 "I would still like to be able to do all the things I could 40 years ago. . . . And I still try to keep in some kind of shape, . . . especially with grandkids. But unfortunately the joints aren't allowing it to happen." *Male, 60ish*

441 "I know as far as physical activity, I dread the day . . . where I can't do that anymore. I really do. . . . I look at my father-in-law who's well into his 70's and he's at a point where . . . physical activity really is done for him. And that's hard for him because he was . . . an outfitter. . . . He has to use a handrail to pull himself up two steps. And I look at that and think, 'Oh man, I hope I *never* get to that point.' " *Male, 30's to 40's*

442 "Agewise, I believe I enjoy [physical activity] more now because I have time to stop and look at the beauty in the [outdoors]. . . . I step out with my dog in the morning, and I hear an early morning pheasant." *Male in his 70's*

443 "As I've gotten older I've slowed down. . . . Let me put it this way, seven-year-old kids have a lot more running ability than I do." *Male in his 60's*

444 "Last weekend I went . . . and climbed and looked at petroglyphs. . . . I don't have a problem keeping up with 16-year-old kids." *Male, late 50's*

445 "My kids are pretty well grown, so you don't have the physical activity associated with chasing children around like you do when they're tiny."
Female in her 40's

446 "I still try to jog three days a week. But as I've gotten older, things don't work as well as they once did. . . . I can't just jog and enjoy it for the most part because there is always an ache or pain." *Male in his 30's*

447 "Sometimes you think about growing older, and you know you're going to go downhill. I think you want to hold that off and try to do as much you can as long as you can." *Male, almost 60*

448 "It's not like when you were younger. . . . You didn't think about [physical activity], you just *did* it. And I think as we change in our lives, physical activity, as taking time out for ourselves, becomes more difficult to schedule."
Female, late 40's

449 "[When you get older], you don't walk as fast, and you get tired faster, and getting older you just kinda slow down. I still enjoy [physical activity], but it's not as much fun." *Female in her 60's*

450 "Most women won't do strength training. . . . For some reason, [they] have been brainwashed into thinking that that's not something that women do. Women do aerobics. Aerobics are fine, . . . but you need to maintain muscle mass." *Male in his 30's*

451 "Guys like weights. . . . For a period of time there, [hydraulic resistance] was kind of the thing. It was a good strength workout. But I think it flopped and fell out of favor because . . . you weren't moving stacks of weight, . . . and guys like to see what's going on. With [hydraulic resistance machines], you really didn't know exactly how much resistance you were moving." *Male in his 30's*

452 "Women are more social, period. . . . Sometimes I think they talk just to talk, but that's the way that they let the other woman know that they're concerned. That's why [circuit training for women] . . . works the way it does because you go around in a circle. And it's everybody's facing each other. So everybody's talking. It's a social thing." *Male in his 30's*

453 "[When women work out], it's more [for] physical appearance. . . . Women aren't so concerned about how much [weight] they are lifting. They are concerned about firming and toning, losing inches and things like that."

Male in his 30's

454 "My husband is on his feet all day, turning wrenches, doing these things. I sit at my desk eight hours. . . . We have different kinds of exhaustion when we get home." *Female in her 30's*

455 "[In high school], there were all these short jokes, even with people I ran around with. . . . I always felt it would be nice to be bigger, just from the standpoint of not being picked on or having to be afraid of . . . getting your ass kicked. But it always would have been nice to be big enough to, if you had to, clean house, . . . live in peace, 'cause I would be sick to my stomach to go to school." *Male in his 30's*

456 "The place that I go work out is more for women, and I've noticed that around surrounding communities, they have a lot of places for women to go work out. But . . . there's no physical activity center where men can go work out and I think a lot of men . . . would feel uncomfortable going to the [workout facility in this town]. . . . I guess men aren't supposed to work out [in this community]." *Female, mid 20's*

457 "My attitude towards physical activity has changed. . . . It used to be that I would go to the gym and sweat and just kill myself and lift weights, and now it's more I hope to get a few aerobic tapes in the evenings if I have time."

Female, early 20's

458 "Sometimes I push it so hard that I get . . . tunnel vision. My vision starts to come in when . . . I start to hit it too hard, . . . really working, . . . trying to top a ridge or . . . packing your elk out. . . . It kind of takes some of the fun out of it. Basically you're not getting enough oxygen." *Male in his 30's*

459 "After my heart attack, [my wife and I] got into some cardiac therapy under a controlled set of exercises three times a week. . . . When we are out for our evening walks . . . we [walk at a more leisurely pace]." *Male in his 70's*

460 "A few hunting trips with my husband when we were first married . . . required a lot of effort getting into snow that was really deep. . . . [It felt like] you were going to die before you made it back to the top of the mountain. . . . We lived through it, . . . but . . . [it was] exhausting." *Female in her 40's*

461 "My husband . . . [and I] go out and go walking. . . . He picks up a pretty good pace and I'm a short little kid, so my legs don't go that fast. . . . But usually [my husband] will go by himself 'cause then he can just toodle right along, get his heart rate going. Me, I'm slower than the second coming." *Female, late 40's*

462 "I enjoy different things now, less strenuous things. Like now I prefer golf to jogging." *Male in his 30's*

463 "[My husband] can walk three miles an hour and I can only walk two. So I'm always asking him to slow down so I can rest." *Female in her 60's*

Analogy of inactivity and frog in pot of water

464 "[An inactive lifestyle is] kind of like the story of the frog that's in the pot. If you turn the heat up fast, he jumps out. . . . He notices the change quickly. But if you turn [the heat] up slowly, he'll stay in and boil. So, a lot of that's how life is. Your life changes slowly. So if you have an unhealthy habit, . . . you are not going to notice it until you are having problems with your health." *Male in his 30's*

---

465 "We have a stationary bike and I rode it for a while, especially after the accident, because I was always trying to recondition my leg. And I did really well while I was doing the therapy, but as soon as that was over, [the bike] pretty much has gone to rust." *Male in his 40's*

466 "I spent 11 years in [another town] where they do have a rec facility that's reasonably priced, and . . . I was there at least five days a week, playing an hour to two hours. . . . That's something that I miss here." *Male in his 30's*

467 "I like recreation programs that they have for kids. I think this town does an excellent job in that category. . . . I'm not sure that there couldn't be more physical education classes for older people." *Male, mid 70's*

468 "[I wish we had] a place in town that doesn't cost much that I could walk and have the kids play at, or [a] swimming pool, something that's close enough and doesn't cost much." *Female, mid 40's*

469 "It seems to me that the whole idea . . . is that you really got to . . . as a community say 'People are different.' You can't just offer two racquetball courts . . . and say that's good enough. . . . You've got to offer swimming. You've got to offer softball. You've got to offer a lot of stuff." *Male, 30ish*

470 "In a small town there are just not a lot of things to do. I think we're lucky to have volleyball and that kind of stuff. But it would be nice to have more activities available, especially for the winter months." *Female, 40ish*

471 "They schedule [our swimming pool] to be open, [but] when [you] get there they're closed. You know it doesn't take very many times like that and you kind of quit going." *Male, 30's to 40's*

472 "As soon as I got [my exercise bike], I started using it and I loved it. I was so excited, and fax machines were just becoming the thing to do and so I said I'm going to fax the president of the company. I just said, 'I love your machine.' He called me and he said, 'Can you come down for an interview?' And I said sure! . . . So they interviewed me. . . . [Now, that exercise bike] has been sitting on the back porch way too long. And people joke about stuff like that. 'Oh, yeah, we had that and we sold it,' or 'We had that and it's in the garage.' I know that happened to us." *Female, early 60's*

473 "I'm not one that sits in front of a TV. . . . I like to get out. . . . I've gone to the health gym a couple of times, but it got too expensive . . . so I couldn't do that." *Female in her 60's*

474 "You see so much about exercise on TV. You see all these different things on TV about different systems and all this equipment and all these things that you can buy to get you in shape. And they've got so many things out there that they're throwing at our society to make people think that they need to be using their stuff to get in shape. You know it's a big business. There's a lot of people making a lot of money selling stuff that people end up storing in the basement."

Male in his 30's

475 "I started watching on TV professional basketball, professional football, those type of things. And that led me into the physical activity. . . . So I would say that's the big influence there. Yeah, at a young age that's kind of what started me." *Male in his 30's*

476 "I remember coming upon Jack LaLanne on TV one time. I thought he was just a pretty neat character. . . . He was probably the original [exercise] guru. . . . I guess that was probably my first real routine of exercise." *Female, 50ish*

477 "I smoked for 40 years. . . . I quit [over 20 years ago], cold turkey. . . . I've never smoked one since. . . . I enjoy everything better—breathing, non-stuffiness. I think I see everything in a clearer vision. . . . I'm breathing better. I can exercise, walk, hike, eat, sleep, and I'm not coughing." *Male in his 70's*

478 "I'm having a little trouble quitting smoking. I mean I'm having a lot of god damn trouble quitting smoking, and I know I should. . . . You know it's [easier] to sit down and smoke a cigarette and drink a cup of coffee than it is to go over and get on the [exercise machine] and do a few reps or a few rows or something. . . . What's it going to be like five or ten years down the road there? You know, wheezin' old man! Not good. Not at all." *Male, mid 50's*

479 "I quit smoking when I was probably 20. I smoked almost four packs a day. I was in the military and it just got to the point . . . where I couldn't hardly breathe. . . . And then after that I have just been relatively healthy the rest of my life because I could see the difference of what, like, smoking, for example, could do." *Male, late 50's*

480 "I'm getting older and smoking is not good and does all kind of weird things. I think, beyond looking just at what's going on right now today, a person needs to look down the road a little bit." *Male, mid 50's*

481 "This area is very fortunate that we have a wide variety of [physical activity] options, and my work also offers [any] one of the three health clubs, [and] if you go as a family, they'll pay . . . the fee . . . because they believe in wellness for their employees." *Female, early 40's*

482 "I think of all the necessary work to do on a ranch, pretty well keeps you conditioned. When you have to bring this hay in and feed it, and you have to take the used hay back out, . . . that's . . . pretty well conditioning you."
Female, mid to late 70's

483 "I used to work in the oil field and [that job was] way too [physical] and it caught up with me." *Female, late 40's (suffers from back problems)*

484 "My primary job is for a construction company, so our season is like a whole other life than the downtime. So we're talking 50-hour weeks. Plus still holding down a 20-hour second job, so 70 hours of your week is gone. Trying to fit in exercise just went away." *Female, early 40's*

485 "I work at the hospital, . . . so it's pretty physically active just doing that. I'm hefting patients all the time and . . . running around the hospital a lot. . . . I walk a zillion steps." *Female, mid 30's*

486 "I'd like to slow down [my physical activity] a little bit, but I've got four years, one month, and 26 days left, and I'm going to retire." *Male, late 50's*

487 "When I grew up you didn't do all this stuff like they do now, all the machines . . . and the running and all this stuff. Really, it just was work; . . . you got your exercise just working." *Female, late 70's*

488 "Something has to be done to help young couples where maybe the woman doesn't have to put in an eight-, nine-hour day at work. . . . You [can] get up early [and exercise], but sometimes if you're up all night with a baby, you just physically can't; I mean you're just exhausted. And it's tough because a lot of young couples, they both have to work." *Female, late 40's*

489 "In the summers . . . I love to walk and I'll get up early in the morning and go walk for an hour. Then when school starts again and I have to get up and get my kids ready to go, my exercise program just falls apart." *Female, mid 40's*

490 "It was real freeing for me to realize that in carrying my one-year-old around and vacuuming the house I am getting . . . physical exercise . . . that benefits my body." *Female, late 30's*

491 "We have a weight room at the bottom of my workplace, and I try to go there . . . and work out . . . on the treadmill and try to at least run a mile and a half or two miles every day." *Male, 30's to 40's*

492 "Before I retired [four years ago] I was very active. . . . I worked on one of the production lines and it was very active." *Female in her 60's*

493 "I was a self-employed contractor. I was up at daylight every morning and going 'til dark and never had to worry about gaining a pound." *Male, 70's to 80's*

494 "Sitting behind a desk can [make you lazy]. Your mind is constantly going . . . [so] your body's not tired at night, but your mind's going all day and so you're a zombie in your brain." *Female, 40ish*

Physical activity and the military

495 "My father was in the Army. It is a great way of life. There are risks and you better know about that. They tried to [recruit] me in high school. There was a lot less of me back then. Looking back on it, that was one defining moment in my life. The guy doing the physical said, 'Have you used an inhaler?' . . . And I said, 'Well, I could tell the truth, which is yes, or I could say no and I could go in the Army.' But I told the truth and that cut me out right there. And that in a way was a defining moment in my life. . . . I went to college, and [physical activity wasn't promoted] unless you're in the athletic department." *Male, early 30's*

496 "I'm in the National Guard, and I have a PT test coming up, which is physical training, and so I'm supposed to pass my push-ups, sit-ups, and two-mile run, which I don't think I'm going to do. Push-ups I don't have to worry about. Sit-ups kill me. I keep telling my recruiter guy that they [need] to make a special section for women that have had children. He doesn't like my excuses."
Female, mid 30's

497 "I spent 25 years in the United States military. . . . I enjoyed the physical part of that." *Male, mid 50's*

498 "After my heart attack, [my wife and I] got into some cardiac therapy under a controlled set of exercises three times a week. The doctor informed me that I absolutely should . . . do it." *Male in his 70's*

499 "I was going to have my ankle fixed a year ago. . . . Went to the doctor. He looked at it and said, 'Yep, we need to do surgery,' and [he] said, 'This is when we need to do it, . . . and you are going to be laid up . . . for about six weeks.' That [would have included] opening week of elk hunting. . . . He [laughed and] said, 'We ain't doing the surgery.' So it didn't get done, and it still hasn't been done." *Male, 40ish*

500 "[My husband] had a heart condition, and he had to walk every night, and we just started walking, until he got to where he couldn't walk anymore. And then after he passed away I just kind of went into a slump and didn't want to go out walking by myself, so I didn't." *Female in her 60's*

501 "But to think of [regular physical activity] in the exercise way, I've never paid very much attention up until [my heart attack]. I wasn't a weekend warrior that went out and wore myself out over the weekend, although there were times that we did that. . . . But to have a regular program, no, I had never given it a thought until after my heart attack." *Male in his 70's*

502 "I think [it] would really help if we were getting cooperation of the medical profession. And I don't know how you'd implement that, looking at the whole person. . . . There seems to be, and you notice on TV, they have all of these prescription drugs. 'Ask your doctor about them.' How many doctors are prescribing because the person asked them rather than because the person needed it? . . . And every time a new drug comes out, it's got a fancy name and a fancy price and that's what they prescribe for the patient." *Female in her 60's*

503 "The doctor told me a long time ago to stay out of the sun. So I took him very much at his word. And I do walk some, but I don't . . . every day. . . . So I don't do an awful lot of physical activity." *Female in her 60's*

504 "[My doctor encouraged me to be more physically active because] I have diabetes, and I have high blood pressure and cholesterol, the things that happen to you that you really don't want." *Female, late 60's*

505 "My doctor said I need more [physical activity]. . . . I suppose I do, but there's always something going on that I can't fit it in." *Female, 40ish*

506 "I've got a little heart problem, and . . . if I'm going to take care of this heart problem, I need to get off the old couch." *Male, mid 50's*

Changes in society

507 "We used to have chores . . . just to keep a household going. . . . Now, the hardest thing a kid does is work the TV or run to that computer and play on that damn thing. [In the past, we were] getting the wood and the coal and the slop bucket or carrying out the wash water. . . . There was more physical activity to keep a home going." *Male, 70ish*

508 "I don't think the majority of kids nowadays have physical activity like we had when we were kids because I can remember *always* being physically active from the minute I got up until I went to bed at night." *Male, 40ish*

509 "I think our culture has changed so much that we are becoming a more sedentary-type people. And I see . . . kids and the kind of activities they are involved with, whether it's video games or whatever, that require just minimal motion and activity. . . . We're not generating much interest in being active at an early age and I think that converts right into . . . adulthood." *Male, early 40's*

Having a baby

510 "I haven't been active for nine months. I just had a baby a little while back, so I haven't done any activity." *Female, late 20's to early 30's*

Small high school

511 "I came from a very little high school, so I got a chance to play ball. I wasn't a good athlete, but I got in shape playing ball anyway. I think that we should have intramural sports and everybody ought to get the chance to play."
Male, mid 70's

Hunting

512 "I was going to have my ankle fixed a year ago. . . . [The surgery and recovery would have included] opening week of elk hunting. [The doctor] said, 'We ain't doing the surgery.' So it didn't get done, and it still hasn't been done."
Male, 40ish

High altitude

513 "Where . . . high altitude is concerned . . . [and] with the aging process . . . I'm recognizing how that affects everything. . . . I probably enjoy [physical activity] less [now than when I was younger] because it gets harder."
Female, late 40's

Stairs

514 "We lived in a house that had three floors, . . . and I can remember when I first moved in . . . it was tough, . . . but it's amazing, over a period of time, . . . you get to the point where you don't even notice." *Female, late 40's*

Chapter Two

FOOD AND EATING

Take pleasure in eating and honor the gift of food.

Guiding principles from Wellness IN the Rockies

515 "I enjoyed the time that we were able to sit as a family, and that was a pleasurable thing that probably influenced me more than anything. And . . . those [meals] were few and far between. . . . That was something I can remember, but I think the most [important] thing is just the pleasure of being as a family and enjoying a good cooked meal. It was tasty." *Male, mid 50's*

516 "A friend of mine took me to a place because he knew I liked calamari. . . . And it cost me seven dollars for the sandwich, and it was huge. . . . They bake their own bread there. It was two big thick slices and . . . you had to hold it with two hands . . . and I ate that thing and I enjoyed it. And we got about halfway back [to his home] and I said, 'We gotta go back.' And he asked, 'Why?' And I said, 'Because I gotta have another one of those sandwiches!'. . . That was the best sandwich I ever ate in my life. . . . I'll never forget." *Male, early 50's*

517 "When we're camping, it doesn't matter what you eat, it always tastes good. And if you go on a hiking trip, . . . it seems like the food is better. And actually that does [remind] me, whenever I had a job [where] I was physically active, . . . [food] was more enjoyable to eat because you were hungry." *Male in his 30's*

518 "A couple weeks ago [my wife and I] stopped at a restaurant and I had a pot roast dinner and I really enjoyed that experience. . . . And it just reminded me of how things were when I was younger, as a kid. A Sunday afternoon meal with my mother and dad, and I just enjoyed eating it because it tasted good and because it refreshed some of those memories from another time." *Male, mid 50's*

519 "I enjoy eating. Everybody has to eat. I like good food. . . . But now it doesn't have to be where I'm miserable when I get done eating. . . . I finally got this mind set that I feel better if I don't overeat." *Female in her 60's*

520 "My grandma cooked all kinds of food [for a holiday meal on Sunday]. . . . And it was good food, especially compared to Taco John's. It was *really* good food. . . . So many of our holidays are based around food, . . . the highlight of the day is to eat with your loved ones." *Female, early 20's*

521 "I work in the restaurant business as a waiter. I've come to the point where good food is important to me. . . . I mean, it's almost like an art to me. . . . It's really a neat thing when you can have a good meal." *Male, mid 20's*

522 "My wife makes the best chicken and dumplings in the world. There is no match whatsoever. So when I know we're going to have chicken and dumplings, why would I want to go out and try somebody else's? It's not going to be that great of an experience." *Male in his 70's*

523 "After high school, I went over to [Europe] and worked in a restaurant there, and every meal they made, we would eat as a family before we'd actually work. It was just so delicious. . . . It wasn't anything really fancy. . . . It was their family dinner." *Female in her 20's*

524 "I'm not much as for quantity as I am quality. . . . And I like good vegetables. . . . We made tacos the other night and I *love* tacos. And you go get some of these good . . . tomatoes . . . vine-ripened. Get some of those and some good lettuce and cheese and some olives, and . . . I could eat that just as good on a Sunday as I can on a Tuesday. I feel good about it." *Male in his 50's*

525 "When I came home from school, [I could tell] what we were having for dinner just by the smell. You associate smells with food, some of the foods with different occasions, and it was a great time." *Male in his 50's*

526 "I guess that I like eating food that has [more fat]—I mean, it isn't exactly healthy for you but I enjoy it. What tastes good to me isn't always what most people consider healthy." *Male, early 30's*

527 "I always enjoyed food. You can tell by my [gestures to body]."
Female, late 60's

528 "Me, just being fat, you know . . . I like to eat. That sounds terrible, but I like to eat food. I just enjoy eating food." *Female, mid 20's*

529 "I eat food because I like it. . . . Even though I know I have to watch what I eat, I still eat because I like to and not because I need to." *Female, late 20's*

530 "There are some foods out there that I really enjoy and I am a hearty eater, so to speak. . . . I pretty much like everything. . . . That's why I have to force myself to exercise. I like food so much." *Male in his 30's*

531 "[In terms of enjoying food], I . . . think, in general, of times when . . . you go to a good restaurant—. . . just how excited you are to go try . . . your favorite food." *Female, early 20's*

532 "I ate at a restaurant yesterday and had a big greasy hamburger. It was really good. . . . It just satisfied that hunger craving I had. . . . I look at it and say, 'That's probably not good for me,' but . . . it sure tasted good."
Male in his 20's

533 "Eating is just a daily fact of life, and . . . if you enjoy being a participant, I think that's joyful." *Female, early 60's*

534 "I remember times when I was . . . having a hard time [my mom] would go to the kitchen and [give] me a plate of cabbage and homemade noodles and put lots of butter on it. It was just really neat. It was a good treat as a kid."

Male, early 40's

535 "[The heavy kids] go home and they eat because they don't want to have to deal with life. My wife, she's skinny for years, but . . . yet to this day her way of dealing with stress or dealing with whatever is to not eat. When I deal with it, I eat." *Male, 30's to 40's*

536 "If you had a bad day at school, . . . you got in trouble or whatever, Mom made you your special [food]. There was Mom's medicine factor to meals sometimes. . . . I think those thoughts still hang with me." *Male, mid 30's*

537 "There's comfort to food. . . . Feeling the need for food—like now, sometimes when you get kinda blue, it seems like [eating] is just something to do." *Female, mid 70's*

538 "I got married and my mother-in-law was a wonderful cook and food was offered to you all the time. . . . It all tasted so good. It was easy to eat too much, but food is comfort too." *Female, mid 70's*

539 "There's a salad that my mom always makes . . . [and] I'll always associate it with my mom. It's kind of a comfort food to me. If I get homesick for Mom, . . . I can make that salad and remember my mom." *Female in her 30's*

540 "And I love to cook, and it kinda shows. And when I'm bored, that's what I turn to rather than the physical activity. It's, 'Let's make something good to eat.' " *Female, mid 40's*

Memorable quotation

541 "You'll be walking through the store and you'll hear a little kid say, 'Now that guy is pretty fat.'. . . I mean, they're not meaning to do harm. They're just little kids. . . . But being teased about it would force me to go home and have some ice cream or something. Kind of kill the pain with food." *Male, early 20's*

542 "I have [food] issues . . . that I'm trying to slowly, slowly resolve and keep resolved, because I've walked down this path a lot, and then I jump back, and I don't know at what point I do that. But I need to stop that pattern because I have this pattern going that's awful. Realize [poor eating habits]. Go do something about it. It's getting better. Go back to the old habits. [I do that] *over* and *over* and just keeping playing the tape. And it just makes me wonder at what point what happens that I say, 'This is enough,' and truly go get past that. And so [dieting] is a huge part of my life. And I wish it wasn't. I'm ready to put it aside and get on with things that are more important. 'Cause like [someone else] said, dieting *isn't* the most important thing in the world, and I hate that it's such a priority to me." *Female in her 30's*

543 "[Twenty years ago I lost 100 pounds] and I stayed that way for probably almost two years. I did it with starvation. At first I started with [a meal replacement drink,] and it was so much like not eating at all that pretty soon I decided this stuff's expensive, I can't see that I'm benefitting from it, so I just pretty much quit eating. Sometimes I'd go four or five days without eating. . . . I lost a lot of weight that way. I lost over 100 pounds in four months. That's probably why I didn't keep it off, too. 'Cause I didn't form good eating habits. But the problem with dieting is you don't eat like everybody else. . . . When I sit down to a meal I want to enjoy what everybody else is enjoying." *Male in his 40's*

544 "Well, it was quite a few years ago I started going to [a diet program]. And I would just let myself get so hungry, I would just hit the cupboards, refrigerator, the freezer, everything. And I just let myself get too hungry and I had to eat. . . . I don't know how many times in my life I've dieted. And now I'm doing it again." *Female in her 60's*

545 "I started dieting when I weighed 250, and I dieted myself up to 350. It's just what happens. . . . Every time I got my weight down to about 220, then I would go back up. I would let it get back up, and it would be ten pounds heavier than it was the last time I did it. [I went on that] Optifast program . . . which turned out to be really bad for a lot of people. A lot of people . . . [from] that class had gallbladder problems, and I think out of the 20 people that were in that class that I went to for six months there was only one that . . . when they got done with the liquid diet was able to maintain their weight." *Male in his 60's*

546 "Currently I only eat when I'm hungry so I don't get obsessed with food. . . . After being on those silly diets, I remember craving food . . . because all I thought about all day was food. . . . If I'm not hungry I just don't eat and I save [food] for later . . . , which I was trying to teach that to my mom, but I don't know. It's not really something you can teach to someone." *Female, mid 30's*

547 "More than ever in my life, I try *not* to eat to keep weight off. . . . It doesn't help that at work all the girls are dieting . . . and it almost makes you feel like, 'Gosh' . . . especially when they're thinner than you are, and they're doing that. . . . I skip meals . . . in hopes of maybe I'll lose some weight, which I know is not the answer to losing weight, but I do it sometimes though." *Female, early 20's*

548 "I tend to put on considerably more weight in the winter. . . . And it seems like every year, as I get older, I'll put on a couple more pounds and those don't come back off. I might gain ten pounds, but you know somewhere in there I would lose eight." *Male, 30's to 40's*

549 "[My mom and I] always eat at [our favorite restaurant] and we have this one salad that I just *love*. But after going to Weight Watchers I found out that my favorite salad, that I think I'm doing so well, has 20 points in it in the medium, and sometimes I get the full. And I'm only allowed just over 20 points, so that uses my whole day in one shot. So we decided we would still go to [the restaurant] and I had to order the little fat whatever salad. I *hated* it. Shuckee-darn, [that restaurant] will never be the same for me. . . . We were both grumpy because we were just eating this tasteless thing. . . . So it was not the same and it was kind of a bummer. . . . I left there still wanting the salad." *Female in her 30's*

550 "I did the phen-fen thing and that did help. And then I heard it was dangerous, so I quit. . . . I probably lost 30 pounds. . . . You hardly even notice 30 pounds on me, I'm so big." *Male, late 30's*

551 "I've been overweight all my life. I was 10 pounds, 12 ounces when I was born and I've been big ever since. And I've been on many diets all through grade school, junior high, high school. And I probably haven't dieted in the last ten years. I figure why bother? I watch what I eat. I don't eat a lot of fried stuff. But I just take it one day at a time. 'Cause I figure, you know, I like who I am. . . . And if somebody doesn't like me because of the way I look, they lost a friend . . . . So that's just the way I look at things." *Female, early 40's*

552 "I would literally have to starve myself [to lose weight]. It would be like a piece of fruit for breakfast—and I've done this before—a piece of fruit for breakfast, salad for lunch, and for dinner I may have some protein and another vegetable. And then I can lose the weight, as well as running like three or four miles a day. Then I could get down to a decent weight. But you eat like that, and I can't function. So it's hard!" *Female, late 40's*

553 "There was a summer that my husband [was away] for three months, and so I was home alone. And I focused very intently on losing weight while he was gone. And I lost like 25 pounds. [I'd] go home and grill myself one little tiny chicken thigh, and that was it. And I focused on [losing weight] all summer. And as soon as he was home and I had somebody to cook for again, the meals were no longer quite as torturous. I remember feeling that they were torturous—to go home and eat that chicken thigh one more time. And when [my husband] was home, it was back to cooking and enjoying food a little more."

Female, early 40's

554 "I was really starting to feel the weight. It wasn't so much feeling uncomfortable with myself as the way I felt. The shortness of breath, some of the warning signs of possible diabetes, and some different things that you think like, 'If I don't get a hold of this thing now it's going to be too late. And I'm really going to pay the price.' . . . I graze [food] continually, and so I had to do something, and the support that I get at [my support] group too is wonderful. . . . I have to be accountable to somebody, 'cause I can just avoid my little scale at home. Push it to the side. Or I get on it and push it around and think, 'Okay now if it's over here a little bit it might be a few pounds lighter.' Hop off and get on it in another spot. Oh, I know [all the tricks to get the scale to read lighter]. But when I have to go to a meeting and weigh in, I have to be accountable to that person, or I tell myself I do." *Female in her 30's*

555 "[On weigh-in days] I'd say, 'Oh it's weigh-in day. Mother, can I have a water pill?' And so then I'd borrow a water pill from her and I did not like the feeling that I got from that. It was not healthy, and I dehydrated myself for sure." *Female, early 60's*

556 "My weight . . . varies all the time . . . . I eat a lot, and I'm like, 'Geez, I'm starting to get kind of chubby.' So then you just don't have a Snickers bar and you maybe try and eat just one portion instead of two." *Male, mid 20's*

557 "You play football and you bulk up and you'd then go into wrestling season and you'd literally starve yourself to death. . . . You'd go in and you'd lose ten pounds in a night. And then hold it off to make weight, and then you'd binge the next day." *Male, almost 50*

558 "Not too long ago, I went on a very restrictive diet to lose weight. . . . Things were going wonderfully. I went to see the doctor, and I was anemic. . . . And he said, 'I think you better eat,' which was wonderful news. . . . I can breathe in when I go by a restaurant and gain five pounds." *Female in her 60's*

559 "I [lost over 20 pounds] in the last five weeks, just eating healthy . . . and actually I feel great just to get that little bit of weight off. It's a lot easier to move around and breathe." *Female in her 20's*

560 "I've lost about 30 pounds over the last four months without even really trying to. . . . And the minute I say the word 'diet,' I'm going to go find a chocolate bar, so I'll warn you. I refer to 'diet' as behavior modification."

Female, early 40's

561 "My husband was a wrestler in college and I mean he dieted *all* the time. . . . And so now dieting is real tough for him because he just hates it. And he goes overboard when he does decide to diet, so it makes it really tough for me because I just want to maintain a certain diet, and he goes up and down."

Female, late 40's

562 "I knew I was getting in a slump from when my husband died. I was . . . just sitting home every day and doing nothing except eating. . . . And one day, when I bent over to tie my shoe, all of a sudden I couldn't get my breath. I couldn't bend over without gasping for breath. . . . I had never been this heavy, and I thought I got to do something about this . . . before I get any bigger. . . . I joined [a weight control group] and I've really enjoyed it because . . . I can still eat any food I want. I just have to count the points and know how much I can eat each day and it's been satisfying." *Female in her 60's*

563 "Twice in my life I've lost 150 pounds going on a straight liquid diet. . . . I got to looking pretty good, but as soon as I tried to go back to normal food, [the weight] all came back." *Male in his 60's*

564 "I went on [meal replacement drink] and lost, like in six months, I probably lost 20 pounds. . . . But it didn't stay off. It found me again." *Female in her 20's*

565 "These quick-fix programs or these extreme programs don't work; they only make matters worse. I can tell you that . . . 'cause I've tried every one of them. . . . I couldn't count them all." *Male in his 60's*

566 "These fad . . . diets . . . that you see on TV, . . . you can lose weight with them, but you'll gain it right back. . . . You can gain the weight you lost and more back." *Male, early 20's*

567 "[After dieting], my weight crept back on. I'm probably at the highest I've ever been in my life. Even pregnant I don't think I weighed anywhere near this. And I talk to my doctor . . . and he said, 'Well, . . . cut down sugar and fat.' Well, it's such a great idea if you can really do it." *Female, early 60's*

568 "I was one of those who went on every diet and they didn't work. . . . I'd lose weight, but then I'd gain ten pounds more than I was." *Female, mid 60's*

569 "On the day that you're going to weigh in, . . . [food becomes] almost an enemy then. . . . Then we would go out afterwards . . . and we would eat, visit, and enjoy food." *Female, early 60's*

570 "[When you're dieting,] you have to have a certain type of food every day, . . . which would get very boring. . . . You get through eating that and get to lose weight, then you're going to go back to your regular way of eating and you're going to put [the weight] right back on again. . . . Since the fifties, I've just kinda gone up and down. . . . [I] just yo-yoed." *Female in her 60's*

571 "I have many family members, [and] we're always dieting, and we're always talking about food, and we're always talking about the fact that we're always talking about food." *Female in her 30's*

572 "When you're married, say a guy tries to go on a diet . . . but his wife's not on it. When she tried to do it, it was the same thing. And lately, we're both in the same mind-frame working towards the same weight, whereas before we were kind of at odds." *Male, early 30's*

573 "My mom got a little heavy, and . . . she was always trying to diet, and I guess it made such an impression on me. I didn't see much difference in her. . . . I determined that I would never diet when I was old because it seemed like such a hassle that didn't do much good. . . . I haven't tried any diets and I've probably stayed about the same weight as I would whether I dieted or not, or maybe I'd be heavier." *Female, mid 40's*

574 "I've always been working on my weight. Always. I've been to this and every diet you know. You're always working at it." *Female, late 60's to early 70's*

575 "I did belong to Weight Watchers and then joined TOPS. . . . It has kept me from ballooning. You need that scale every week." *Female, late 60's*

576 "I think whenever I try to diet, . . . I just don't feel good. And I get the shakes or whatever. So I just kind of figured out to just cut back and not do the diet business. . . . I just don't feel comfortable dieting—physically comfortable."
Female, 30's to 40's

577 "My mom was always dieting, and I'm probably . . . a little bigger than she was at her biggest. And since she was dieting, it makes me feel like I'm too big because she felt like she was too big." *Female, mid 40's*

578 This person served as a missionary for her church and described how the experience impacted her relationship with food: "It was constant rejection all day long. . . . I kind of went into a depression tailspin. . . . I got moved to another place. . . . I just started working [harder] trying to do more than I could, . . . but they still were rejecting us all the time even though they were really good people. And so finally I started going off the deep end and I started eating too strict [a diet]. . . . [The more] I stressed out, the less I could sleep and I started dropping weight, a whole lot, and then I started probably having hallucinations, and I ended up really skinny. . . . And it ended up that I had a nervous breakdown, and I was sent home. But food was part of that. . . . After I came home . . . my body just needed to rest and I just slept for months. And I gained a whole lot of weight, like 70 pounds. . . . And so that was a major experience with . . . food." *Female, mid 40's*

579 "I don't know why or who started it—my husband or me—that if I lost weight to be in a certain size then he'd buy me . . . a pretty dress. And so probably then is when I concentrated most on not eating as much. . . . But then I got the pretty pink dress to wear." *Female, mid 40's*

580 "When I was in high school . . . a lot of times I got really busy and I didn't eat, or my friends weren't hungry at lunch, so I just wouldn't go eat. And I know a lot of times . . . I would end up not eating all day. And because of that, I probably wasn't at the healthiest weight. . . . I was so *tiny* in high school."

Female, mid 20's

581 "My wife will leave to visit with her mother, and I'll go three days without eating. . . . Sometimes I'll drink things I shouldn't drink, but mostly I'll just even drink water or a soda or something, but I won't eat for sometimes three days. And then it's like, 'Oh, I got to eat,' and that's not healthy . . . by any means."

Male, early 30's

Memorable quotation
582 "When somebody was selling vitamins, he made up this beautiful song that you had to get to the right weight so you'd look good in the coffin." *Female, mid to late 60's*

583 "I used to eat just enormous amounts and . . . don't know why I did. I didn't feel good after I did it, especially as much as I ate, but . . . I really abused [food]. . . . I always ate too much. . . . I have no concept of being full. . . . You're supposed to become satisfied and . . . if I get going I can put away staggering amounts. I don't know . . . how much [a stomach can] take, but I have no concept of being full. I eat until it's gone. But that's improved over the last couple of years. But, boy, when I was in my early 20's I could eat six quarter-pounders, and . . . I just liked eating. And it went along with watching TV. They go together. And . . . why I don't feel full, I don't know. . . . I have to sit there and think to stop because I can just keep packing it away." *Male, late 30's*

584 "I notice that when my life isn't balanced, that [overeating] will just be all part of it. . . . It's not the *cause,* but it's . . . one of the *symptoms*, and so if I've not taken enough time with the Lord or with my family or my work—just the balance not being there." *Female, 40ish*

585 "Almost after every meal, I want something sweet. And I don't know if that goes back to when I was a kid, 'cause that was . . . the routine. You ate the dinner and then if you ate everything on the plate, then you got the sweet thing. Then you're so dang stuffed that you couldn't enjoy the sweet thing. But we'd eat it anyway." *Female, 40ish*

586 "You can have all this great information [about healthy eating,] and you'll still be crazy when it comes to food sometimes. . . . I just looked at myself in the mirror one day and I said to myself, 'Why can't you stop when you know you should? Why don't you just take in a normal amount?' " *Female, early 60's*

587 "[There are] times I don't feel like I'm in control, that I just want to continue to eat, and I know I shouldn't be doing it, but I'm doing it anyway. . . . And I know better. . . . But just *knowing* better and [still overeating] . . . that's irritating to me." *Female, 40ish*

588 "I have learned . . . never to overeat. When you've eaten so much, there's a time to stop. . . . You sleep better at night . . . if you don't gorge yourself and overeat. . . . There was a time when I was kind of overeating, and I couldn't sleep good, . . . couldn't even run good. . . . Then I realized if I ate less I felt better." *Female, mid to late 70's*

589 "I went to school with a girl, she would never exercise when we exercised. She would never slow down on lunch. She . . . just gained a lot of weight. And I thought, 'I do not want to end up like her.' . . . I think she died in '94, and . . . I do not want to end up like that." *Male in his 30's*

590 "I like bars, cookies, pies, cakes, whatever. And that's why I have my [weight] troubles. I've got a sweet tooth and I very seldom bake anymore.... If I bake now, I usually eat it all. So, I very seldom bake." *Female in her 60's*

591 "I binge.... I don't know why I binge.... I don't get fat when I go to the restaurant; it's what I do in private." *Female in her 60's*

592 "Sometimes . . . I eat too much and regret it later.... I think, 'Oh, I shouldn't have eaten that. I shouldn't have eaten all those M&M's.' "
Female in her 20's

593 "I can definitely see that if you eat to overindulgence that's going to affect your physical well-being, and it's going to affect your life span." *Male, mid 50's*

594 "Overeating food can keep a person from enjoying [food]. If a person eats too much, it takes a little while to wear that off and a person doesn't feel as well for a while. So if we actually realize what's happening, and we're disciplined enough, then we'll try to just eat a little less and feel better." *Male in his 50's*

595 "Order of the Eastern Star, . . . we call it the Over Eaters Society because those ladies prepare meals all the time. Of course, the men love it."
Male in his 70's

Buffets and Potlucks

596 "I've learned that when we go to a potluck, don't be in front of the line. There are too many decisions. Stay until some of the rest of the people have eaten." *Female in her 60's*

597 "I find myself getting some very serious guilt trips on [eating]. For instance, [I] had an experience of going to a buffet type of a restaurant. I came to be glutton in those periods of time and suffered for it.... [I say] I'm just not going to eat that much, but I do.... I'm old enough to know better."
Male in his 70's

598 "My parents were always the type that they loved those buffet-type places. They would love to just chow and my mom would pick four desserts and that always embarrassed me. It's like, 'Mom, that just looks like a glutton.' ... My parents would just shovel their food in, whether they were hungry or not, and it used to bother me, especially as I got older." *Female, mid 30's*

599 "The problem with buffets is that you will take more food than you would normally.... They just have . . . so many wonderful choices." *Female, early 60's*

600 "I sometimes go into buffet-type restaurants and I look around and I figure about two-thirds of the people there eat more than they should. Many of them are overweight, and seeing them just heaping their plates up, I think that's wrong. I don't think a person should overeat. . . . I just see too many people go back for seconds and thirds and heap their plates, and . . . they're not healthy."

Male, mid 70's

601 "But every now and then lately, especially if I'm out of town working, and I've worked hard that day, . . . I try to find a smorgasbord or buffet . . . so I can . . . I guess you'd call it pig down. And after I've done it, I don't like to eat for about two more days 'cause I've got to get rid of what it did to me. . . . I don't [usually] eat a lot. . . . But it's just sometimes I overconsume." *Male, 60ish*

602 "I don't like buffet places. . . . My dad loves [buffets] and I just rebel. It's like . . . I can't go to a place where there's so much out there that you just don't get to taste the food." *Female, mid 30's*

Family Holiday Meals

603 "My family [overeats at holidays]. They just eat all day long, never become comfortable. Got the turkey and dressing and then the pecan pie that we love, and it never ends." *Female, early 20's*

604 "Easter stands out, . . . overdid everything as usual. And then afterwards you feel like you are going to die for awhile, but then you do get better, usually."

Male, 40ish

605 "[Family holiday meals are] where you eat until you're stuffed, and then you wait a few minutes, and you go back again." *Female, early 20's*

Self-therapy to curb overeating

606 "This is probably silly, but I wanted to give myself shock therapy. So I took some old jam and was giving myself shock therapy saying, 'Look at yourself! You're eating whether you enjoy it or not. Why are you doing this?' And so I'm smearing jam on my face and I'm putting some in [my mouth], but I'm spitting it out and just saying, 'See what you're doing to yourself? You're just taking in food. You're not enjoying it. Just cut it out!' I just thought that was a self-inflicted shock treatment. It was just bizarre, but I'm going to say I was more careful after that."

Female, early 60's

---

607 "I can remember when we were little growing up, my dad and mom would make my [siblings] eat everything on their plate, and I had one . . . brother who would not eat it. And to this day, he does not eat vegetables. . . . He doesn't eat all these vegetables because he had to sit at the table and stay there until he ate them. . . . And my brother would sit *forever* and not eat his vegetables because he didn't want to, and my dad would make him sit there. And I knew I would just not do that to my kids and make it such a big deal." *Female, 30's to 40's*

608 "My mother always cooked very big meals . . . and we couldn't leave the table until we cleaned up our plates, 'cause we [were] always told [about] starving kids. . . . We ate whether we [were] full or not. [You] were never told to quit eating when you were full. You just cleaned up your plate."

Female in her 60's

609 "[My dad] would fix you a plate that was about like a serving platter thing— 'No, you can't get up from the table until you eat all that.' Well, Mom, she'd feel sorry for us and she'd be there helping us out a little bit, or kind of get rid of [the food] real fast. . . . There was not a chance in God's green earth that a child can finish a plate that he piled up. Like I said, Mom was helping us out. She was trying to eat some and throwing it to the dog outside, throwing it in the garbage real fast. It's called portion control—geez, Dad! But you had to finish that plate before you got up from the table." *Female, late 40's*

610 "I struggled to get rid of [the concept that] you had to clean your plate and eat everything that was on your plate no matter what. . . . My mother—oh, God bless her, my mother! You didn't waste food. Now I know you've heard about those hungry starving children in China. Everybody knows about them. Like that one bite you take or don't take is going to make a difference. . . . I have a hard time, even like when I would clear the table after a meal, if there was a tablespoon of this or a tablespoon of that left, and it wasn't enough to really do something with, rather than throw it away I'd eat it. . . . I just decided that I had to make a real effort not to [always clean my plate]. . . . I still kind of have to clean my plate, but I don't have to clean the whole table." *Female, 50ish*

611 "What I remember vaguely [from my childhood] is there seemed to be some honor in cleaning your plate. You ate everything that was put in front of you, and I think part of that was [my parents] going through the Depression where things were tougher, and you [didn't] waste." *Male, almost 60*

612 "My folks made me clean my plate. . . . One thing I'm trying to do more in the last few years is get away from the old habit of always cleaning my plate. . . . I think that maybe when you're full, you should quit eating." *Male, almost 60*

613 "I came from parents who [said], 'Here's the food. You eat it.'. . . But if I didn't eat it say at breakfast, then I could have it again at lunch. I mean, it's not that they were wicked parents. . . . They were brought up during the Depression, . . . which [40-some] years later, I understand that. But food oftentimes was somewhat of a battle." *Female, mid to late 40's*

614 "My mom comes from a very meat-and-potatoes [family,] . . . and actually, she's a great, great cook. . . . But it was pretty much a home where she valued good eaters. She didn't like finicky, picky eaters. . . . And my . . . daughter can eat like a small horse . . . and my mom just rewards that. . . . It was a clean-your-plate kind of family." *Female, mid 30's*

615 "[I remember] that big Norwegian hand that my dad had—hands twice the size of mine—and he'd reach over and say, 'Did I tell you to clean your plate up?'. . . I mean [that hand] was just like a sledge hammer. . . . And you know, to this day . . . if I'm . . . watching TV or something, I'd rather go get just what I want, because if the wife puts that [food] on that plate, no matter what, I'll clean that plate up." *Male, 70ish*

616 "My parents felt that I should always clean my plate up, and one time I had a pickle on my plate and I did *not* want to eat this pickle, but they would not let me leave the table until I ate the pickle. They were already sitting there eating their dessert, and so I put whipped cream on the pickle in order to get it down, . . . but I did eat it. Oh yeah, you didn't cross Dad on anything." *Female, late 30's*

617 "I don't like cereal, but that's the one thing my mother would say, 'You eat that.' And then you'd sit there. It would get soggy. The corn flakes would get soggy. She would go make the bed and you would slip [the cereal] in the garbage can. She knew exactly what I was doing all the time because I would probably still be sitting there." *Female in her 50's*

618 "We ate oatmeal at camp and you had to eat it before you cleared the table. I got real good at putting the jelly with the oatmeal. . . . I had a whole thing of jelly with just a little oatmeal." *Female, 40ish*

619 "[My husband] just hounds [our son] and hounds him until he cleans his plate and I'm thinking, 'Don't do that.' Our son is not skinny. He's a well-fed child, but I mean that just starts bad habits to where that's how you get overweight children." *Female, late 20's to early 30's*

620 "[Growing up, it] was, 'Eat 'til you're full and then some.' And when the plate's clean, *then* you can consider getting up." *Female, 40ish*

621 "When I would go to my grandma's house as a child, the rule was you finished what she put on your plate. And . . . I've noticed since, I feel guilty when I don't eat everything that's on my plate. Even now, . . . I feel like I need to finish everything that's on my plate, whether I'm hungry for it or not."

Female, early 20's

622 *If your husband wants your children to clean their plates, but you prefer to let them stop eating when they are full, how do you handle this?* "I try to do it my way by putting less food on their plate. Then if they have to clean it up, then it's not that big of a deal." *Female in her 30's*

623 "If I order something at a restaurant, I feel—this might sound weird—but I [feel] I got to eat it. Or, if I'm at home and my wife fixes me a plate, I got to eat at least what is on the plate." *Male, early 30's*

624 "[When I was young], we couldn't fight, and we had to eat what was on our plate. . . . I learned really young that if there was a vegetable or something that was going by my plate that I didn't want, I didn't say anything. Then I'd only get a little spoonful. But, if I said anything, then I got two spoonfuls and had to eat them all." *Female in her 30's*

625 "I grew up . . . during the Depression years. The thing I remember the most was, 'Clean up your plate; you can't waste the food.' " *Female, mid to late 60's*

626 "I got really good at hiding the food [I didn't want to eat]. [I used] the dog, the cat, my pocket, [the] tablecloth." *Female, 40ish*

Humorous quotation

627 "My girlfriend's . . . brother . . . would slide the peas underneath the edge [of the tablecloth] and when you picked up the tablecloth, there would be the peas."

Female in her 50's

628 "I think about lunch, because I did overeat. . . . I was really hungry, and I had been really good . . . and came home and I just was ravenous, and so I had like one of those . . . rice bowl things—you stick it in the microwave. And then I had like three honey sandwiches. I have no idea why. . . . I think about that because I was like having my third one and I'm like, 'You're really not hungry anymore, so why are you having this sandwich?' And I'm like, oh, screw it. I'll start [eating better] tonight. Have another one. . . . But it's like, why am I doing this? Because I had just been thinking about how I needed to cut these calories, . . . and I think it just put the idea in my head." *Female, mid 30's*

629 "I am kind of a chocoholic. My dad always used to get those big Hershey bars, . . . and . . . we nibbled on them. . . . And this one time . . . I thought I would get a piece of it, and it was all gone. And you know, I went [into] a panic and it scared me and it scared me so badly that I didn't ever touch another piece of it for at least two years. . . . That really frightened me. . . . It had become an addiction and I had no idea that it was." *Female, mid to late 70's*

630 "I remembered gaining a lot of weight my freshman year and I think a lot of it stemmed from being depressed. . . . [I was] away from home maybe for the first time and had that freedom to go to a candy machine, . . . but I remember just being obsessed with having those Hostess cupcakes. Even after eating a good meal in the cafeteria, I remember going down to those machines and having to have those chocolate cupcakes." *Female, mid 30's*

631 "I can't control chocolate. . . . I just go home and I have [a chocolate chip cookie], go sit on the couch, go get another one. . . . I have a hard time controlling some things. Then I'll go on binges and then I'll be really good and then I just fall apart again. I don't know how to change that." *Female, early 20's*

632 "I have a stepdaughter that's fairly heavy for her age. I see her struggles. . . . She has an appetite problem because that's one thing her mind has control over. 'What am I going to eat next?' instead of 'What am I going to do next?' "
Male, early 40's

633 "I looked at the choices that we had [to eat for lunch]. None of them looked really good. I almost didn't get anything and then, I saw chicken nuggets and french fries, both fried foods, and I said to myself, 'I don't want fried foods,' but I ordered them anyway. . . . It was kind of a compulsive thing. I just ate them. I can't say I enjoyed them really." *Male, early 30's*

634 "I think I probably have a weakness for ice cream that I can't control. And if it's in the house I usually don't have a lot of self-control." *Male, mid 50's*

635 "I had a grandma who, if you didn't eat a certain amount of food, thought 'Well, you must not . . . love me'; . . . she just kept stuffing it and stuffing it and stuffing it. You almost felt guilty *not* eating. . . . It's almost like [she] equated . . . how much you ate with how much you loved her." *Male, 30ish*

636 "If we had a [family dinner], then the guys tried to see . . . how many plates of food they could eat. There was a real emphasis on that. . . . You couldn't really say you were full because [the women] would cook you a plate of food anyways. And then it was kind of rude if you didn't [eat] it." *Male, early 40's*

637 "When I was little, . . . breakfast . . . was always the hot cereals. . . . And I just *hated* cooked cereal. . . . And my dad and I would get into [it]. I think it was kind of a contest of wills. . . . The funny thing was once we got cold cereal he didn't eat [the hot cereal] much either. . . . I think it was just misery enjoys company. . . . He was going to make us suffer if he had to." *Female in her 40's*

638 "I graduated as a 98-pound senior. I went into the [military] with not much more [weight] than that. And all the time there, they tried to fatten me up, and it didn't work." *Male, early 50's*

639 "When I went into the military, . . . you ate at the same time at the chow hall, and it was all just so structured. . . . That was the only time I made a major jump and I gained weight." *Male, 70ish*

640 "When you were a kid, if you went to any of my aunts' houses, that was usually a first question they'd asked you: 'Are you hungry?' Usually my one aunt would say, 'You look too skinny, I'm going to make you some food,' whether you were hungry or not." *Male, early 40's*

641 "This manager of the apartment house always . . . made the meals for whoever was living there. . . . She probably made a little too much. . . . For breakfast, she'd make four slices of toast and at least two eggs and some other things. . . . When I came there, she . . . actually said she thought I couldn't push a shovel. So she was trying to get me [to gain weight]." *Male in his 50's*

642 "I got married and my mother-in-law was a wonderful cook and food was offered to you all the time. And she would have her feelings hurt if you didn't eat. . . . Food was a big part of their life." *Female, mid 70's*

643 "My grandmother gives [homemade chocolate chip cookies] to me, so I feel like I can't refuse them, and then I feel guilty if I throw them away."

Female, early 20's

644 "I finally learned that food does not control me. And that took me a long time to learn that because in the seventies I was anorexic and then I went bulimic. . . . Anorexia is when you're obsessed with being thin and you're obsessed with numbers, and no matter how small or skinny you look, even if your bones are showing, you're not thin enough. Bulimia is where you can consume huge amounts of food in a . . . sitting and you may even do it in private, like eat all the box of Twinkies on your own and then you get rid of it through throwing up or using laxatives. I could never throw up, but I could use laxatives, and I knew that my electrolytes were going to make me have a heart attack, and I think I just got tired of that and got out. . . . [I was] *very, very* [lucky]. . . . I took back the control from food. I don't use food to reward myself or punish myself. I don't use it to satisfy how I feel. If I'm hungry, I eat. If [I'm not hungry,] I don't, but I had to learn that because I was addicted. . . . We are so bombarded that we have to look a certain way that when I gave up thinking, 'I don't have to look *any* way,' I let go of the anorexia, I let go of the bulimia. . . . And it's like an alcoholic. I was addicted to that *thought* of food. I needed to have it. I needed it to make me feel good. And I didn't like that."

Female, late 40's

645 "I went to high school with a girl who just got home from a treatment center. She has bulimia. And I know so many [girls], even now, that have eating disorders. . . . I just think that it's so sad that our society is so focused on how our bodies look that people will do anything to have the body that they think they should have. . . . It just saddens my heart to know that there are girls who hurt themselves to look the way that they think they should. And I just feel so horrible for this girl who had to drop out of college and leave basketball, which is what is putting her through college, because she had a problem. And I know the root of it is not to please yourself, but to please others." *Female, early 20's*

646 "My . . . daughter has eating disorders and has really struggled with that as I think probably I did. . . . And I probably still do struggle from eating disorders; they just flip-flopped [from undereating to overeating]." *Female, mid to late 40's*

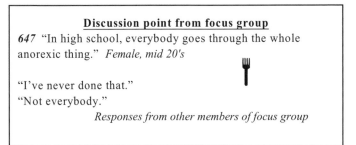

Discussion point from focus group
647 "In high school, everybody goes through the whole anorexic thing." *Female, mid 20's*

"I've never done that."
"Not everybody."
Responses from other members of focus group

648 "As soon as I walk in the house, I want to start eating. . . . I've tried to sit down to the organ and play. I still want to walk out there in the kitchen and find something. . . . It's just that I need to be putting stuff in my mouth, and I think that that's just maybe the way that I've done [it] all my life. . . . You go out in the fields and you worked as a family, [and] as soon as you walked in the door, why you ate and went back outside, and as soon as you walked in the door you ate. And I think that probably that's the way my life was. I ran home from school and jumped off the bus, ran in. Mother had hot bread and jam and a glass of milk. And I don't know if . . . I just carried that over subconsciously. I don't really know, . . . but I want some help." *Female, mid 60's*

649 "When my [siblings] graduated and left home, . . . my mom . . . never learned how to cook smaller portions, and I'm not blaming her, but she'd cook these huge meals just like they were still there. And the worst part about it was me and my dad would eat it. And there still wouldn't be anything left over, but . . . we didn't need to be eating that much." *Male, early 40's*

650 "Until I was about 11 years old, I was very undersized and very small . . . . So [my parents] were always feeding me things that were actually a no-no—beef tonic, [brewer's] yeast. . . . And they were afraid we had worms. It was very popular to be afraid your kids had worms. And so they were always giving us stuff for that too." *Female in her 60's*

651 "Growing up on a farm, my favorite time of the day was four o'clock in the afternoon. . . . My grandparents lived on the farm and you always waited for them to bring tea and cookies. . . . Those are really fond memories. . . . I spent an awful lot of time with my grandparents, and I don't think today, at least with my own [kids], I don't spend that kind of quality time—having tea and cookies with my kids. And I think they miss out on that. When they get home from school, they've got to fend for themselves." *Male, 30's to 40's*

652 "My parents thought that I was heavy. And I remember my mom put us on a diet—all of us. And I remember I lost like ten pounds. I looked in the mirror and it scared the hell out of me! But it felt like [food] was a battleground the whole time. And I don't remember [my mom] being mean, or my dad. I remember thinking, 'I shouldn't be eating this,' and 'I shouldn't be doing this,' and I think . . . I made it worse." *Female, early 40's*

653 "When I was in . . . sixth, seventh, and eighth grade, . . . some of the kids didn't like school lunch and there was a little store across the street from the school that served hot donuts and ice cream. We had that at least three times a week and I think back to that and think, 'Why did I do that?' But, it was a social thing because most of the kids went there." *Female, mid 60's*

654 "If I would go to other friends' homes and . . . if they'd invite me to have lunch . . . with them, I'd watch how they did it and how they offered grace and other things and their customs and to me it was fascinating to see, . . . and I really enjoyed that." *Male, in his 50's*

655 "I guess what you are raised on entirely has something to do with how you choose to eat. . . . I know when I was a kid we drank a lot of milk, and I still drink a lot of milk. . . . And then being around the beef, we ate that, and butter. Those kind of things influence how you . . . feel about food." *Male in his 40's*

656 "When I was growing up you would just come up to the table, and you'd just sit down and you ate, and no one said, 'Do you like this? Do you like that?'—you just ate. . . . Now the little kids sit down and [say], 'I don't like this' and 'I don't like that' and 'I don't want this.' " *Female, late 70's*

657 "There are a lot of things I [wish] I wouldn't have eaten as a kid. It probably would have made me healthier now. But when I was a kid I ate a lot of junk food. My lunch in junior high was a Texas donut, a glazed donut about as big as a basketball, and one of the big two-liter bottles of Orange Crush."
Male, early 50's

658 "My mother worked all her life, and my dad worked all his life. . . . They were going their separate directions, and I was kind of left on my own with not too much adult supervision. I got it once in a while if I got out of line. So meals as a family were something you remembered." *Male, mid 50's*

659 "You can walk into a school lunchroom and smell the smell, and it will bring you right back to the lunchroom when you were hiding stuff in your darn milk carton." *Female, 30's to 40's*

660 "When I grew up, we had the old A&W. And we used to [eat] hamburgers all the time. That was a big thing when we got something like that in our small town. When you got those greasy old french fries and greasy old hamburgers, you remember things like that. Yeah, and I know it's not the best, but it seems like that's part of life." *Male, mid 50's*

661 "When you were a kid, if you went to any of my aunts' houses, that was usually a first question they'd asked you: 'Are you hungry?' Usually my one aunt would say, 'You look too skinny, I'm going to make you some food,' whether you were hungry or not." *Male, early 40's*

662 "When you're at home and you're a kid, you pretty much got to eat what you're given." *Male, early 30's*

663 "Food has always been a stumbling block, learning what is *emotional* eating, what is *physical* eating. . . . I will go everywhere from the table looks good 'cause I need some fiber to I forget to have meals, I forget to eat. . . . I mean I'll be so busy I'll almost keel over, and I'll realize that I haven't eaten all day. It's a real broad range for me." *Female, early 40's*

664 "I finally learned that food does not control me. . . . I took back the control from food. I don't use food to reward myself or punish myself. I don't use it to satisfy how I feel. If I'm hungry, I eat. If [I'm not hungry], I don't, but I had to learn that because I was addicted. . . . And it's like an alcoholic. I was addicted to that *thought* of food. I needed to have it. I needed it to make me feel good."

Female, late 40's

665 "Food was not necessarily a real important thing to me. . . . If I'm busy doing something else, I never even think about food. Like [my husband] would come in and say, 'Are we having some lunch?' 'Lunch? What are you talking about, *lunch?*' " *Female, mid to late 40's*

666 "I spend too much time thinking about food. . . . Get up in the morning, what's for breakfast? Ten o'clock you start getting hungry, so it's what's for lunch? About two o'clock you start worrying, what's for supper? What am I going to cook? . . . I think I live to eat food." *Female in her 30's*

667 "I am in recovery and I am an addict when it comes to *everything*: drugs, food, sex, everything. I go all or nothing. When I was on drugs, I got pretty skinny. . . . And then I quit doing drugs, and food became my addiction."

Female, late 20's

668 "There is a tribe in . . . Uganda. . . . [Whenever] they kill an animal, everybody gorges themselves. . . . They have this fear that they are going to starve to death, so whether they are full or whether they are hungry, they still stuff themselves. I probably think that way also sometimes. . . . And I guess one of my poor eating habits is eating too fast, and I think I need to just relax a little more and eat slower and not be thinking that I'm going to starve."

Male, early 40's

669 "[When] you get hungry, you just eat to get rid of the pain, the feeling of hunger. . . . I mean, you should try to eat good, wholesome, quality foods, but mostly you're eating to get rid of that cotton-picking pain. You aren't thinking about every bite of food you take, what kind of nutrition and stuff that's going to provide your body. It just takes care of the cotton-picking hunger pains."

Male, mid 50's

670 "I don't know how to make food not be a battleground. . . . I think a whole lot of it would solve itself if we didn't focus so much on it. It just feels like we're pounded day in and day out. Like I watched a program on TV last night . . . on obesity in America. And it just seems like everywhere you turn we're being bombarded with how bad we are. We're fat and we eat too much and we don't exercise enough. And it's all negative, and it's constant, and it's day in and day out." *Female, early 40's*

671 "When I was growing up, people used to tell me, 'You've got to watch what you eat, you'll gain weight and you don't want to do that.' And I used to say, 'Leave me alone.' But now I realize they were right. I don't think I eat as much as I used to." *Male in his 30's*

672 "If you're addicted to alcohol or cigarettes or something . . . it's hard, of course, but you can get over it . . . , whereas with food, you have to have it every day." *Female, mid 20's*

673 "I probably enjoy food more now than I ever have because I don't feel like it's in control of me, even though it never was. I wanted to think that I had no control." *Female, 40ish*

674 "It's just a thing I have. If [food] is there, I'll eat it. If it's not, I won't."
Male, early 30's

675 "We were always very lucky to have whatever [food] we wanted, and we never went hungry, so maybe that's why I have my attitude of I'll eat what I want and I will be happy." *Female in her 30's*

676 "[Food] is just something to keep your body going. . . . And I think when you get older, your body doesn't need as much . . . food to keep it going."
Male, early 60's

Humorous sidenote
677 What are some of your experiences regarding food?

"Oh, food. Wow. Oh my goodness. Food. I'm a garbage pail."
Male in his 70's

678 "When I was little, I hated Chinese food, . . . but then . . . we decided to host a student from Taiwan, and . . . one day he brought a bunch of friends and they made an authentic . . . meal. They brought their woks and their steamers and all this stuff and it was *so-o-o good.* And from then on I fell in love with Chinese food, and I still love it today." *Female, mid 40's*

679 "I always enjoyed food—you can tell by my [*gestures to body*]. . . . I was definitely fullblood German, and [eating] was one of the things we really enjoyed." *Female, late 60's*

680 "I served a mission, . . . and there's several Spanish people down there and . . . a few families . . . owned restaurants. . . . I learned to love Mexican food."
Female in her 30's

681 "I had a friend in Switzerland, and we went over and visited her, and their breads are just [delicious]. . . . That's one time in my life that I remember eating . . . good food—really good food. . . . We went for a little tour, and we got cheeses and breads, . . . and that's what we ate. . . . These are weird things to bring up. . . . I haven't even thought about that forever." *Female in her 20's*

682 "[My son] brought to my attention . . . he [has] never lived any place for more than three years in his life and I didn't realize that we had moved that much. But in the course of that moving, I realize how often I'd gleaned a recipe from some aspect of where we were. . . . We spent a year in China, so whether it was the . . . favorite foods that we adapted from there or just friends, . . . that's been an interesting aspect of my . . . life." *Female, late 40's*

683 "I went over to France and worked in a restaurant there and every meal they made . . . was just so delicious, except for one time they had cow's tongue, and that was really gross. . . . [And] there was sheep brains, and I wouldn't try that. . . . And I actually didn't mind escargot. I didn't enjoy it, but I would eat it. . . . It's like chewing gum. It's just rubbery. But I really enjoyed their food."
Female in her 20's

684 "[I like] going out to different restaurants. [I was on] vacation last year, . . . and family members took me out to different restaurants, and I love to try different ethnic foods." *Female in her 60's*

685 "My father was in the Navy . . . [and] he knew about Spanish foods and Oriental foods. . . . We started learning at a fairly early age to like [ethnic] foods. And then as I grew up, I branched out into other areas. . . . I don't think there is a single ethnic food that I wouldn't care for." *Female in her 60's*

686 "I have no concept of being full. . . . When I was in my early 20's I could eat six quarter-pounders. . . . Why I don't feel full I don't know. . . . I have to sit there and think to stop because I can just keep packing it away. . . . I enjoy it, too, and I'm a pretty good cook, so it tastes great, and it's an effort to stop. . . . I still have an enormous appetite." *Male, late 30's*

687 "The workshop that I participated in really taught you the sensation of *hunger* and *fullness*—what it was about and that food was . . . something to fill your stomach, to continue to keep your body going, . . . and so you were never deprived of any food. It was just, 'If you want that hamburger, why don't you start with a half and then if you still feel hungry and your stomach really is still saying *hungry*, well, then eat another fourth of it,' instead of taking the hamburger and saying, 'I'm not done until this is gone.' And so that was a *huge, huge* eye-opening event for me. . . . I've lost about 25 pounds with that method of eating." *Female, 40ish*

688 "I eat too much of certain things. Like, I really like my meat, so I'll eat lots of it sometimes. . . . I'll eat and then I won't feel anything . . . until I've finished eating and then all of a sudden my stomach starts to hurt me because I've eaten a little bit too much. Hopefully . . . I'll . . . eat to where I still feel slightly hungry, but I'm not full." *Male, early 30's*

689 "I took back the control from food. I don't use food to reward myself or punish myself. I don't use it to satisfy how I feel. If I'm hungry, I eat. If [I'm not hungry], I don't." *Female, late 40's*

690 "I don't obsess about [eating]. I just think each time I eat, 'Do I need to eat any more? Am I full?' And sometimes I eat too much. Absolutely, no question about it. I never get it perfect every time, but I don't worry about it anymore. . . . It's funny how I used to look at the food and go, 'Okay, how many calories? How much should I eat of it?' " *Female, 40ish*

691 "I think there's a trigger . . . in your body that says . . . it's time to quit [eating]. . . . You overeat, . . . you get uncomfortable, and I don't like that feeling. . . . Just don't stuff yourself. . . . It's something you learn. . . . It's just like getting stuck with a pin. It hurts you, and you don't do it." *Male, early 60's*

692 "I eat when I'm hungry. I've always been that way, every since I was a kid, apparently. At least that's what my mom says. I eat when I'm hungry. . . . I've always been that way, so I don't know any different. . . . I enjoy [eating] everything in little portions. Eat ten times a day if you want to, a little bit at a time. See, that's what I do." *Female, late 40's*

693 "Coyotes . . . always take the easy path, and so . . . they get trapped. If they took the hard path, . . . they'd be around a while. Well . . . life is the same way. . . . You could take the easy path and not . . . exercise and eat a lot and [that] gets you into trouble. . . . But . . . you've gotta have . . . willpower." *Male, early 60's*

694 "I remember telling my mom this and I still feel this way to this day. I will be glad when I am a grown-up because I will not eat anything I don't want to . . . and I still don't do that. I am not a clean plater. You would think someone who is heavy [would clean their plate], but when I reach the stage where I am full, I stop. . . . I just don't eat when I am full. . . . My husband will say, 'Oh I'm so full.' I hate that feeling. I hate that overfull feeling." *Female, mid to late 40's*

695 "I'm . . . postmenopausal . . . [and] something . . . started maybe about four years ago. My body chemistry changed, my metabolism changed, my appetite changed. Over the last four years I've gradually . . . shed . . . a pound or two a month. . . . I can leave a half a cookie sitting in front of me. I can leave a half a hamburger. . . . I look for small meals . . . at the restaurant." *Female, 60ish*

696 "If I could just stay away from the cookies. . . . It's terrible, because [my wife] will cook me oatmeal or anything in the world and all I do is [eat] cookies. . . . This winter's been the worst. And I think that's a lot of the weight problem. Just a bad habit I got into here. . . . I get a craving for the cookies. Also, [I] can read the paper and eat. It's terrible to tell you. I will eat 10, 12 cookies. Drink that coffee and eat them cookies." *Male, mid 50's*

697 "At Thanksgiving, . . . I was able to just eat one helping, . . . and I was satisfied. And I don't think I'd ever had a Thanksgiving or Christmas that I hadn't loaded my plate twice. . . . That was cool." *Female, 40ish*

698 "When you're single, . . . [you can eat] just little stuff through the day since [you] don't have to worry about anybody else. The dog has a bowl full of food all the time, and every once in a while I hear it gnawing in the dish, and that means I'm hungry too." *Male, 70ish*

699 "I think that food is something that God has given us to not only nourish us but for us to enjoy as well and to bring us pleasure. But if we don't handle it wisely or in moderation or balance, then that's when it is . . . negative."
Female, late 30's

700 "I've had lots of changes [with eating] throughout life, but currently I only eat when I'm hungry, so I don't get obsessed with food. If I'm hungry, I'll find something in the cupboard to eat. And that seems to work good for me."
Female, mid 30's

701 "I know that I use food as a tranquilizer. I'm very aware of that. And I know that both of my heavy daughters use it as a tranquilizer. They've led stressful lives. And I know that when I get really stressed, I want to eat. And I think that's probably the biggest reaction of all normal people who are heavy —that food is their tranquilizer." *Female in her 60's*

702 "I think a lot of the eating is when you're lonely. You just want to do something, but you don't know what, and it's so easy to pick up and nibble on something. You think it helps you, but first thing you know you want more. Whatever it is [you're missing, food] isn't satisfying it." *Female, mid 70's*

703 "I can tell you I probably felt guilty about eating since I was in junior high, guilty that I wouldn't eat the right things or guilty that I would eat too much. I think food is just a whole bunch of guilt. . . . And so I eat my sausage egg McMuffin, and it's peaceful. And then I feel guilty because that's not exactly a good breakfast, but it was peaceful. . . . So I think food is just a whole lot of guilt." *Female, early 40's*

704 "[I] got down to probably 40 pounds from my goal weight. Then my mom passed away, and that shot all that completely to smithereens. And then [my weight] went back up again." *Female, early 40's*

705 "I could keep [my weight] off for a while, but . . . I think stress plays a part in there. If there was a stressful time, then I would tend to put [weight] back on. . . . I [also] eat when I'm tired. Somehow I must equate that to energy. . . . Probably about 20 years ago . . . I was going to go eat something and [my son said], 'You're tired, why don't you go take a nap instead of going to eat something.' Well the light bulb went on. And I thought, 'You know, that's really what it is.' . . . But it didn't mean I didn't [eat when I was tired]."
Female, 50ish

706 "I was probably an emotional eater. . . . I was home a lot and there's too much temptation, and I would eat when I wasn't even hungry. . . . I did have emotional roller-coaster rides with [food]." *Female, early 60's*

707 "When I hit that depression stage and start eating that candy or junk food or whatever, in the moment it makes you feel better, but then later you think about what you ate and it is a horrible thing." *Female, late 20's*

708 "Any time that I'm bored . . . I eat, or if I'm upset, I eat. . . . My friend . . . when she's upset can't eat, . . . but I am completely the opposite, and if I am upset, then I clear out the cupboards. . . . I think that I like to eat, and sometimes that's the way I answer some of my problems." *Female, early 20's*

709 "When [I had cancer and] I was going to radiation and chemo, food was just not good and it was *really* difficult to get anything down. I got sores in my mouth and it was very hard to eat. And things didn't taste good. . . Then maybe the next day I could eat something that I couldn't the day before. . . . For someone who liked food, it was real difficult not to be able to eat. . . . I was overweight when I got cancer. I think it was the fact that I was a little overweight that helped carry me through the fact that I couldn't eat for months. I think since, hopefully, I am cancer-free now, I hope, it's like I'm going to be sure I have extra weight on if it comes back, so I have something to ride to get through the next step." *Female, mid to late 60's*

710 "I just saw on the news that [being] fat was worse than smoking. Smoking kills you off when you're in your 50's and 60's. Being fat can get you in your 40's, so it's just terrible for you. . . . My folks would help if I wanted a gastro-bypass. I just worry that it would ruin my life. If they screw up, your life is ruined. If they don't, you're in a lot better shape. . . . But the most important thing is just not to get fat in the first place." *Male, late 30's*

711 "My mom is diabetic, so I guess growing up I watched how she ate, and everything had to be monitored and this and that. . . . So I always felt like I never wanted to be in that kind of situation." *Female, late 20's*

712 "[When I was young], my mother tells me I was skinny. I was super active then, . . . and she said I was skinny. . . . [My mother] told me that I had a stomachache a lot. . . . The only thing the doctor said was, 'She'll outgrow it—give her some hard candy to suck on.' Well, I loved that doctor, [but] I always thought, 'Momma, I need medicine.' " *Female, early 60's*

713 "I've had quite a bit of medical problems. As I grew up, I was always having a stomachache. . . . From the time I was about six or seven years old 'til I got out of high school, . . . I had a stomachache so much of the time. . . . I didn't enjoy eating when I was a kid. . . . I was undernourished when I grew up because I didn't like to eat very much." *Male, mid 70's*

714 "I have been taking insulin since I was five years old, so [I] have to watch [what I eat]. Maybe that's been a lifelong education, working with dietitians and different doctors that know various things. Some think they know more than others, but that's been something, just to try to balance the insulin, the food intake. I think I have gotten better at it. But it's always interesting to me. I've got a pile of books, and I test my blood sugar, in some ways experimenting—if I eat this and I do this, what happens and what length of time does that last? . . . I mean you can really get lost in the detail." *Male in his 40's*

715 "I know that I've had physical reasons [for gaining weight]—the . . . non-functioning thyroid, . . . but we discovered that about five years after I gained all that weight, which was too late. . . . Once you get fat, it's nearly impossible to get rid of it. . . . Once it's there, it doesn't go away. . . . And some bad eating habits certainly [contributed to my weight gain]. I'd get my folks to stop for fast food several times a week. And . . . we liked eating, period. And so I got fat . . . pretty quickly, inside of a year or two. I went from a real skinny kid to a fat kid." *Male, late 30's*

716 "I know it's a lot harder [to eat] now because I have diabetes, and I can't eat a lot of things that I would love to eat. And I think—it's just as well I can't eat them. And it's quite a change from [when I was younger and food was scarce]. I mean, just to have food to eat, and then all of a sudden you can't eat this and you can't eat that." *Female, mid 70's*

717 "Well, I don't get to eat much any more 'cause my insides are bleeding. . . . Well, they give me tons of pills that are supposed to have all the vitamins and everything. Better living through chemistry, I guess. . . . At my current rate, I won't be around anymore, so that's the extent of my food enjoyment. . . . Food doesn't make the passage through the system the way it should." *Male, 40ish*
(seriously injured while in military special forces)

718 "In the last two years, . . . serious food elimination [due to food allergies] . . . [has] changed my eating drastically. The list of things I try to avoid is not fun." *Female, late 40's*

719 "I stay right around [200 plus pounds], but I figured that ain't too bad. I take medicine that keeps the weight on me." *Male in his 40's*

Humorous sidenote

720 "I enjoy most foods. . . . Broccoli . . . I don't care for."

Didn't a president get himself into trouble by saying something like that?

"I'm not the president, though." *Male, mid 70's*

---

721 "My husband says, 'Do you want me to get you a box of chocolates for Valentine's Day?' I said, 'Are you kidding, why would I waste calories on just any box of chocolates? Unless you can find me [fine chocolates], forget it.' "

Female, late 30's

722 "My husband's an old country boy, and his idea of food is meat and potatoes, and just a plain thing—[he doesn't] want it doctored up. If he wants meat, he wants meat! If somebody asked me to make something fancy, I'd turn them down 'cause I wouldn't know how." *Female, 70ish*

723 "I just love that camp food. It's simple food, but there's nothing nicer than the aroma of coffee and bacon cooking in the morning. . . . I like good coffee. During the war when coffee was rationed, it was the most disappointing thing. They would say, 'Come in for coffee,' and it was just slightly browned water. I like good coffee. So I always say, 'Yes, it is my starting fluid in the morning, and my go fluid during the day.' " *Female, mid to late 70's*

724 "If I'm hungry . . . but I'm not hungry for peanut butter, I won't just pull it out because I'm hungry. I'm so picky on what I'm hungry for, it's funny. . . . And I just talked to a friend recently about that. Her and I are the same weight. We don't eat stuff that we don't like. We talked about how we would scrape the pumpkin out [of pumpkin pie] and just eat the [filling], whereas most people would just be courteous and eat the whole thing." *Female, mid 30's*

725 "I don't enjoy eating. I don't enjoy what other people [enjoy]—like my mom can't control herself with chocolate, but to me there's no enjoyment or no pleasure in that kind of stuff. A treat for me would be like homemade beef stew. . . . [Not enjoying food] is why I gained so much weight. too. I was eating one meal a day and perking up with Mountain Dew, so my metabolism just kind of [*sound and gesture of downward trend*]." *Female in her 20's*

726 "Being raised on a ranch, our meals were meat and potatoes. Bacon for breakfast and ham and beans for lunch and maybe a beefsteak or ground beef for supper. And [when] you're raised on that you develop . . . a taste for it or else you hate it, one of the two. . . . So that was really hard for me later in life to get away from that mind-set, simply because that's the way we ate." *Male in his 60's*

727 "The worse [the food] is for me, the better I like it. So, I don't eat as much of that stuff as I'd like to—red meat and fried stuff. I love french fries and that sort of thing. If I shouldn't have it healthwise, it's probably one of my favorites. But I am conscious of not doing it. . . . I had a good steak [last week], . . . now I won't eat anything like that for awhile." *Male, early 80's*

728 "If I could do the cooking in my household, I would have more vegetables than anything else because I love vegetables. I'm a vegetable freak. . . . When there's carrots and broccoli, everybody takes a little . . . so I just clean the whole pot up." *Male, early 50's*

729 "I guess the way you eat is kind of how . . . you've been brought up. I grew up on a farm where we did a lot of milking, so I like milk and . . . we eat a lot of meat. We eat a lot of potatoes and a lot of the basics, . . . and I still enjoy doing that every day. . . . I eat what I like to eat." *Male, early 60's*

730 "My mom was really good at making cakes and now my wife and my mother-in-law make really good food, desserts. . . . After a meal, I feel like I need to have dessert 'cause I enjoy it so much. Well, it's just funny to where you feel like you need a dessert because you're craving it. . . . It's like the meal isn't complete if you don't have a small dessert or something." *Male in his 30's*

731 "But you got to have a little spice of life, I guess. You know once in awhile . . . you get a craving . . . that you just need a greasy old hamburger. [When] I grew up, my dad had fried eggs and greasy old eggs. And my wife gets a little mad because about once a month on Sunday morning I'll have to fry up some greasy eggs. You cook them in bacon and so you know they're slimers."
Male, mid 50's

732 "I kind of got off fast food and all that because I realized just how bad it tastes. . . . I might even be considered a gourmet [cook]. . . . I watch cooking shows on cable, and so I'm kind of an enthusiast, which is what a gourmet is."
Male, late 30's

733 "My wife calls me a meat-and-potatoes kind of guy. . . . I don't like food mixed together. In fact, when I eat my food, I'll eat one thing and then I'll move to the next thing and eat it. I don't mix my foods. . . . My family goes nuts over pizza. Well, my definition of [pizza] is barf on bread. . . . In my adult years, I've never liked pizza." *Male in his 40's*

734 "Probably my weakness is I like sweets and salty things—like a lot of people." *Male in his 30's*

735 "You can only eat so many pieces of carrot and celery, fruit. I mean, that gets old." *Female, late 40's*

736 "I don't make anything from scratch. . . . I like steak and fries, pizza, things like that." *Male in his 30's*

737 "If it came down to where there's only two things that could be left on the earth to eat , . . . hot dogs and hamburgers would be perfect for me."

Male, mid 20's

738 "I'm not too much on vegetables. I'm real big on meat. I like meat. You can [serve some] vegetables, but don't give me vegetables with nothing [else] to eat." *Male in his 40's*

739 "I'm pretty easygoing about food. I'm quite varied in taste and likes. . . . I'll try most anything." *Male, early 40's*

740 "I've always had kind of a desire for sweet foods, . . . but I know that a person should keep it down to a minimum." *Male in his 50's*

741 "I like baked goods and that's my downfall. I like bars, cookies, pies, cakes, whatever. . . . If I bake now, I usually eat it all, so I very seldom bake."

Female in her 60's

742 "We lived in the country. . . . Our meals were based around protein—what beef were we going to grab out of the freezer? And still to this day, when I think about having a meal or cooking for friends, . . . the first thing I still do is, 'Okay, what meat am I going to have?' " *Female, early 40's*

743 "I eat a lot of . . . eggs. . . . And when I eat eggs, it ain't nothing for me to eat three or four at a time, . . . eight or nine a day." *Male in his 40's*

744 "[A] lot of my likes now are different than when I was younger, especially like cabbages and fruits and vegetables. . . . I like a good small steak once in a while, but I'm more into a variety of food." *Male in his 50's*

Memorable quotation

745 "You know in your head what you're suppose to [eat], but that doesn't always mean you can sit down and do what you're supposed to do. You know what [food] is healthy. You know what is good. But your senses, I guess, can kind of just override all that just real easy. [It's a] long way from your tummy to your head sometimes." *Female, 50ish*

746 "I found that one thing I do like is potato chips and peanuts. . . . But I found that if I just took a small portion and just nibbled on it slowly until finally I got the taste, that would be satisfying instead of just gobble down three or four handfuls. . . . I'd just take a little bit and I wouldn't be denying myself the taste, but I would savor it more. I'd either get bored with it or I would get full. Then I was satisfied." *Male in his 50's*

747 "I kind of have a philosophy that I'm going eat everything, just in moderation. I don't want to deprive myself, 'cause I've learned throughout my life [what] my personality type would be if I didn't eat sweets anymore: I could see me one whole day binging on them." *Female, mid 30's*

748 "We got three sizes of plates in our cupboard, . . . the big ones, the medium, and you got these little saucers. And I've learned that if I put the small plates on the table, . . . that [even though] you put what you want to on a small plate, you get less [food] out [of the serving dish.] And you still get to feel good 'cause you cleaned the plate up." *Male, 40's to 50's*

Experiences from a selective eater

749 "The workshop that I participated in really taught you the sensation of *hunger* and *fullness* . . . and that food was . . . something to fill your stomach, to continue to keep your body going, . . . and so you were never deprived of any food. It was just, 'If you want that hamburger, why don't you start with a half and then if you still feel hungry and your stomach really is still saying *hungry*, well, then eat another fourth of it,' instead of taking the hamburger and saying, 'I'm not done until this is gone.' And so that was a *huge, huge* eye-opening event for me . . . realizing that . . . cleaning your plate isn't what it's about. . . . And it's also not about going down the diet aisle, that eating cardboard isn't the answer either. And chocolate isn't put on the earth to torture us. It's to be taken in reasonable quantities. . . . If you like the juicy part of the hamburger, then why are you eating the part that's all crispy? . . . So pick the parts of the food that you like the most so you don't feel like you're deprived when you're done with that meal, that you've gotten the best, juiciest parts of the dinner and you've left behind the parts that are really [not] appealing to you. . . . I'll have a plate of potatoes, corn, dressing, and turkey. . . . Then I'll go around that plate and I'll say, 'Ooh, I really like this part of the turkey and this part of the potatoes,' and then I'll put the other stuff aside and then when I'm full I didn't miss the best part. But I have to be conscious to do it." *Female, 40ish*

---

750 "When I was a kid, I just abused [food] terribly. You know, fast food. I ate unreal amounts of it, and it's because it is easy to abuse it. You know, you drive in, and they give you something and you drive home and eat it. . . . But I really got off of it in the last year. So that's not an issue anymore. . . . I just don't eat that stuff anymore. . . . I think I just outgrew it, and I realized I didn't like it anymore." *Male, late 30's*

751 "I think when I was younger I was just [thinking], . . . I'm just going [to] grab that cookie, and I'm going to jam it in my mouth 'cause it's a good cookie. But now I'll think before I pick up that cookie. I think, 'Do I really want to have that cookie?' " *Male, early 20's*

752 "Occasionally, I'll skip going for seconds . . . . I eat about the same as I always have. . . . A few small things have changed from 2% to 1% milk, eating fat-free sour cream. Pretty small things like that." *Male in his 20's*

753 "My weight . . . varies all the time . . . . I eat a lot, and I'm like, 'Geez, I'm starting to get kind of chubby.' So then you just don't have a Snickers bar and you maybe try and eat just one portion instead of two." *Male, mid 20's*

754 "When I go shopping, I shop on the perimeter of the store and stay away . . . [from] the processed food." *Female, late 20's*

755 "[Eat] moderately. I mean, you can enjoy a piece of pie without enjoying the whole pie." *Male, almost 50*

756 "Mainly for me at this point [the key] is identifying when I'm eating from emotion and when I'm eating from hunger." *Female, early 40's*

757 "I try to eat five little meals a day. It makes me feel better than my not eating all day long and then just wolfing down a huge dinner." *Female, mid 20's*

Summary eating strategies for one female
758 "Don't obsess about food. Learn what it's like to be hungry and full. Stay within those boundaries. Find out what makes you overeat or undereat. Turn off the TV [and] do things with your family. Eat what you really like. Leave food on your plate." *Female, 40ish*

759 "I think food is almost like a history book to other lands and other cultures, . . . whether it's spices or preparation or utensils or whatever, and I think it's a history lesson all at one table sometimes." *Male in his 50's*

760 "[After one of our family] trips, . . . my parents had a little bit of money left over and they took us to dinner, and we actually got to eat lobster. And I remember that very vividly. We went to a nice restaurant near our hometown and had lobster. In fact, we kept the shells we were so enthralled. I had never seen anything like that before. So we took these stinky lobster tails home with us, we thought it was that cool. I couldn't have been much more than 11, 12, 13, somewhere in there. That was a positive experience that kind of opened my eyes at the time, . . . there's something else out there [besides] roast beef."
Male, almost 50

761 "We just had a family get-together Sunday. . . . And that's interesting to me to get together with something like that because everyone brings something and it's not just the foods that you're used to making or what your family is used to eating. And it's just different things they put together that you think, 'Ooh, I can't believe somebody would eat that.' Or, 'I never thought of putting those things together.' So that's always interesting to me, what someone else eats—what they dare bring to public." *Female in her 30's*

762 "My mother . . . [didn't serve] meat and potatoes every meal. And then we would go places. . . . So I . . . was exposed to a variety [of foods]. . . . And I still will try [different foods]. I have some friends that I don't even like to go eat with them because it's just blah. You know it's going to be the same thing every day. . . . They won't try anything other than this basic bill of fare."
Male, early 80's

763 "I really enjoy meals that have a variety of foods in them [so] that you can try a variety of things. I enjoy going to restaurants and getting things that I can't make at home or I don't make. Sometimes I . . . order something that I think I shouldn't have ordered . . . [because] it was really not what I wanted, but I like to experience different foods." *Female in her 20's*

Humorous sidenote

764 "There are very, very few foods that I won't eat. So green beans didn't grab me by the throat, throw me down, and make me feel bad—or cabbage or spinach or any of those things."
Male in his 50's

---

765 "I have [two children] and it doesn't matter what I cook, one of them, if not both of them—'Oh, yuck. I don't want this,' to the point that it's become such a battleground, I don't want to cook. I don't want to eat at home. The [older child] is good enough to make . . . macaroni and cheese, and . . . make it for his [sibling], and so fine, just go do it, just so I don't have to listen to you guys whine and complain. I'm tired of cooking and having people complain."

Female, early 40's

766 "My husband likes to go home for lunch, and I like to go out for lunch because as soon as we get home, he sits down with the newspaper and I'm to cook lunch. Well, *I'd* like to sit down with a book and he can cook lunch. And he doesn't understand why I don't like that and I don't understand how come he can't understand [my frustration]." *Female, early 40's*

767 "Yesterday I went and bought some good steaks at the butcher for Sunday [dinner]. And I made the steak and some fresh strawberries and fresh asparagus. And [my oldest son] wouldn't eat any of the steak—wouldn't even take a bite—so he ate I think six strawberries, and he whined the whole time about having to eat the asparagus. [My youngest child] ate half my steak and about three bites of the asparagus—whining the whole time that he didn't want the asparagus. No, he didn't want strawberries. And my husband's steak I overcooked—but too bad. And [my steak] tasted pretty good, but [the meal] was not real pleasant." *Female, early 40's*

768 "I have a brother . . . and I just thought he was disgusting. . . . He would come home and would get one of those big long ice cream spoons and go and get the peanut butter and sit in the family room, watch Scooby-Doo, and eat peanut butter. . . . Ughh—that's just gross. And I don't like peanut butter. . . . And I don't like Scooby-Doo either." *Female in her 30's*

769 "When I was . . . in high school I got really sick and they didn't know what was wrong with me. So they were going to do tests. . . . I had to drink two gallons of apple juice in a 24-hour period of time, no other food . . . . To this day I can't stand apple juice. I don't even like the smell of it. It's just gross . . . . [If my children have apple juice], their dad feeds it to them 'cause I can't even stand the smell of it." *Female in her 30's*

770 "From the time the first dandelion came up or anything green, Mom got 'em and cooked 'em. I hated greens of all kinds and I still do. . . . We didn't have too much to eat, so I don't blame Mom at all, it was just—we didn't like 'em."

Female, mid 70's

771 "I have never been the kind of person who had to be seriously watching what I ate in terms of weight. . . . If anything, there are times when I think I probably need to put on a little bit more [weight] . . . . But I've never had food binges or really serious cravings that would cause weight gain."

Female, late 40's

772 "With my first baby, I wasn't gaining weight at all. . . . They finally told me if I didn't start gaining it, I'd have to go into the hospital until I gained weight. The worse place . . . to gain weight is in the hospital, so I went home then and I just ate fat stuff. I mean, I would eat what I wanted, when I wanted. My poor husband gained ten pounds because I wasn't cooking low fat. I didn't buy low-fat stuff because I needed the fat calories . . . . They wanted me to gain 25 pounds in that pregnancy and I barely gained it. The only thing I changed was I just didn't pay attention to my fat intake. And now I really don't either."

Female in her 30's

773 "I always struggled to get to the . . . weight that I wanted to be. Like my [football] playing weight . . . goal was always about 205, and I could never break about 198, especially once the season hit. All of a sudden you're fighting just to keep . . . [from] dropping pounds. And that's something I've never really understood. . . . I'd watch some of the other guys on our team, offensive linemen . . . up at 340 and 330 trying to cut weight and struggling to do that, and here I'm struggling to put it on. . . . I tried like crazy, . . . eating and lifting hard and taking supplements, . . . peanut butter and jelly sandwiches five, six times a day, so . . . I just couldn't figure out why it didn't work for me." *Male in his 20's*

Followed by a response from another focus group member: "If I had eaten like that, I would have been the size of the whole offensive line and the defensive line all in one person." *Male in his 60's*

Memorable quotation

774 "I can tell you a little story about fried chicken. . . . My first wife made my favorite meal, fried chicken, mashed potatoes and gravy, for dinner and half-way through she told me that she was going to leave me. So I'm really superstitious about when my wife cooks fried chicken. Yeah. I always give her a bad time: 'You want to tell me something now or are we going to eat?' "

Male, mid 50's

---

775 "I'm not a breakfast person . . . . In fact, my wife will write 'eat your breakfast.' . . . I can tell for me, [I need to] afford [breakfast the] time to do it right so I keep my [energy] level going, especially with this job, because some days you don't know when you're going to be back, and especially when you've got a problem come up. It's going to be long, long days, and if you don't eat breakfast, it catches up with you." *Male in his 40's*

776 "I used to be able to go all day without eating if I didn't have a chance to, but now . . . I feel like woozy if I don't eat. And my mom used to have the same problem and I used to like think, 'Well, why can't you go without lunch? Can't you wait until supper?' And now I know why she used to have to eat. Your body is saying, 'Yes, you do need to have these meals.' " *Female, mid 30's*

777 "Before [my current job], I did construction, and it seemed like if you weren't eating proper you just didn't have energy to make it through the day. You had to eat decent meals appropriate to keep your energy levels up to make it through the day. And especially when it was really cold, that's when it zapped you the most. It seemed like if you didn't eat your breakfast and have a good lunch, you were zapped." *Male in his 40's*

778 "[After I lost the 25 pounds], I see a couple very minor little differences, but for the most part, I still feel pretty big. I'm starting to feel a little bit better. I think it's more energy from being thinner . . . . I don't actually think it's self-image that's the major cause of my feeling better, but I think it's just because I'm losing weight I have more energy, and I'm actually eating so my body has something to make energy with." *Female in her 20's*

Humorous sidenote

779 "People really have these [life-changing] experiences and they can really remember them?" *Interviewer: Well yeah, we've had some people.* "You didn't think they were lying?"

Follow-up at end of interview: That pretty much finishes the interview, but I want to ask what you think the most significant thing was that we talked about today. Is there any particular topic or issue that really stands out to you?
"Not really. I'm going to go off and try to have some life-changing experiences. I'm going to write them down and I'm going to be ready next time [you do this interview]." *Male in his 50's*

---

780 "When I grew up, it seems like from the time we were little, food was used as a reward. . . . If you cleaned your plate, you could have dessert. If you do this, you can have an ice cream. And it's been really hard to overcome that with my own kids, not to do that, to avoid that issue. It's been something that's been difficult to do." *Female, mid 40's*

781 "Well, it took a lot of years to realize this, but there's things that trigger you [to eat]. And in my case, due to things that happened in my life and the way I was raised and even my marriage relationship, there's things that trigger eating. To me, it was kind of a reward or feeling better, to eat. And so that's something that I still have to fight. It's been something that's been wrong with me for a long time, but that's one really important thing to realize—if you eat to feel good or reward yourself for something, that's probably not a good thing." *Male in his 60's*

782 "I will have a bowl of ice cream before I go to bed every night. That's my reward. Worked my tail off today." *Female, late 20's*

783 "When my mother wanted to give us a reward for something good that we had done . . . she would ask us what we wanted for our reward and I know I always wanted . . . chocolate pudding, and I just loved it. . . . That was my reward." *Female, mid to late 70's*

784 "Most of my life I have been more on the heavy side, and I've tried not to pass that on to my kids. But, we were also given food for a reward. [During my childhood, we were often] rewarded with food." *Female in her 60's*

785 "I really enjoy my coffee and people are always telling me, 'Oh, that's going to kill you,' but I am still here. . . . When I've been working hard and come to the house like late in the afternoon, a cup of coffee is a reward."

Female, mid to late 70's

Humorous sidenote

786 What have been some of your experiences with regard to food and eating?

"I do it often. Every day." *Female in her 30's*

787 "I love french fries and that sort of thing. If I shouldn't have it healthwise, it's probably one of my favorites. . . . I had a good steak [last week], . . . now I won't eat anything like that for awhile. Last night I had shrimp. Tonight I think it's fish, and so I try to kind of space [sic] myself." *Male, early 80's*

788 "I'm a real advocate in everything in moderation. I think if you eat any one thing too much, it's probably going to cause problems. I think we'd be healthier as long as we had that variety of foods. . . . I think reports come out that kind of scare us and later we find out they are not true. Some [foods] are bad for you and the next thing you know they're good for you." *Male, almost 60*

789 "I had a friend that worked for the same agency I did. . . . He had a lot of health problems. He would not watch his diet and I was on him quite a bit to try to get him to watch his fat and keep away from salts and everything. But I had little influence on him. . . . He died at about . . . 55." *Male, mid 70's*

790 "After I cut weight severely [for wrestling], then the sweets was what I wanted. And so that lingers to this day. I mean . . . I love doughnuts. Pastries and those kind of things are favorites. And I have them almost every day. Not good, and I know that, but I can go for four or five days without it and then I think I'll just have one and then it's not good. I struggle with that. I eat two good meals a day, and the third one is pretty crummy." *Male, almost 50*

791 "I thought that I needed to stay super, super skinny to [please] the person I was dating. . . . I wasn't eating healthy. . . . And I think now. . . I . . . realize what healthy eating is and what you can do to stay healthy." *Female, mid 20's*

792 "I went to [college], and [the nutrition class] and college algebra had the two highest levels of failure there 'cause it's not just talking about food. There's a lot of knowledge . . . that goes along there as far as calories and breakdowns of nutrition. . . . The things which are recommended for your body intake are real because your body has certain needs and demands for either building or maintaining. . . . We know about them, but quite often we don't [follow good nutrition]. 'Well, today I'll do this, and then tomorrow I'll start doing [something better].' " *Male, early 40's*

793 "[With] my father and mother, it was always meat and potatoes. And that's the way you grew up. Every night it was meat and potatoes. And maybe that's what caused some of my problem because my dad had a heart attack and so did my mother. And maybe that's because we grew up . . . with too much greasy foods. I don't know for sure, but these last few years, [I'm] trying to change a lot of my habits of eating." *Male, mid 50's*

794 "Basically, like most people, I tend to enjoy food that I shouldn't. . . . I've been trying to force myself to eat things I never thought I'd eat, finding out they're not so bad after all, even love them. . . . Now I'll see something I used to shovel down [and I'll think], 'You know, that's disgusting.' " *Male, early 30's*

795 "We had bread and potatoes and meat, and that was what I grew up with. . . . I never went to bed hungry, but [there wasn't] variety. I didn't even know what broccoli and cauliflower [were] . . . . I can't blame . . . my mother that I'm overweight, but I think that does play a big part in my life." *Female, mid 60's*

796 "I've been trying to have a tray of fresh vegetables with dip 'cause carrots are boring. I figure it's better to have the carrot—even if you're putting it in some Ranch dip—than to not have the carrot . . . . So, I've been trying to [eat better]. I haven't done very good at it. I go in spurts." *Female, early 40's*

797 "I know the value of nutrition. I know the importance. I know the Food Guide Pyramid. I know that you should eat oils and fats sparingly. I know that you should eat a lot of fruits and a lot of vegetables . . . . And lately, my cholesterol has been a little higher than what it used to be. I don't know if that's because of my diet or if it's genetic, but it definitely opened my eyes as far as my lifestyle and eating." *Male in his 30's*

798 "I'm really trying to get in a lot of fruits and vegetables, so that was, I guess, it was almost a—I felt like it was a *duty*." *Female in her 30's*

799 "I stopped [eating] my Oreos and milk at eight o'clock in the evening. I'll have a bowl of oatmeal for breakfast. . . . I've cut milk from [whole] to 2%."
Male in his 70's

800 "[My children] like really more healthy eating, not so much fried foods and lots of fruits and vegetables and dark bread, and I just cook healthier because of my children." *Female, late 70's*

801 "I've studied a little about food. I've studied human anatomy and how the body uses food and all that kind of stuff. . . . [You] can . . . look at . . . the label, and . . . then you can tell how much you should eat, but it doesn't mean you always follow that." *Male in his 30's*

802 "You're susceptible to a lot of diseases if you don't eat right. I've got a daughter that has a problem eating right, and . . . she gets sick very easy. . . . We've got to keep well fed because if you don't, you're going to get sick. . . . And the cycle just continues." *Male, early 50's*

803 "My husband and I belong to . . . [an organization in town], . . . and when we have our meetings, we eat out. So we went to this restaurant and our meal was . . . enchiladas. . . . It [had] this cream sauce over it, sour cream, and . . . I . . . scraped the sour cream off, got down and I could see that there was still cream cheese and sour cream, and I thought, 'Now wait a minute. Here I am, I'm going to the gym, and do I want to eat this?' So I ate a half of one. They didn't serve a salad, and . . . when we got in the car I said . . . , 'Tonight's the last night. I'm not going to [eat] like that.' I [said], 'I don't want to eat that stuff and then have to work three hours at the gym to get half of it off. . . . That's just stupid.'. . . I decided that if you make a plan, it's just like a goal in your life. You have to set a goal or you never go anywhere." *Female, mid 60's*

804 "I should be doing more and taking care of the old body a little better. You only have one [body], and you better take pretty good care of it. I had a heart attack . . . about ten years ago, which I never dreamed that I would have. It makes you worry about it all the time. 'Should I do this or that?' . . . And that's why I think I'm not doing right now the best. I should take care of myself. . . . I have a real bad habit of eating cookies . . . . I mean I'm just trying to break it, and . . . my wife's trying to break me of it. Instead of eating cereal in the morning I eat cookies. And it's just a bad habit. . . . You only go around once. And there's a lot of good things out there to see, so we've got to take care of [our bodies]. . . . I'm finding out here lately, since we have grandchildren, . . . that it's meaning more 'cause I hope I can watch them grow up a little bit. . . . I hope I can share a lot of my life yet . . . . You know you've got to do the best you can. . . . It all comes down to [bad habits] some years ago. It's caught up [with me]. I should have started taking better care of my life and my body years ago instead of just these last few years." *Male, mid 50's*

Memorable quotation
805 "I've always been very successful in most anything I've ever done, both athletically and otherwise . . . . My [child] has had a learning disability that we've really struggled with because in my family . . . there's been real achievers. My wife's family is very competent and always had people that did well, and then this [child] comes along and really struggles with [almost] everything. . . . It's kind of an eye-opener to me and makes you realize how fortunate you are when you're healthy. And then these things that you don't have any say over anyway don't happen to you." *Male, almost 60*

806 "[Previously], I would eat . . . fast food. . . . I would eat a lot of frozen food because studying doesn't leave much time for cooking healthy or for shopping for healthy food. The frozen foods were . . . fast. . . . It doesn't take you an hour; it takes you three minutes." *Female in her 20's*

807 "Yesterday was one of those days where I was [working] all day and didn't have much time, so I stopped and got a hamburger at McDonald's and the whole time you're doing that you're thinking 'Gol', this isn't great and I know better, but it's quick and I've got to get back to [work] and it's just faster.' "

Male in his 40's

808 "I think there's this time factor that comes in where I just don't have the time to make a meal, so a lot of times I find myself ordering out or buying frozen [prepared foods]. . . . That's nowhere close to anything I enjoy."

Male, early 30's

809 "I work several jobs and my wife works and . . . quite often at the end of the day we just don't have the ambition to then put together a fully balanced nutritious meal. And when you go out and eat, you just get what sounds good, not what's nutritious. Actually, that happens fairly regularly." *Male, early 40's*

810 "We all know how to eat better than we do, but some things are easy and some things quick and sometimes you're in a hurry." *Male, early 40's*

811 "[Eating] last night . . . was very frustrating because I couldn't sit down and eat because the phone was ringing off the hook at the front desk. So I went to eat a bite and I'd run to the phone, then I would come back and eat a bite and then go back and answer the phone." *Male, early 30's*

812 "When my husband and I first got married, I loved to cook for him because he liked the things that I cooked. . . . And then, since we've had the kids, just forget that idea. . . . And I still enjoy cooking when I have the time. I don't like having to try to figure out something for dinner at five o'clock on Monday night." *Female, early 40's*

813 "What I do all the time is basically the easiest and the fastest because I work and have . . . kids." *Female in her 30's*

814 "Even though I've taught [my children how to cook], it's been easier [for them] to go out or go buy something quick. [Maybe it's] just the speed of our environment. Nobody wants to take the time to cook a home-cooked meal or even sit around the table and be a family." *Male in his 60's*

815 "For the last 12 years I've worked a rotating shift . . . . That really messes with your life. It messes with your eating habits. It messes with about everything you can imagine." *Male in his 40's*

816 "Alcohol puts a lot of pounds on you. . . . [Drinking] was a way of doing business back in [another state]. [Customers] would come in and at four o'clock in the afternoon they would slap a 12-pack down on your desk and they'd say, 'Let's go.' . . . It got to be a very bad routine and actually kind of nice to break."
Male, 30's to 40's

817 "[For lunch today I] ate . . . while I worked at my desk, which unfortunately happens way too often at my job. . . . [It] was not very relaxing. . . . It was like, 'Inhale while you're at it.' " *Female, early 40's*

818 "I used to work at a [local grocery store] and there I couldn't eat, but now I have a desk job and all I do is sit and type. Man, I eat all the time. I graze. . . . I know I've gained pounds since I've changed jobs." *Female, late 20's to early 30's*

819 "When you're raised on a farm, . . . you eat three heavy meals. You work hard. . . . When you go to a physical environment that you don't work as hard, you still have the same kind of memory about the kind of foods you like and how you like to eat them. And three heavy meals with heavy foods isn't as acceptable as it was when you were burning the 6,000 calories a day." *Male in his 50's*

820 "When I first went to basic training, we were in such a level of physical and mental conditioning at that point you looked forward to going to the chow hall. You ate everything they gave you whether you'd ate it in your life before or not. . . . I felt like I needed that food to sustain my physical energy to make it through the days." *Male, mid 50's*

821 "I work from 3 to 11. . . . I come home and eat at 11 at night, . . . so [I'm] sleeping with a full stomach instead of being active. . . . And then I'd wake up in the morning, . . . [and] it's too late for breakfast, too early for lunch, so then you eat a big breakfast/lunch combination." *Male, early 30's*

822 "I went to work at a bakery. That just kinda went downhill with the [good] diet thing. They don't work well together and I've never been this heavy in my life." *Female, late 20's*

823 "I was in a flight training program . . . where all you did was wait for a plane and then you would fly for an hour or so, and the rest of the day you would just sit around and eat. . . . And I gained weight. . . . I didn't even realize it and I didn't like it." *Male, almost 60*

824 "[When we] first got children, [we] really struggled. . . . You think people on food stamps would be emaciated, but it's not that. . . . And I'd have to say during those years we were eating a lot of stuff we probably shouldn't have, but we did it simply because we were so poor it seemed like a little luxury. It wouldn't hurt anything. And then it became a habit." *Male, early 30's*

825 "I started going to [a weight control program] last year and it's taught me a lot, that you eat 'til you're full and then you push it aside. At first, [it was hard] . . . because when you go to a restaurant you think, 'Well, I'm paying for this so I need to clean up my plate; . . . I'm wasting money if I don't eat all my food.' And now I can leave it. . . . It doesn't bother me." *Female in her 60's*

826 "When [you're at a buffet, food is] too available and too prevalent. . . . You make yourself eat more than you need just because it's there. . . . I want to get my money's worth and I want to try that and I want to try that." *Male, early 40's*

827 "Before I married, we would go out to eat a lot. And then I [got] married and you have no money. . . . We're on such a limited budget because I've chosen not to work; . . . we're just on the bare minimum of being able to eat. And sometimes before payday, we're getting low and . . . our [kids] fix meals right now and they say, 'I don't know what to fix, there's nothing here. . . .' We're probably getting more down to basics when we don't have as much money. . . . We probably have maybe a healthier fare than we would if we had more money." *Female, mid 40's*

828 "I've gone to a fine restaurant before where the cuisine was really good and the ambiance was really good and the presentation of the food was really good. It would have been a very good experience—and I went and paid for it and that was a less good experience." *Male in his 50's*

829 "I don't want to have to pay more money for my food. It seems like anything that's good for you costs more." *Male in his 40's*

830 "Income and resources affect people. I just see my paycheck and I feel the tightness now. . . . It's expensive to eat properly, but it can also be expensive to eat junk food. Making the shift from [junk food to healthy eating] can be hard."
Female, late 40's

831 "My mother put food on the table and said, 'Eat it.' . . . My mother never made [very good] wages. . . . We didn't have a lot." *Female, 70ish*

832 "I hate spending a lot of money on food." *Male in his 30's*

833 "I don't use food to reward myself or punish myself. A lot of it hit me when I was a single mother and I was constantly thinking about food. And here I was, poverty level, and struggling to keep food on the table. But food was *always* in my head." *Female, late 40's*

834 "When we'd go grocery shopping [when I was growing up], I remember we'd have two or three carts that we'd fill up with food . . . and I just thought it was so fun. . . . But now that I'm an adult, I know that you have to pay for it. . . . An eighth a cart of food isn't fun, price wise, anymore." *Female, mid 40's*

835 "I remember a lot of gravy [when I was young] because it was still Depression-affected years and so my father had to go to [a large city] to find work. While he was gone, my mother made gravy out of everything she could think of." *Female, early 60's*

836 "So, we go in [to the ritzy place] and my wife takes one look at the menu and goes 'Uhhhh!' I said, 'Don't look at the right-hand side of the menu. Just order what you want.' And she said, 'There's nothing in here less than like $35.' I said, 'It's okay. It's fine. [My business associate] will take care of it. It's all right.' She says, 'They're buying $50 bottles of wine!' I said, 'It's okay.' Dessert was like $28. It wasn't for me, but it was a memorable experience because my wife had never done that before." *Male, late 50's*

837 "I don't like buffet places. . . . I don't like to waste money on something I'm not going to taste." *Female, mid 30's*

838 "I think there was a time in college where I didn't eat quite as well or as much as I probably should have. But a lot of that was just the financial situation you're in." *Female in her 20's*

839 "We had [a] place . . . here in town. They had excellent food. It was kind of pricey, but that's all right. It was not uncommon for me to give [the waitress] a $20 tip because the service was phenomenal, and the food was absolutely excellent." *Male, late 50's*

Humorous sidenote

840 *Were you one of those kids who was forced to sit at the table and clean your plate?*

"I was one of those kids that sat at the table and ate [my food] and tried to get some [food] from my brother." *Male in his 50's*

---

841 "I grew up knowing my mother was an excellent cook and she never worked outside of the home. We came home to the good stuff and I loved it. And I love to cook, and it kinda shows. And when I'm bored, that's what I turn to rather than the physical activity. It's, 'Let's make something good to eat.' "

Female, mid 40's

842 "When some young gal gets out of school and gets married, and [she and her husband] look at the bills they got to pay, the next thing you know they're both working. They don't have time to cook the way my mother and grandmother did. . . . So, what do they do? They go buy the stuff on the shelf that's fast to fix and somebody else has already done the work. . . . It's supper, but is it really good for them? . . . They just want something fast and they don't realize it wasn't good for them until 20 or 30 years later." *Male, 40's to 50's*

843 "You could be a bachelor and never get married. You got a microwave and who needs a wife to cook? 'Cause you could go to that store and, boom, boom, boom, your meal's there." *Male, 70ish*

844 "The first time somebody told me they liked my cooking, I wanted to cook more. . . . I do some serious cooking now. . . . And if there's any one thing that influenced my thoughts about food, it's that 'Wow! I can make good food.' You know, people like what I make." *Male, mid 30's*

845 "When I cook [food], I don't care anything about whether I eat it or not later. It's like, ah, I've looked at this long enough. It's important to me that the quality of what I fix is good for others." *Female, mid to late 40's*

846 "I'm glad that I have done as much cooking from scratch as I have over the years. . . . There's just something about putting those ingredients together and knowing how to do it that makes meal preparation enjoyable. And you know what you're eating." *Female, late 40's*

847 "My mother was a lousy cook. And our family agreed by mutual consent that she was a lousy cook. So anything that she cooked, we were tentative about eating. My grandmother was an extremely good cook, and so anything she cooked we really looked forward to." *Female in her 60's*

848 "I like to eat. I'm a pretty decent cook . . . . I can go into almost anybody's refrigerator and fix dinner. I'm not special. I'm old and I've had a lot of experience. You can't live as many places as I've lived and [had] as many different jobs as I've had and not learn something even through osmosis."

Male, late 50's

849 "It was a Boy Scout merit badge that got me started [cooking] and I've cooked pretty much ever since. . . . I really enjoy it. I mean, I buy cookbooks like crazy, . . . and I watch three or four cooking shows on TV. . . . I'm an enthusiast." *Male, late 30's*

850 "My wife's not one of them that experiments a lot with cooking. We have [foods] we like and that's pretty much what we do." *Male in his 40's*

851 "At this point in time, cooking a big meal is not high priority. I'll admit that right now. I enjoy [cooking food] if people enjoy eating it, like for a holiday or something." *Female, 50ish*

852 "I love to cook . . . . I like preparing gourmet foods. When my husband was alive, we had lots of people over for dinner . . . because I liked entertaining at home rather than going out. Now it's a little different, this part of my life."
Female, late 60's

853 "My mother was a very good cook. We didn't eat out a lot. . . . She was home and so she was always cooking. . . . [My wife] turned out to be just a marvelous cook. She has always been in the home too and never worked [outside the home]. We very seldom eat fast food." *Male, almost 60*

854 "My mom is an excellent cook. . . . I'm one of those guys who is . . . lucky because I learned how to make some [of] those things. . . . And I don't have too many complaints about how I cook." *Male, early 40's*

855 "I think just going out and not having to cook is wonderful. We have friends that she cooks one [meal one week] and I cook the next . . . and we vice versa. And I *love* the [days] that I don't have to cook." *Female, 30's to 40's*

856 "My mother thoroughly enjoyed cooking and she was a good cook. . . . I probably took [my mother's cooking] for granted. . . . But . . . later, when I was cooking for my own family, I would consult with her." *Female, early 60's*

857 "My grandmother's way of presenting the food was very good, besides the fact that she was an excellent cook. . . . Cooking must have been a drudgery for [my mother] because she never acted like she was pleased with cooking. . . . Well, I happen to hate cooking. And I had to cook when I was 11 years old. . . . And now because my husband has no conception of time—he's never on time for anything—and so I try to cook things that will keep 'til he gets here, casseroles and roasts and things like that. When it comes to things like steaks and stuff like that, I just don't cook them. He cooks them when he gets home, himself. And he enjoys cooking. That's just fine by me." *Female in her 60's*

858 "I remember around holidays it was such a hassle to cook for everybody. . . . Right now . . . for holidays, you eat all day long, so why cook? . . . We don't cook anymore. And we enjoy ourselves just as much. . . . We always have vegetables and meats and cheeses and crackers. And we just have finger foods all day. . . . But we don't kill ourselves anymore." *Female, early 40's*

859 "I've been a cook for about 20 years. I started when I was a kid. . . . I might even be considered a gourmet. . . . I like all kinds of food, but French is my favorite and I cook it a lot. It's also the process. Making it is fun. And it's kind of challenging to make good food. . . . It's kind of . . . a hobby almost, trying to be a good cook. I'm not bad. I'm not as good as my favorite chef, but people like to come to my house to eat." *Male, late 30's*

860 "I've always enjoyed food and I like to cook. I'm a very good cook. . . . I enjoy cooking and that's probably not a good thing for me either, 'cause I sample it once in a while." *Male in his 60's*

861 "I was not a cook before we got married. I could prepare some things, but there was a lot I didn't know and there's a lot [my husband] taught me. . . . He's a good cook, but he doesn't like the routine responsibility of it." *Female, late 40's*

862 "My sons—I don't know if it's 'cause their dad cooked all these years or what—but they do most of the cooking. The women they married don't know how to cook." *Male in his 60's*

863 "I enjoy cooking. I like to be able to try things like foods from scratch so I could say, 'I did that. I've made that.' " *Female in her 30's*

864 "Well, I enjoy [food] more when I didn't cook it, [when] somebody else made [it]." *Female in her 20's*

Changes over time with men and cooking

865 "I would bet that in today's society that males are more adapted to cooking their own meals and taking care of themselves than . . . a few years [ago]. Like my dad, . . . if Mother was in the hospital or gone for some reason, he could fry eggs. We would get sick of eggs 'cause it was eggs three times a day. But I'm a pretty good cook and love to cook. And I think a lot more males today are like, from a divorce or something, able to be better cooks than in years past." *Male, 70ish*

---

866 "I love steak. . . . I swear I eat about as much now as I did when I was in high school. People look at me and wonder where in the hell does he put it all? . . . I got a prime rib, which I dearly love, and I like them just rare enough that if I could get the vet, there is still hope. Anyhow, when I finished this thing that looks like a roast, . . . one guy came over and, 'Well,' he says, 'I lost. I bet my partner you'd never get around that, but you did.' " *Male, early 80's*

867 "[My dad] would fix you a plate that was about like a serving platter thing—'No, you can't get up from the table until you eat all that.' . . . 'It's called portion control—geez Dad!' But you had to finish that plate before you got up from the table. . . . And then as I got to be into junior high, early years of high school, he didn't do that anymore because [I got to] the rebellious stage, I guess. 'Dad, you are not going to fix my plate for me!' " *Female, late 40's*

868 "I always tell [my mom] that I don't feel guilty coming to her house because it would be rude if I didn't eat her food. But then I have to go home and my kids are like, 'I want to go to Grandma's house. We get lots of food there!' "

Female, mid 30's

869 "We were taught to clean our plates up, and we were served large portions and I think back in those days . . . [people] felt that you weren't healthy unless you had some weight around your hips." *Female in her 60's*

870 "My wife makes me go on that half rule, . . . have a portion and . . . eat half of it and then put the rest back. . . . [She's] trying to get me to lose a little weight because . . . she wants me to stick around a little longer." *Male, mid 50's*

871 "You went through a line [when I was in college], and you served your plate. And serving a plate from a line and from a table was an entirely different thing. [It required] learning how to judge what was a reasonable amount. So I did put on weight that first year." *Female, late 40's*

872 "When we first were married, I used to make . . . these army-sized helpings and we would just have a *ton* of food. . . . [Now] I try to eat five little meals a day. It makes me feel better than my not eating all day long and then just wolfing down a huge dinner." *Female, mid 20's*

873 "My parents . . . put potatoes on my plate and I ate it. They put oatmeal in my bowl, and I ate it. I had brothers and [my parents] didn't see the difference that maybe girls needed less than the boys. . . . We all got the same amount."

Female, mid 60's

874 "The problem with buffets is that you will take more food than you would normally. I had a small piece of steak and a lot of salad. . . . I was real careful."

Female, early 60's

875 "It wasn't a clear-your-plate kind of table when I was younger, but if you put it on your plate, you ate it." *Male, 30's to 40's*

876 "I can eat more than my husband. It takes more to fill me up."

Female in her 60's

877 "We have kind of a policy, my wife and I, that we eat desserts, probably a dessert every night for dinner, but we make them smaller than we used to."

Male in his 50's

878 "My mother always told us when we were children, 'Don't take more than you can eat.' " *Female, mid to late 70's*

879 "When I would go to my grandma's house as a child, the rule was you finished what she put on your plate." *Female, early 20's*

880 "If I'm sitting and watching TV or something, I'd rather go get just what I want because if the wife puts that [food] on that plate, no matter what, I'll clean that plate up." *Male, 70ish*

881 "If I'm at home and my wife fixes me a plate, I got to eat at least what is on the plate." *Male, early 30's*

882 "Basically my parents would put the food on our plate and you had to eat everything." *Female, late 40's*

Memorable quotation

883 "A person said that the average American digs his grave with his teeth. . . . So if you watch what you're eating, you don't dig quite as fast." *Male, early 80's*

---

884 "Most of the time eating is a chore. I do not like to cook. I do not like to prepare [food]. Don't like to wash dishes. . . . I've never gotten too turned on about it. . . . I'm bad at grocery shopping, too. . . . I don't like wasting time. It's almost like eating and cooking and all that is a waste of time to me. . . . There should be something else that I could be doing or something. . . . I don't eat fast, but . . . I want to get done . . . so I can do something else. . . . It would be nice if [eating] was optional." *Male in his 30's*

885 "I don't know that I really *enjoy* eating. I mean, it's just something you do. . . . Cooking is something I *have* to do. . . . Buying groceries, the same thing. Everything associated with food—it's just something that has to be done. . . . [When I was young], I'd rather be outside helping my dad than in the house cooking. That was where I liked being . . . outside." *Female in her 40's*

886 "I don't live for food. I eat because I have to, I guess. . . . I'd rather hold my grandbabies and tend them than eat." *Female in her 40's*

887 "Food for me is—I mean not that I don't enjoy it—but sometimes I just think it's kind of time consuming." *Female, mid to late 40's*

888 "I guess I'm just lazy when it comes to food. . . . If I run out of pop and I don't make it to the store for a couple weeks, so be it. There isn't any pop. But if it's there, I'll have it instead of water." *Male in his 30's*

889 "Food was not necessarily a real important thing to me. . . . I mean, I guess I kinda figured you ate 'cause you needed to eat. . . . If I'm busy doing something else, I never even think about food." *Female, mid to late 40's*

890 "When the gardens are out, oooh, I just love to make homemade vegetable soup with fresh vegetables out of the garden. That's my Saturday activity."
Male in his 50's

891 "Everybody would raise their own gardens. . . . And over the years, you'd find yourself trading recipes and trading ideas." *Male in his 50's*

892 "I just hate [vegetables]. . . . Grandma always had gardens and the only way I would eat [vegetables] was peas had to be fresh out of the garden and corn had to be Grandma's sweet corn." *Female, 40ish*

893 "[When I was growing up], we had to sit down for dinner and [my mom] always made this bowl of huge dinner with all these foods and you had to have the whole table set and you didn't get served from the pan to the table; you had to have it in a serving dish. . . . [Now with my family], we sit down and eat and you take the pan from the stove to the table and you have a fork and whatever you need and you eat and then you're out the door and doing something else."

Female, 40ish

894 "So when my mother remarried, the dinner table was the battleground. If there was a problem, if there was whatever, it was addressed at the dinner table and it was horrible. I got when I was probably about 13, 14—I just wouldn't eat." *Female, mid to late 40's*

895 "It's really embarrassing, but I go and have a sausage egg McMuffin for breakfast because I can do it on the bank run. . . . And I get my bank deposit, and I go over, and I swing through McDonald's, . . . and I go to the bank and I go back to work. And it's peaceful and it's quiet and I don't have anybody yelling at me, and maybe that's why I do it as much as anything. . . . I eat [at] McDonald's not because it tastes good but because it is a quiet meal. And I don't have to listen to anybody argue, whine, complain, fight." *Female, early 40's*

896 "There's a restaurant, . . . and it's in an old cathedral and it has water coming down the wall. They serve Italian food and my husband went to Italy . . . and so we really like Italian food. And we took our family there and it was fun. . . . The atmosphere was just so fun and the food was so good that it was really a joy to eat there with our family." *Female, mid 40's*

897 "I'll give you a typical me and my wife and the kids at home. [My wife and I] will probably eat in the living room. I don't watch much television, but the television that I do watch happens to be right at six. . . . [The] kids eat in the dining room, and they have their little pow-wow and they like it. . . . They do their thing, and . . . it's kind of time alone for [my wife and me], too. So it's good both ways." *Male, early 30's*

898 "At home, . . . the table is just in the middle of everything. So it's like we're eating in the setting of the sink and the [dirty] dishes." *Female, mid 40's*

899 "I went to [a local restaurant]. I don't really care for [it]. . . . The service isn't . . . good. I pay for service. We had [another] place . . . here in town. They had excellent food. . . . The service was phenomenal, and the food was absolutely excellent. . . . I like food prepared well—a nice clean plate."

Male, late 50's

122

Changes in society

900 "Part of our society's problem [is] everything's gotten so much faster . . . 'cause [everyone's] just going 90 miles an hour all day long until it's time to go to bed at night. . . . So . . . what comes down from [fast living] finally hits us, and . . . now we're seeing the . . . brunt of the storm with . . . child diabetes."

Male, 40ish

901 "It seems to me like our society today has quite a [focus on food]. . . . 'What did you eat?' and . . . 'I went to lunch.' I think we're more prone to eating anymore as a . . . social event." *Female in her 50's*

902 "One day [my daughter] said, 'Mom, when you grew up, were there heavy girls in school?' and I said, 'No.' I could think of one. And I do believe it is [because] we didn't have the pop and the chips and all those kinds of things."

Female in her 50's

Media influences

903 "You can try educating people, but . . . you're competing against the entire advertising media. You're competing against schools being sponsored by soft drink companies. . . . When I went to school, . . . they didn't sell soft drinks. They didn't sell candy bars and potato chips." *Male, late 30's*

Plentiful food

904 "Sometimes I think that people in our country are spoiled because not enough of us have gone hungry to appreciate the food we have. I have never gone hungry." *Male, almost 60*

College

905 "I'd have to say my weight problem probably started [in college] because they [practically give pizzas away to college students]. . . . We all came from little towns. We didn't have [delivery pizza]. We had someone bringing pizza to [us]. . . . I'd have to say it was like I was at a fork in the road; I took a fork. And eating college cafeteria food [would have been better] than pizza. . . . And I'd have to say that set quite a few habits that should have maybe not been set."

Male, early 30's

Winter

906 "I grew up in California . . . . When it gets hot, you don't want to eat. . . . But I notice here in the wintertime I eat a little more. Maybe sometimes a lot more than . . . I should during the wintertime, especially when you're just sitting around waiting for the cold snap to go. Now when the summer comes I won't eat as much." *Male, 60ish*

907 "When I was younger, I could eat whatever I wanted to. I was active enough that it never showed. Now that I am older, I have tendencies to eat whatever I want to, [and] it's just a bugger to try not to." *Female, late 20's*

908 "[My husband and I are] only eating one meal a day, and nobody will believe me, so I don't tell them very often. . . . We just figure we aren't working like we used to. You don't need that much food." *Female, 70ish*

909 "The only one that could ever eat what they wanted and never gain [weight] was my husband, . . . and now those days are gone for him, too." *Female, 50ish*

910 "I think when a person gets into maybe the high school and college years we somewhat get away from paying much attention to how we eat. . . . But then later on, we start thinking it's probably important again. Maybe when it's a little bit too late. . . . My wife and I actually do spend quite a bit of time at the grocery stores in the produce area." *Male in his 50's*

911 "I understand as you get older sometimes you've got to limit what you eat. . . . I'm not looking forward to that, but it might come someday. . . . My dad . . . the last few years— I don't know [if it's] a midlife crisis or what, but he's turned into a health nut. . . . I get a lot of . . . 'When I was young I should have been healthy instead of eating some of that.' " *Male in his 20's*

912 "Normally, if I don't eat at like six, I don't eat because I . . . can't eat late anymore." *Male in his 60's*

913 "But the last ten years I've gained about ten pounds. . . . When I was younger, I never gained any weight. I had to eat just to keep it on." *Male, 40ish*

914 "When I was younger, hell, I ate anything—as much as I wanted to. When you're young, you don't think about those things. When you get older, you have a bad night when you get up and the food's coming back up and you're coughing up stuff. That never happened when I was young. 'What the hell is wrong here now?' So you're more in tune to . . . how much you eat and what you eat as you get older. . . . You watch what you eat when you get older." *Male, 70ish*

915 "Since I've gotten older and less active, . . . I've watched my weight go up. . . . That's just the way it is. . . . It usually hits when my pants get to feeling they're too tight. And it's either buy a new wardrobe or lose a little bit of weight. . . . And I haven't had that problem until just the last year or so. Before that, my weight . . . pretty well . . . just stayed where it was." *Female in her 40's*

916 "I smoked for 40 years. . . . I quit [over 20 years ago], cold turkey. . . . I've never smoked one since. . . . It has increased my taste buds, but I enjoy everything better, breathing, non-stuffiness. I think I see everything in a clearer vision." *Male in his 70's*

917 "I've smoked for 35 years. My doctor forced me to quit ten years ago due to my health problems. After I quit smoking, I gained a lot of weight. When I was smoking, I would grab a cigarette and get some coffee. Now it seems like I grab for food instead of a cigarette." *Female in her 60's*

Food and Eating - Medical

918 "Not too long ago, I went on a very restrictive diet to lose weight. . . . Things were going wonderfully. I went to see the doctor, and I was anemic . . . and he said, 'I think you better eat,' which was wonderful news. . . . And the doctor has never since said anything to me about my weight. Now, he knows and I know that I'm too heavy." *Female in her 60's*

919 "My cholesterol's marginally high, so I probably should be more careful about [eating meat] than I am. It helps that I exercise because . . . my good cholesterol's very high. So when the doctor looks at [my cholesterol] he says, 'Well, you're marginal, but your HDLs are pretty high so I won't spank you.' " *Male in his 50's*

920 "[After dieting], I was glad to be at my goal weight, but then my weight crept back on. . . . Even pregnant I don't think I weighed anywhere near this. And I talk to my doctor . . . [and asked], 'What can I do?' And he said, 'Well cut out or cut down sugar and fat.' Well, it's such a great idea, if you can really do it." *Female, early 60's*

921 "I do think . . . our doctors today maybe don't put enough emphasis on foods and diets. You are what you eat. I think that is probably where more problems come from than we recognize . . . is poor diet." *Male, almost 60*

922 "I wish the medical profession was a little bit more into treating the individual. . . . I think that would really help if we were getting cooperation of the medical profession. And I don't know how you'd implement that, looking at the whole person . . . . There seems to be, and you notice on TV, they have all of these prescription drugs. 'Ask your doctor about them.' How many doctors are prescribing because the person asked them rather than because the person needed it? . . . And every time a new drug comes out, it's got a fancy name and a fancy price and that's what they prescribe for the patient." *Female in her 60's*

923 "[During family get-togethers, we] have three big meals a day, which I don't think is necessary, but my mother-in-law's headstrong and she's from the old school of three meals a day." *Male, early 50's*

924 "My husband eats three hearty meals a day, but that's all he eats. I would eat the three hearty meals, plus I'd have many, many, many snacks in between and he does not snack. And so I know if we'd sit at the table he may eat more than me *then*, but I continue the meal. Or, I've already *had* the meal *before* we sat down and then I eat another one. . . . He eats the three meals and that's very satisfying to him. I graze continually, and so I had to do something to [control my weight]." *Female in her 30's*

925 "I don't eat much breakfast. . . . It's a time factor, too. I have to be to work at six in the morning and I don't want to have to get up that early to have breakfast. . . . And recently, I have kind of cut my dinner out, too, trying to help lose weight. I'm drinking [a meal replacement drink] to take the place of those [meals]. But I still eat a pretty big, good supper. That's one of them things that's hard to give up." *Male in his 40's*

926 "I never looked forward to sitting down and eating dinner. [Meal time was a battleground when I was growing up] and I think that has played a part with me now. . . . It's almost like I can say, 'Okay, here we go, everybody eat.' I have rebelled against the structure [of family meals]." *Female, mid to late 40's*

927 "I married very young, and when you get right on a ranch it's big meals. It's three meals a day, and they were big meals." *Female, mid to late 60's*

928 "Some people space breakfast off like it's no big thing at all. . . . My philosophy is you've got to have those three [meals] in there at seven, twelve, and five—breakfast, dinner, and supper. I'm from the old school, . . . you better have them. I don't care if you're not hungry, . . . put something in your system. You need it." *Male in his 70's*

929 "I look back at my mom and we had three meals a day, every day. You could set the clock by when we ate. . . . That was a positive thing. . . . Now I miss breakfast or eat supper at nine at night. . . . Busy lifestyle. . . . I miss the regularity." *Male in his 20's*

930 "[When I was in college], I started making sure I at least . . . had time to eat two meals a day because I don't think there's any college student who eats breakfast. Even though we know it's the most important meal of the day, . . . I think we would rather sleep." *Female, mid 20's*

931 "Last night . . . I didn't get home until 10:30 and didn't feel like cooking, of course. And nothing was really open to go get anything to eat, so I ended up eating chips and a pop for dinner." *Female, early 20's*

932 "I have a boss that continually wants to . . . go out and have a big lunch. . . . But I know that when I eat a big lunch . . . it takes me a couple hours to really get going again. . . . It makes me feel lethargic. . . . So that's why I just basically don't eat much lunch. But then I kind of pig out a little bit more in the evening." *Male, 60ish*

933 "I eat usually twice or once a day. I would like to get where I would eat five or six times a day, just smaller portions and more spread out, but it doesn't happen that way." *Male, early 30's*

934 "When you're single, [meals] don't matter. . . . I don't have to worry about anybody else." *Male, 70ish*

935 "I usually eat twice a day. My breakfast . . . is around ten, and then I'll eat [at] maybe two or three and then I'm done. I'm one of those people—I can't go to bed on a full tummy." *Female, late 40's*

936 "Lunch is my time to separate myself from my work. Unfortunately, a lot of days I can't do that. I'll grab something and run, but . . . [lunch] is how I kind of separate my mind from what I'm doing." *Male, 30's to 40's*

937 "I try not to eat a large meal during the day. I kind of snack on fruits and vegetables and then eat with the family at night. It's what I'm trying to do. It doesn't always work." *Female in her 30's*

938 "[My husband] always has to have a breakfast. . . . [Breakfast] means you got up in the morning—you're still kicking!" *Female, 70ish*

939 "One thing I do horrendously is I don't eat breakfast. I'm not a breakfast person. I get up and try to get to work as quick as I can, so usually a pot of coffee is what I call breakfast. And I know that's not the grandest thing in the world." *Male, 30's to 40's*

Family meal time

940 "[When I was growing up], dinner time was a family time. And at my house now, it's not. It's crazy. . . . I even wonder sometimes why we have a dining room with a table in it." *Male, 30's to 40's*

941 "I really tried to snack on more things like celery and carrots. . . . Although I like them, after a while it gets pretty boring. . . . But you push through, just to see if it'll work. And it definitely works." *Male in his 50's*

942 "We love to make popcorn and watch a movie and it's kind of like a family gathering thing. . . . Oh yeah, the smell of popcorn just kills you."

Female, late 30's

943 "I've changed . . . . Instead of having three meals a day, I have snacks too—midmorning with the kids. If I don't [eat a snack, I get] kind of shaky. . . . And then after school I have a snack and sometimes before bed. Probably if I cut out my bed snack it would help my weight a little." *Female, mid 40's*

944 "[My husband and I] have three meals a day . . . , and in between I like chocolate. And my husband, he has a sweet-tooth more than I do, so we kind of eat sweets in between meals." *Female in her 70's*

945 "I guess I was a picky eater. My mom always said I was very, very picky. And I guess I am picky in the fact that now if I'm hungry and I look in the cupboards, but I'm not hungry for peanut butter, I won't just pull it out because I'm hungry. I'm so picky on what I'm hungry for, it's funny." *Female, mid 30's*

946 "I'm probably not a real big 'meal mother,' but I let my kids snack throughout the day when they are hungry." *Female, mid 30's*

947 "I really don't eat near as much as I used to, just because I'm not as active. . . . The only thing now is I find myself eating more sweets when I'm sitting at a desk most of the day. Sometimes there's a bag of licorice hanging around and I'll eat that a lot more than I used to." *Male in his 20's*

Snacking and emotions

948 "I snack all day and I love food. And anytime that I'm bored, it almost feels like I eat. . . . And if I am upset, then I clear out the cupboards and I just start eating, and eating, and eating, and eating. I think that I like to eat, and sometimes that's the way I answer some of my problems." *Female, early 20's*

---

949 "I had . . . cut [pop] way back . . . until I started school again. And it just killed me. And I don't know whether it's because they have pop machines there or you're trying to stay up late . . . . I can go weeks for a while without having one and then all of a sudden I'll have a horrible craving." *Female, mid 30's*

950 "When I was married to my first husband, he'd call me 'my own stupid self.' . . . When my kids were taken away, . . . I was so glad I was not a social drinker . . . , because I swear if I was, I'd be an alcoholic today. I was drinking 12 and 24 packs just about every day of Pepsi. . . . [Even though] I've cut down so much, . . . I still like my Pepsi, and that's part of the reason that I'm heavy. I got really depressed and started drinking Pepsi, *lots* of it. And I was so glad that I got help. I mean, I still drink Pepsi; in fact, I wished I'd had one earlier."

Female, early 30's

951 "When I was a kid, we drank a lot of milk and I still drink a lot of milk. And I can see I have never been weaned yet. . . . I still drink probably three or four big glasses of milk a day, at least." *Male in his 40's*

952 "They have a pyramid of food . . . but I never see them put [in] . . . soft drinks. My daughter feeds it to her little girl. . . . She goes to McDonald's or somewhere [and] . . . I . . . just . . . say, 'They sell milk here.' "

Female, mid to late 60's

953 "I would drink like four Pepsi's a day. . . . I would not eat. . . . And . . . [I thought] how terribly unhealthy that was . . . , but I lost lots of weight."

Female, mid 30's

954 "For years I drank a lot of caffeine. Since [last summer], our whole family's just cut it right out. We just decided we were going to do it and we did it. . . . I sleep better at night. . . . And I drink caffeine-free Pepsi and Mountain Dew now, but not near to the point I was then. I mean, I've cut back on that too, but [I] still drink it. [I] still enjoy it." *Male in his 40's*

955 "I lost 45 pounds [one] time and kept it off for a number of years. [Then] I moved to another location where drinking [alcohol] was part of their society, I guess, and [I] quickly put the pounds back on." *Male 30's to 40's*

956 "I'm amazed by the kids that come into . . . where I work and don't buy a pop, but they go and buy water. It just boggles my mind 'cause I'm trying now as an adult to retrain myself to drink water, to crave water when . . . I'd rather go grab a can of pop or iced tea. . . . I'm not saying it's *working*. Some days are better than others. The thoughts are there." *Female, early 40's*

957 "We didn't drink anything [but milk] as kids. We drank milk, and if you had something else it was a real treat because it was so unusual."

Female, late 40's

958 "At an early age I got started on pop and I drank it really heavy. If it had been booze I'd have been in the clink a long time ago. . . . I haven't drunk enough water. There would be days that I'd go and maybe not drink anything but maybe milk and half a dozen pops a day." *Male in his 20's*

959 "[Now] I just try to stay away from pop as much as possible. . . . I used to drink two of those two-liter bottles of Pepsi a day, and that would be without breakfast. I'd get up in the morning and before lunch I'd have one and a half of them bottles gone. [For lunch, I'd] go around the drive-in and get a hamburger and milkshake and a great big pop." *Male, early 50's*

960 "I think I drank way too much pop. I was drinking six of those Big Slams a day. I haven't had one in five weeks. I feel so good." *Female in her 20's*

961 "When I gained weight in the Army it was 'cause it was handy to the [post exchange] every night. And boy, you'd drink several beers. And I gained, I'll bet, 20 pounds." *Male, 70's to 80's*

962 "I think the public should have more choices of a diet drink available. . . . I don't like sugar . . . but there's not a lot of [nonsugared beverage] choices out there." *Female, early 60's*

Cultural change toward soft drinks

963 "I remember growing up, it was a real treat to go to town and get a pop every now and then. And now, it's just how many have you had before breakfast? And so that's one of the things . . . if we become addicted . . . it becomes a way of life." *Male, early 40's*

964 "You're running 'til eight o'clock at night. What do you do? It's really easy to drive through the fast food place. And sometimes that's not fast enough." *Male, 30's to 40's*

965 "We always ate fast food because both my parents worked. And this is a very common story these days, in this culture. Everybody's working, nobody wants to cook, so they go out to McDonald's.... [When I was young], I loved going ... to McDonald's. Kids love going there. It's marketed to kids."

Male, late 30's

966 "When I was a kid, I just abused [food] terribly. You know, fast food. I ate unreal amounts of it, and it's because it is easy to abuse it. You know, you drive in and they give you something and you drive home and eat it." *Male, late 30's*

967 "I hate McDonald's.... And having two kids in [this town], and they think that's the only place there is in town to eat. Every once in a while, I put my foot down and say, 'No, we're not going to McDonald's.' ... But that's their favorite place and I get sick of it.... I eat [the food], but then afterwards I feel blahhh, ... and I just—yuck, yuck—I think, 'Why did I waste those calories?' "

Female in her 30's

968 "Me, just being fat, you know food's enjoyable and I like to eat. That sounds terrible, but I like to eat food.... I'm just as guilty as everybody, too. There's some weekends where I just don't feel like cooking anything, so we'll go to McDonald's, and I always feel sick after I eat at McDonald's."

Female, mid 20's

969 "I eat [by myself at] McDonald's, not because it tastes good but because it is a quiet meal. And I don't have to listen to anybody argue, whine, complain, fight." *Female, early 40's*

970 "My mother was a very good cook.... [My wife] turned out to be just a marvelous cook.... We very seldom eat fast food." *Male, almost 60*

971 "[My husband and I] noticed that we had gained a lot of weight. When I look back at pictures now, I think, 'Oh Lord, I *did* gain a lot of weight.' But it was basically because [we were] going out to eat all the time.... [Since then my weight has] definitely gone down and I lost a lot of fat ... that had built up from eating McDonald's and Burger King." *Female, mid 20's*

972 "Since I've moved out of my parents' house, I eat out *all* the time. And probably my biggest downfall is that I eat at Taco John's at least . . . once a day." *Female, early 20's*

973 "Yesterday was one of those days where I was [working] all day and didn't have much time, so I stopped and got a hamburger at McDonald's and the whole time you're doing that you're thinking, 'Gol', this isn't great, and I know better, but it's quick and I got to get back to [work] and it's just faster.' "

Male in his 40's

974 "I'd have to say my weight problem probably started [in college] because they [practically give pizzas away to college students]—five bucks—you can get a medium pizza. We all came from little towns. We didn't have [delivery pizza]. [In college], we had someone bringing pizza to [us]." *Male, early 30's*

975 "I think sometimes when we get busy, it's convenient to go to fast food, which is probably more than we should. . . . Sometimes life is just so busy I don't make it home to eat, so I guess I just drop by the Burger King or something. And that's not great." *Male in his 40's*

976 "We took a trip . . . for my husband's . . . work . . . and we didn't have a kitchen. We were living in hotels. . . . By the end of the trip, I was sick of [eating out]. And a lot of it was fast foods 'cause we were in a hurry. I was so sick of that food. It's really gross, though my daughter learned to like french fries." *Female in her 20's*

Memorable quotation

977 "Everybody's working two and three jobs. It's so much easier to go out and get a hamburger than it is to have to cook something. . . . It's just so easy and it's cheap. . . . I spend a lot on food when I cook it myself. When you go to McDonald's, you pig out for five or six dollars. It's cheap and easy. . . . You don't have to clean anything up. . . . You have your work cut out for you."

Male, late 30's

978 "I don't like buffet places . . . . I can't go to a place where there's so much out there that you just don't get to taste the food. So I like the fancier restaurants that do come in the courses . . . . I think I love that you get your salad first and then a relish tray and then maybe a soup. . . . Where if it's all on a big plate, you don't remember what you had. . . . I really enjoy food. Maybe that's it."

Female, mid 30's

979 "My wife's an excellent cook and we don't eat out very much. We eat at home most of the time. . . . I do notice this, that in my neighborhood probably 60 percent of the meals are eaten out of the home today. There's lots of people that don't eat at home. And I think that when you go out to a restaurant, you don't get proper food. I don't care what you say." *Male, mid 70's*

980 "Most restaurants I think actually serve too much, but I don't ever get a doggie bag." *Male, early 80's*

981 "[In terms of enjoying food], I . . . think, in general, of times when . . . you go to a good restaurant, . . . just how excited you are to go try this new place and your favorite food. Or, even though you're stuffed, how good it feels after you eat it, 'cause it's just really good food." *Female, early 20's*

982 "I like to eat out more than . . . make my own food just because it is so difficult to find a common ground with [my] family." *Female in her 30's*

983 "A couple weeks ago [my wife and I] stopped at a restaurant and I had a pot roast dinner and I really enjoyed that experience. . . . And it just reminded me of how things were when I was younger, as a kid. A Sunday afternoon meal with my mother and dad, and I just enjoyed eating it because it tasted good and because it refreshed some of those memories from another time." *Male, mid 50's*

984 "It was a tradition in my family [that] we had dinner that my mom prepared for us. . . . And now that I'm married, I find it kind of strange, I guess. Whenever we visit my wife's family, they always eat out. That's their family tradition. . . . Probably four or five nights a week they go to a restaurant. . . . And that's just kind of what's been in my wife's mind." *Male in his 20's*

985 "My parents had the means to go out to eat every day, five times a day, if they wanted to, but we did it very, very seldom. Maybe like once or twice a month Mother would say, 'Well, let's go to this restaurant. Your father wants to take us out to eat.' And I don't know that we really enjoyed that as well because it was more of a formal situation than it was of us gathering around the table . . . and being able to enjoy each other." *Male, 60ish*

986 "I prefer to relax and sit down and eat. [There are] few things in life that you get to enjoy, and eating is one of them. You might as well take your time and enjoy it. I enjoy eating." *Male, 70ish*

987 "At my house, we always hurry through [eating] and it's just something you have to do and get through it. . . . We take [eating] for granted." *Female, 40ish*

988 "[For lunch today I] ate . . . while I worked at my desk. . . . It was like, 'Inhale while you're at it.' " *Female, early 40's*

989 "My wife and I have a more difficult time eating a full meal . . . with others because we take more time at mealtime than most people do. We kind of have that as our social time together, and we don't eat so fast." *Male in his 50's*

990 "I'm [from a large family], . . . so when the food was put on the table everybody ate real fast so they would get their share. And I still do that today. I can eat my meal in 15 minutes. Everything. But the problem there is you're not paying attention to your body. You're eating until [your food is gone]."
Female, early 40's

991 "If we're going to go out [to eat, the kids] want to know if it's fast food, where we will be blasting through a restaurant, or slow food, where we actually sit down at a restaurant. And the same distinction for at home. If . . . we're going to get together as a family, which is hard to do, . . . they make that distinction. 'Well, this is slow food, we're going to sit down.' " *Male, mid 30's*

992 "I guess one of my poor eating habits is eating too fast, and I think I need to just relax a little more and eat slower and not be thinking that I'm going to starve." *Male, early 40's*

993 "If . . . we go to a restaurant, I would just as soon get it and take it home and eat it. . . . I don't like eating in front of people, possibly because of my weight. Also, because inevitably you're going to spill something on your shirt. . . . Or a lot of times, being big, someone is thinking, 'Look at the fat guy with his chicken nuggets.' And of course, 90 percent chance no one is thinking [that], but it is in the back of your mind. . . . I think I just prefer to eat at home because I'm just more comfortable there." *Male, early 30's*

994 "I'm not a 'closet eater,' . . . but I sometimes don't feel comfortable with eating certain things in public and I'll take it home." *Female, early 60's*

995 "When I was growing up, my dad was an oil field worker. We were 'oil field trash,' kind of thing. But one thing, we always had food on the table. . . . Probably some of the most fond [childhood] memories . . . [I have are from] just sitting down and eating dinner together. . . . It's not the food so much, but maybe the social time around the food. . . . Dinnertime was a family time. And at my house now, it's not." *Male, 30's to 40's*

996 "Food for my family was always the celebration. Okay, what are we going to have? I've grown up with that. And I have trouble with that because it's like, 'Okay, what are we going to have?' Unfortunately, my husband likes to eat just as much as I do and my whole family is overweight." *Female, late 40's*

997 "I think I always enjoy meals when it's with a family gathering. I really like the holidays. The food always seems to taste better when you're with your family. I do believe that, definitely. . . . I'll go home and eat lunch with my family . . . . I mean, we focus on having meals together. And I think that's important for families to sit down and eat. And I remember growing up that we would . . . typically have supper together. . . . That's something that has always been important to me, to sit down as a family and eat together, just 'cause it's a time when you can share what's going on for the day." *Male in his 30's*

998 "[Where I came from], just about everything you do revolves around beer or food or both, usually. . . . With my family, every time we get together we talk about what we're going to eat." *Male, 30ish*

999 "I have one brother, . . . and his wife watches what they eat, . . . and he keeps his weight very good and has no problem. And our [other] brother, his wife doesn't care and she cooks all the stuff in the world. . . . I think my mother would have cringed and turned over in her grave, maybe even arose from it. . . . He looks terrible and has back problems and everything else because he is overweight, and yet he was never that way until many years after he got married." *Male, 60ish*

1000 "[In my family when I was growing up], I think there was too much emphasis sometimes on how much you could eat . . . , kind of like this challenge or something. And I kind of wish I didn't get taught that." *Male, early 40's*

1001 "[Family] mealtime . . . always had that pleasant feeling because [Dad] would always visit with us when we ate our meals. I always think of a mealtime then as being a lot of fun, . . . a together time." *Female, mid 70's*

1002 "[When I was a child], a family was all together when they ate. I suppose that helped make food a more pleasant situation. Now everybody seems to eat single file. Somebody's always going to get somebody or something."

Male, early 80's

1003 "We always had our places [at the dining table] . . . . You never sat in any different place at the table; you always sat in the same spot." *Female in her 30's*

1004 "Sundays [we eat together], but I mean, [with] teenagers, they're in and out the door as much as possible. There's always [food] there, but we don't always eat all at the same time." *Male in his 40's*

1005 "I do miss the family [sitting around the table]. I've tried to do it a few times, but it just doesn't work, so I've just accustomed myself to [the chaos] ."

Male, early 30's

1006 "Growing up on a farm, all the main events really rotated round a meal. It's the only time that you got to see the whole family together. . . . And that's the time you could see your dad." *Female, late 40's*

1007 "My mom came from a big family and everybody got together for every holiday and cooked everything under the sun. And I always thought it was kind of a pain." *Female, 40ish*

1008 "I think the biggest thing [about food was] just hoping to have enough on the table to feed everybody. . . . On Sundays when you didn't know you were going to have anybody, and all of a sudden, the whole family came and there were 17! But I usually had something I could throw together. But that was fun. . . . Man, you were busy and you didn't sit and think about it. You just did it."

Female, mid 70's

1009 "Family get togethers [are] always special. . . . I always liked going out to my one uncle who . . . cured his own venison sausage. That was my favorite. Everybody could drink all the pop and have all the sweets and I'd sit there with a big salami stick—chewing on it." *Male in his 40's*

1010 "Our breakfast meals tend to be kind of 'everyone on your own,' except on weekends. . . . Dinner, we're together, but breakfast and lunch we [usually aren't]. We may read a book or play a game of solitaire while we're eating [alone]. . . ." *Female, late 40's*

1011 "Our holidays are based around food. . . . The highlight of the day is to eat with your loved ones." *Female, early 20's*

1012 "I'll find myself looking forward to a meal with my parents because I get to talk to them, . . . see what they're doing, they see what I'm doing . . . . I look forward to that. . . . The food is just a little bonus." *Male, early 20's*

1013 "My daughter, about a year ago, decides that she thinks she wants to be a vegetarian. So, this is a whole new concept we've been working with. . . . And she's not that horribly strict about it, especially if she doesn't like what I'm fixing." *Female, 50ish*

1014 "To me, . . . the enjoyable times that have anything to do with eating [are] usually because [of family]. We have a little tradition in my family. . . . Twice a year, we go and we have a family birthday party. . . . We buy all of our kids dinner, . . . but that's secondary. It's the time spent with our families that's really the important factor." *Female in her 40's*

1015 "The family dinner at home shapes the relationship you have with your family, versus everyone kind of fend for yourself, go-go and eat-out type of thing." *Male in his 20's*

1016 "Eating is a family thing. To eat alone, you grab a sandwich or something and eat on the run. But with a family, you sit down, and there's conversation."
Female, 70ish

1017 "Our little family heritage—it's always been, . . . we're always eating."
Male, late 30's

1018 "I keep talking about the Depression days. Probably the nicest meal that . . . [mother] would make for us would be fried chicken. And she would *raise* that chicken. . . . [She'd serve] fried chicken and either potato salad, which she would make her own salad dressing, . . . or else mashed potatoes. . . . After she fried her chicken, then she would put it in a big black, heavy cast-iron kettle and it would steam until tender." *Female, mid to late 60's*

Humorous sidenote

1019 "My mom always told me that I would have enough time in my life to learn how to cook when I got married. And so she never really taught us. I knew how to make spaghetti. . . . But I really never learned how to cook a lot of the meals that [Mom] even made for us. There were times where I would cook for the family, but they got spaghetti for the whole week. I remember times where my brother would say, 'No more spaghetti, *please*.' And I said, 'That's all I know how to make.' " *Female in her 20's*

1020 "When my children were little, I didn't ever force-feed them. They didn't eat until they were hungry. And if it was ten o'clock in the morning and they hadn't had breakfast, it didn't matter to me. [It] used to drive my mother crazy because 'they weren't being fed properly.' Well, I don't have children that are overweight. I have children that know when to stop when they're full. And they know the sensation of being full." *Female, 40ish*

1021 "When I was at basic training, my folks were watching the kids for me. And all Dad had wanted them to do was eat like a teaspoon of [peas]. That's [my parents'] thing. You take one little tiny bit. And so it became a battle, and of course my dad won. And I happened to call right in the middle of it, and so [my son's] bawling, and I haven't seen him for three months, and I'm thinking, *'Is it such a big deal that he didn't want the peas?'* " *Female, mid 30's*

1022 "I try to make it a point to be at home during breakfasttime . . . . I guess I'm very family conscious and I think it's important that we try to eat together, and breakfast is the one time when I'm always there. I could easily leave and go to work earlier, but I don't. . . . Some mornings I wonder why, if my wife and daughter get into a fight and I'm sitting there, but I'm there!" *Male, almost 60*

1023 "[When I was growing up], I think there was too much emphasis sometimes on how much you could eat . . . , kind of like this challenge or something. And I kind of wish I didn't get taught that . . . . With my . . . kids, I kind of try to protect them, and if somebody is trying to make them eat more than they want to, I just say they're full, they don't need to eat anymore. I think it's important that we don't do that to kids." *Male, early 40's*

1024 "[Adults] don't have much involvement as far as what we're teaching the younger generation, or even ourselves, [about food and eating]. . . . When I was in school, you had a meal, and we ate that meal. Or your mom packed your lunch. Now we give [kids] *choices*. They eat pizza and fast foods, french fries, and that's what these kids eat. I won't let my kids do it. So you either eat the meal at school, or you don't eat. That's your choice." *Male, 30's to 40's*

1025 "[My wife's] dad made them eat everything, clean their plate down to the glass. Now she doesn't want our kids to . . . have to do that, so they pretty much . . . choose and pick what they want to eat. It isn't always what I would like them to eat, but I'm fighting both ends [my wife and my kids]." *Male, 40ish*

1026 "I'm in the unenviable position of having to advise my children, 'Don't let this [overweight problem] happen to you. . . . Do as I say, not as I do.' Now that's a drag." *Male, mid 30's*

1027 "I never make food a power issue or a struggle. I don't make [my kids] hide their peas under their plates or anything like that. If there's a meal and it's fixed . . . they have a choice to eat it. If they don't want to eat it, they don't have to eat it, but they don't get to eat snacks or dessert or anything else after that. . . . It's not something for me that's worth making a struggle . . . . With teenagers, there's always enough to argue about. It's just not something to create an issue over. I want eating to be something that's pleasant and enjoyable and not a fight with kids . . . ." *Female, late 30's*

1028 "I'm *hoping* that I'm being a role model to my kids 'cause I don't make them clean their plates off if they're not hungry anymore. I think I grew up in probably the household that said, 'There's kids starving overseas, you need to eat everything.' . . . If the kids aren't hungry, I just say, 'Okay, you can save it.' " *Female, mid 30's*

1029 "I just decided if [my kids] didn't want to eat [something], that was fine. They weren't getting anything else. I'm not cooking two meals by any means. But I didn't make it a big issue because it was such a big issue when we were little." *Female, 30's to 40's*

1030 "[Because of my childhood experiences with large meals and expectations to clean my plate], most of my life I have been more on the heavy side, and I've tried not to pass that on to my kids." *Female in her 60's*

1031 "I've tried lots of different things [to lose weight]. I've done Herbalife. . . . I've done the SlimFast. I've done cutting calories. I've done all of those things. But . . . in trying to be an example to my kids, I don't want them to think that you can just take a pill and your weight problems are done."
Female in her 30's

1032 "I . . . ate tonight because the kids won't eat if I don't eat. So even if you don't feel like eating, you sit down and eat something." *Female, 40ish*

1033 "My kids have a sweet tooth and I'm like, 'No. It's bad for you. It's bad for you.' And I'm probably doing to [my kids] what [my parents] did to me."
Female, early 40's

1034 "You don't want to make food the biggest priority—supper doesn't have to be the biggest priority. Food doesn't have to become a power struggle. If the kid is hungry, sooner or later [he'll] eat. So if [kids] don't want to eat right then, who gives a darn? . . . So you've got to just make food not as important as it was when we were kids." *Female, 30's to 40's*

1035 "I was raised in a [big] family [with] . . . the starving children stories . . . . [It was] take and inhale as fast as you can [because] you're afraid you wouldn't get enough. . . . Not that there wasn't ever enough food—it's just that perception . . . when you have [several siblings] and they tell you to look somewhere and you look back and your pie's gone. I needed to stake this out as mine and I'd better put as much on my plate when the bowl comes around; otherwise if I want some more it might not be there." *Female, early 40's*

1036 "I'm [from a large family], . . . so when the food was put on the table everybody ate real fast so they would get their share. And I *still* do that today."
Female, early 40's

1037 "I was one of those kids that sat at the table and ate [my food] and tried to get some [food] from my brother." *Male in his 50's*

1038 "As far as food, I like to eat a lot of red meat. Whether that's good or not, I feel that kind of defines me. I had a roommate once with a vegetarian girlfriend and that was just completely foreign to me. I found out that what I eat defines me. . . . I didn't realize until then that people ate different things. It's a pretty obvious thing, but something you just don't think about. . . . We were excellent friends, but . . . there was not agreement as far as food." *Male in his 20's*

1039 "More than ever in my life, I try *not* to eat to keep weight off. . . . It doesn't help that at work all the girls are dieting . . . and it almost makes you feel [bad], . . . especially when they're thinner than you are." *Female, early 20's*

1040 "This one lady . . . went on that diet where you don't eat any carbs, you just eat protein. Well then when she went off of it, she gained more weight than what she had. . . . And just last Thursday, I took [her] a loaf of oatmeal bread. Very little fat, very little sugar, and [she] loved it . . . . You . . . have to introduce [people] to those things is what I've found." *Female, mid 60's*

1041 "I had a friend in college, who is now my best friend. She's always been slender, the type of person that has to eat to maintain any kind of body weight. We always have fun together, watching what each other eats. . . . I have two other friends that are heavier than I am, and they constantly talk about their weight. . . . I catch myself with a two-edged sword—knowing I am not taking care of myself as good as I can but wondering why they are complaining about their weight and still eating the chocolate bar." *Female, late 20's*

1042 "I hide when I eat. I don't like people to watch me. . . . There are very few people that I can eat in front of." *Female, late 20's*

1043 "I used to hide when I ate. I've actually gotten to where I don't do that anymore. I think I did that mostly because I was told [by my ex-husband], 'Don't do that because you're so big.' So I was like, 'Fine, I'll show you,' and I ate it anyway. . . . [I stopped hiding when] I told [my husband], 'You know what? You're an asshole and I'm going to show you what I'm really made of.' And that's when I decided I'm not hiding it anymore. And when I quit hiding it, I actually started losing the weight. It was a weird thing. . . . It was like a board hitting me on the side of the head." *Female in her 40's*

1044 "I don't get fat when I go to the restaurant; it's what I do in private."
Female in her 60's

1045 "I can tell you I probably felt guilty about eating since I was in junior high —guilty that I wouldn't eat the right things, or guilty that I would eat too much. I think food is just a whole bunch of guilt. . . . At lunchtime, . . . I'll take my book and sit and read, and I've occasionally had people say, 'Do you want to come sit with us?' No, I really don't because I would just like to be quiet for awhile. I just want to read. . . . And so [reading and eating] is my way of escaping from the world. But then I feel guilty. . . . I ate something that probably wasn't very good for me. I could have gone for a walk instead, but instead I sat and read my book. So I think food is just a whole lot of guilt."
Female, early 40's

1046 "I like to eat not alone. I like to eat [with people], and I like to cook for people." *Female in her 70's*

Thoughts about participating in a focus group
1047 "I think that the essence of [what we talked about tonight] is that we're just all people and we all have something to say, and . . . the answers are not right or wrong; they are our own. And that is what makes them good." *Female, late 30's*

1048 "Regardless of the home that we lived in or the community we've lived in, it always seems that when we have people over, it's in the kitchen. I mean that's where we end up, is around the table, around the kitchen area, which tells me that food and fellowship—socializing—go together." *Female, late 40's*

1049 "When I was in [school], . . . some of the kids didn't like school lunch and there was a little store across the street from the school that served hot donuts and ice cream. We had that at least three times a week, and I think back to that and think, 'Why did I do that?' But it was a social thing because most of the kids went there." *Female, mid 60's*

1050 "When we have those [family] meals, we usually sit at the table like forever—half the afternoon—and just keep right on talking. So the socializing is about as important as the eating . . . . It sure is enjoyable." *Female, 50ish*

1051 "I don't live at home anymore, and it was nice to go home and sit around the table with my family and just talk about things that weren't necessarily really important but that mattered." *Female, early 20's*

1052 "It's just my wife and I now. When the children were home, dinnertime was our social time at our house . . . ; that was the time we were all together."
Male in his 50's

1053 "Sometimes I just think [food and eating] is kind of time consuming. . . . I do enjoy feeding other people and that experience of a social thing and the sharing." *Female, mid to late 40's*

1054 "I always think of a mealtime . . . as being a lot of fun, . . . together time."
Female, mid 70's

1055 "I think the big thing that I enjoyed [about family gatherings], . . . more than . . . even the food, was the association with your family. . . . That was the time that you *really* enjoyed your family." *Male, 60ish*

Memorable quotation

1056 "Everybody has different strong points and weak points, things we do well and things we do poorly, but we all eat about the same. So, when you sit down and eat with somebody, you're both at the same talent level. One guy isn't better than the other and then you can talk on the same level. . . . Sometimes I think that's kind of the idea in the Bible . . . that [eating is] a place where you can really share." *Male, almost 60*

1057 "I don't know how to make food not be a battleground, because I'm obviously not doing very well in my own house. And so I don't know what to do about that 'cause I can't even solve it for myself. I think a whole lot of it would solve itself if we didn't focus so much on it. It just feels like we're pounded day in and day out. Like I watched a program on TV last night . . . on obesity in America. And it just seems like everywhere you turn, we're being bombarded with how bad we are. We're fat and we eat too much and we don't exercise enough. And it's all negative, and it's constant, and it's day in and day out."

Female, early 40's

1058 "My husband—he's a diabetic. So, when he was diagnosed with that, I thought, 'Oh, brother, here we go.' And for a long time, [he'd say], 'You're trying to starve me!' . . . Well, my goodness, . . . he's a big man. . . . So I thought, 'Okay, [I need a] different approach,' so I had to look at a whole different way of cooking. And that didn't go over very good at first. He had a heck of a time. So every once in a while, he had to sneak away and go downtown and get a good ol' juicy hamburger or something—which was all right. . . . He's a good ol' country boy. You know, the meat, the potatoes, the gravy, the biscuits, and all that good stuff. . . . When you get back to the salads and the veggies, all that, he said, 'Wait a minute.'. . . Every once in a while, he'll get a bread attack. Good ol' peanut butter and jelly, and he decides to eat the whole loaf of bread." *Female, late 40's*

1059 "My wife makes me go on that half rule, . . . have a portion and . . . eat half of it and then put the rest back. . . . [She's] trying to get me to lose a little weight, . . . and sometimes . . . [she's] a little obnoxious. Like telling me I look like I'm pregnant . . . , and [it] just gets to the point where it's just an incessant type of situation. I get to the point where I . . . find [myself] sneaking food between meals. . . . At night watching TV . . . [I] wait for her to doze off and go to sleep so [I] can zing down to the kitchen. . . . I think some of the negative connotations that I hear from my wife—I know she is doing it out of love and concern—but sometimes I think . . . I get a little angry, I guess, of hearing it all the time and sometimes think to myself I wish she'd quit harping about that because then I find myself getting a little rebellious and just doing things to go against what she's telling me." *Male, mid 50's*

1060 "The White, U.S. world has a real problem trying to accept their fatness because of all the media that you see. All the messages that we get. And [your size] is not something that's easily changed . . . , and in fact I think . . . [the media] makes us fatter because we get more nervous and eat more."

Female, mid 40's

1061 "You can walk into a school lunchroom and smell the smell, and it will bring you right back to the lunchroom when you were hiding stuff in your darn milk carton. You know that's how food gets . . . into your brain."

Female, 30's to 40's

1062 "If my husband ever says anything about [my] weight . . . I say, 'That's going to make me eat more.'. . . I think he'd probably prefer that I was a skinny, cute wife, and I would too, but it's not worth the defeat." *Female, mid 40's*

1063 "I used to hide when I ate . . . . I was told [by my ex-husband], 'Don't do that because you're so big.' So I was like, 'Fine, I'll show you,' and I ate it anyway. . . . My life changed . . . when I wasn't married to him. When I left, it . . . was just a matter of minutes. It just changed. I can't explain it. It was liberating. It was a weight off of my chest. It was gone and I don't know what it was. I don't know why, but I just quit hiding [when I ate]. . . . It was the best thing and also the worst thing. . . . It was the worst case scenario, but it was the best thing that could happen. My door opened, I took it [and] never looked back." *Female in her 40's*

1064 "I'm almost overeating because I feel the pressure so much to not be. And so, it's like if I was just not even thinking about it, I don't think I'd be . . . eating as much. I think I eat more because I'm constantly thinking about the fact that I shouldn't eat and it's so silly. . . . And I tend to have a stubborn streak and I almost think that that's part of it. It's like, 'Mmm, don't tell me I can't eat because I'm going to do just that.' " *Female, mid 30's*

1065 "I've got . . . daughters that are so heavy that it's affecting their health. But you can't nag at people. All that does is make them eat more." *Female in her 60's*

1066 "If anybody tells me I'm going to have to diet, I just don't do well with that. . . . I think I'm having more problems because I'm feeling pressured to [lose weight]. . . . It's like, no, don't make me." *Female, mid 30's*

Memorable quotation

1067 "The media says you need to be skinny and then exercise people come and say you need to exercise and so it's kind of like this guilt trip on you . . . . They say [being fat] is a health risk, too. So not only do we get it from the media and exercise people, we get it from medicine too, that you've got to be skinny. It probably makes it worse. It probably makes us eat more because it's so hard to lose weight and so hard to exercise [that] sometimes you just . . . give up." *Female, mid 40's*

Chapter Three

BODY IMAGE

*Be critical of messages that focus
on unrealistic body images as
symbols of success and happiness.*

Guiding principle from Wellness IN the Rockies

1068 "I'm at peace with [my weight]. I don't own a scale. I don't need numbers to tell me that my body weight's okay. I'm just okay with who I am. And I think that when I let go of worrying about what everybody else thought, *that's* when I realized I'm an okay person, I don't have to be skinny. I'm healthy and . . . I'm at peace with that." *Female, late 40's*

1069 "I feel blessed to be able to stand up and look in the mirror and have [a body that] functions and I think it's great. I have a good, loving family, friends. What [more] could you want?" *Male in his 50's*

1070 "I've been overweight all my life. . . . And I've been on many diets . . . . [And now] I figure, why bother? I watch what I eat. . . . But I just take it one day at a time 'cause I figure, you know, I like who I am. . . . And if somebody doesn't like me because of the way I look, they lost a friend." *Female, early 40's*

1071 "My body's fine. At this age, . . . everything's starting to go south. . . . But heck, I've earned it. I don't mind it." *Female, late 40's*

1072 "I've always been happy with my body. . . . I've never been concerned with anything negative. My philosophy about any problems is if you have enough forward momentum, you'll be by them before they can affect you."
Male in his 60's

1073 "[From working out], I've noticed that I weigh more, but . . . I have so much more muscle in my body . . . , so I guess I stopped worrying about the number. . . . And I stopped worrying about what my pants size was and my shirt size and . . . as long as I can look in the mirror and I can smile at myself, then that's all that really matters." *Female, mid 20's*

1074 "My body image allowed me to really develop the . . . power to let things blow off. . . . I'm really friends with a lot of the bullies that bullied me back in grade school. . . . And I think that the way I look has kind of made me the person I am today, . . . and I like myself." *Male, early 20's*

1075 "I'm happy with [my body size] I guess. I mean, it's okay. I don't worry about it. My bigger concern about [body size] is more in relationship to discomfort. If I don't keep a handle on [my weight] and it gets away from me a little bit, it's just going to be a lot more uncomfortable just to plain walk and get around." *Female, 50ish*

1076 "I've always been happy with the way I look, . . . with [my] body. There's always room for improvement. . . . You just want to be able to get out and . . . improve . . . your body. " *Male in his 30's*

1077 "I . . . have a physically demanding job where I'm lifting 85 and 95 pounds . . . and I can do it. And if I weighed 115 pounds, I couldn't do that."

Female, early 40's

1078 "I feel comfortable [with my body size and shape], but I always know it could be better. But like I say, I'm comfortable. It's not something that keeps me awake at night thinking about [it]." *Male in his 40's*

1079 "[Positive] body image can be camouflaging what faults you do have and not emphasizing [them]. And then to not talk about it so much. We put ourselves down all the time and that is too bad." *Female, early 60's*

1080 "[There is] potential that is within women that—no matter what your body size is—[you can] *reinvent* yourself. . . . That's a great empowering thing, whether you're on the small size or the larger size or in between." *Female, 60ish*

1081 "I like my lower leg . . . . And I wear shorts usually starting around the end of April 'til October. . . . You can wash lots more pairs of shorts together than you can jeans." *Female, early 40's*

1082 "As long as you're healthy, it really doesn't matter . . . how other people think of you. It's a matter of how you feel about yourself." *Male in his 30's*

1083 "I think feeling good about yourself is more important than how you look."

Female in her 30's

1084 "I would read through different magazines, . . . and I'd always compare myself to [the models], and then . . . I just took a step back, and I looked, and I said, . . . 'I don't have to look like these girls, as long as I'm happy with myself and as long as I have a good self-esteem.' So every day I just . . . wasn't starving myself." *Female, mid 20's*

1085 "I'm average height. I like that. I don't have to always sit in the front row, and I never have to stand in the back row." *Female in her 60's*

1086 "I don't want to do the paper bag on my head thing. . . . I'm okay with where I am [with my weight] because I can do the things I want to do, and for me, at this point in my life, that's a victory." *Female, 60ish*

1087 "[My body size] is what the Lord gave me, and I guess I'm going to keep it, so I'm satisfied with it. . . . I tried [to lose weight] for a long time, and I haven't gained, so I have accepted what I have." *Female, 70ish*

1088 "I think [body image] consumes my whole life at this point in my life. . . . Just knowing [what] my husband thinks, . . . I know guys look and girls look, and there is always somebody better looking, and . . . I always wanted to be skinnier." *Female, late 20's*

1089 "I got to tell you, the first time you've got to go to the big and tall store is a bitch. It is. That's a *rock your world* kind of a deal. Man, am I really that big?"

Male, mid 30's

1090 "I'll give you a phrase I have used in front of the mirror in the morning, and you'll have to pardon this expression, but [I say to myself], 'My God, you old bastard, you passed away about 20 years ago.' " *Male in his 70's*

1091 "I think all of us have a kind of an ideal of what we think that perfect body should look like, and we can mirror that on what we currently look like and feel bad about it. I think that in every case you feel bad about it." *Male in his 50's*

1092 "I dislike the whole midsection of my body, from my . . . stomach to my thighs and all in between." *Female, early 20's*

1093 "I feel like it's impossible for me to feel attractive. Like, I *never* feel attractive." *Female, late 20's*

1094 "I remember as a kid hating to go shopping 'cause you'd have to find clothes that fit. And when you're a size 14 in a size 8 world, it was miserable. And I still don't like shopping . . . . But yet, I've accomplished a whole lot of things and gone to school and have a good job, and I'm well-liked by my clients, . . . but there's this negative thing always in the background." *Female, early 40's*

1095 "I'm a little disgusted with the tire I have built for myself around my middle, and when you put your pants on, having to suck that big deep breath in to button them up sometimes and being too damn vain to go to the next waist size bigger in pants because you're afraid you'll like it so well [that] you'll grow out of that one too." *Male, mid 50's*

1096 "People say I have a pretty face, pretty eyes and stuff, but I don't see where I'm pretty. I've got this big fat apron that I want to take a knife to and cut it off." *Female, early 30's*

1097 "[My body] is ugly, and it's uncomfortable. . . . I hate looking in the mirror . . . . I wish I were skinnier, but . . . I don't need to be Twiggy."

Female, early 40's

1098 "I dislike [my body size]. Yeah, I dislike it. And I tell you what, if there was a quick cure . . . , I'd just love to look, you know, *great.* But, it's the way it is right now. So you kind of have to accept it. But no, I don't like it. . . . I'm overweight." *Female, late 40's*

1099 "My feet are too big. My thighs are jiggly. My butt is big. My stomach has stretch marks . . . . My nose is too big, too. I have a *too big* complex."
Female in her 20's

1100 "I *hate* being overweight. Absolutely hate it. . . . My pants get too tight because I'll be damned if I'm going to go to the next size pants. . . . I think about [my body size] constantly. And my wife says, 'Don't worry about it.' [But] I do worry about it." *Male, 30's to 40's*

1101 "I never liked my body. . . . Never been able to get it to where I was happy with it, even when I was young . . . and in really good shape. . . . Always felt it was too big. . . . I started dieting when I weighed 250, and I dieted myself up to 350." *Male in his 60's*

1102 "[Negative thoughts about my body come from] just walking down the street and looking in the windows of the stores, not liking [my reflection], going to try on clothes and not liking what you see in the mirror—and nothing looks good." *Female in her 60's*

1103 "I was heavy as a child. I look back at it now, and I wasn't heavy, but I wasn't the 1960's Georgie Girl. . . . And I look back at pictures of me now, and . . . I'm fat now, but I wasn't then." *Female, early 40's*

1104 "I don't think I'm in shape and I tell people that, but they're like, 'Yeah, you're fine,' [and I'm] like, 'But you don't see me naked.' I mean, everybody feels that. I'm sorry, when you're standing there naked in front of a mirror, you're going, 'Oh, oh, no.' Yeah, . . . I have stretch marks. Yes, I have a belly."
Female, early 30's

1105 "I was probably 21 when it kind of hit me that the actual womanhood took over, the hips went big and all that kind of stuff. . . . I like the size of my chest. . . . I dislike my hips, my waist, and my behind." *Female, late 20's*

1106 "Right now, I don't like [my body]. I'm too big . . . . It's . . . hard for me to get around because I have more to carry. I can't fit into my Wranglers and look like I want to look. So I don't wear Wranglers. That bothers me."
Female in her 30's

1107 "[I've always been] told, 'You're so cute. You have such a cute face, but you could lose a few pounds.' I'm sorry. I'm the largest sister. I have [other] sisters that are all smaller. It pisses me off. *Why me?* Why do I have the boobs and the butt?" *Female in her 40's*

1108 "I would like to probably have just a few less bulges, healthwise mostly. . . . It would be nice if I just didn't have quite so much." *Female, late 60's*

1109 "Right now, I'm not comfortable with my body size. I have lots of clothes in my closet that are too small for me." *Female in her 60's*

1110 "At the present time, I look at myself in the mirror in a bathing suit . . . and I think, 'Oh, if I could just hold this in. I'm so close. If I could just get down a little bit more, I would be more happy.' . . . [My] hind end and stomach . . . have too much fat in there." *Female, early 60's*

1111 "I'm too big. When I was a teenager, I had a big bust and it bothered me and it still bothers me. . . . I wish I was thin." *Female in her 70's*

1112 "I just feel bad about myself when I can't take my weight off."

Female in her 60's

1113 "[I] don't like [my body]. It's too big. It's not fun to go clothes shopping at all. . . . [I'm] probably about 180 pounds overweight." *Male in his 40's*

1114 "I definitely don't like [the way I look], and I want to change it, but it's not to the point where it's going to get me down emotionally. I don't like the way I look, but I know I can change." *Male, early 20's*

1115 "I, like everybody probably, [have] gone through periods when I didn't do much . . . physical activity—taken a demanding job and didn't have as much time—and I got bigger than I wanted to be and didn't feel as good as I wanted to feel." *Male in his 50's*

Memorable quotation

1116 "Nobody's happy with their body. . . . 'I should be shorter. I should be thinner. I should be broader in the shoulders. I should have more hair or less hair. I shouldn't have to shave so often.' Nobody's happy with their body 100 percent. That's disgusting. Why can't people be people?" *Male, late 50's*

1117 "I was just thinking how incredible it is that every one of us have the same kind of insecurities [about our bodies] for almost the same reasons. . . . We may look different, but it's the same feelings that we have, the same heartaches and trials. . . . We just handle those things differently." *Female, 40ish*

1118 "I didn't ever think [one specific person in this focus group] was teased in school, 'cause I graduated with [her]. . . . As far as I knew, I was the only one that . . . was teased in the school. And I wasn't heavy, I was just blind and wore those thick glasses. . . . It makes me realize . . . that everybody has their own set of troubles and they're trying to get by." *Female, early 30's*

1119 "I always wished I was taller. I'd like to lose some weight too, but then I just finally decided that maybe that's me. . . . I had my last [child several] years ago. I've kind of maintained the same weight, maybe ten pounds back and forth. And so I finally said, well maybe that's what size I'm supposed to be, darn it. I think . . . what discourages me when I try to lose weight is it goes off so slow. Plus then I start working out, so it turns to muscle and it all equals out. . . . So I just decided if my pants fit and my shirts fit . . . then that's okay. [It's] not how much I weigh." *Female, 30's to 40's*

1120 "I've never been this heavy in my life. And I don't know if I'm meaner on myself physically or mentally, but I don't even want to try [to lose weight]."
Female, late 20's

1121 "I've got this big fat apron that I want to take a knife to and cut it off, and I get *rashes* because of it. . . . Where it's dead flesh, it stinks and then I have to wash myself with peroxide and soap and water and put cream on it and it hurts like hell. . . . So I feel really inferior that way, and then when I exercise, sometimes this stupid belly flops." *Female, early 30's*

1122 "Every time I got my weight down to about 220, then I would go back up. I would let it get back up, and it would be ten pounds heavier than it was the last time I [tried to lose weight]. . . . It's been a real struggle." *Male in his 60's*

1123 "When I look in a mirror naked, do I like what I see? No, not really, but I'm not to the point where it repulses me or anything like that, so I guess I'm pretty confident about [my body image]." *Female in her 30's*

1124 "For myself, I know that if there is going to be any change in this body, it's going to be done by me and me alone. My wife can harp and gripe all she wants . . . : 'Honey, you're getting a little belly.' Nothing is going to change this body except me. . . . I stand before the mirror and say, 'This is ridiculous, you look like a walrus.'. . . But on the other hand, I'm [over 70 years] old; who gives a damn? [Friends are] going to be my friend no matter what I look like. So I don't worry about body image." *Male in his 70's*

1125 "[My advice is to] be content as you are and just get clothes that fit you. You might have to go through many different sizes of wardrobes like I have. Just feel like you're a good person, in spite of your weight, which I haven't quite come to yet. . . . [With my large body size], I still can accomplish my goals in life, which are to have children, be a good mother, [and] be creative at home. . . . I am hindered just a little, so I don't get much done . . . 'cause I've given up maybe." *Female, mid 40's*

1126 "I think I might always be heavy. My son says if you can't be one, then be the other, 'cause he knows I've dieted so many times." *Female in her 60's*

Mental war with body image

1127 "[There's a] mental war that's going on in me. . . . I have a brother who has rheumatoid arthritis, . . . and he's about 200 pounds overweight . . . and it is *very* detrimental to his health. And I just swear to myself that I am not going to end up in that place. . . . It's a battle inside all the time, but the health concerns outweigh the other [body image] concerns right now. . . . For the first time in my life, . . . I'm just content where I am . . . . [I have] a unity and feeling of pride in myself. But in that unity [is] also figuring out what has to change . . . for the goal of . . . being able to go out and do anything and everything I want to do and not have health concerns." *Female, early 40's*

1128 "I guess it's a human characteristic: if you walk past a big plate glass window, you're eyeballing yourself and checking out . . . what other people see —finding yourself sucking your gut in and trying to make yourself look decent."
Male, mid 50's

1129 "But my version of myself is I am overweight and, yes, I should do something about it. . . . I don't have an alcohol problem, no drug problem, no tobacco problem. . . . I'm very sellable. . . . Basically, everything is there except for this weight problem I have. . . . I shouldn't say it, but without it, I'd be superman or something." *Male, early 30's*

1130 "I've lost almost 25 pounds now, . . . and I still look in the mirror and I still see the same person. I don't see any differences. . . . I still see me as being obese. Actually, I think I've always seen myself as obese. I look back and I see my pictures and I think, 'Wow, I was so thin!' But if I think about what I thought at the time, I thought I was fat." *Female in her 20's*

1131 "When I lost all that weight, . . . I was still going to the big sizes because there's no way I could not visualize myself there. I would still buy [an item of clothing] without trying it on, take it home, and it would be [way too] big on me." *Female, early 40's*

1132 "I was always big. I don't think I ever really thought about it. . . . I think it was just kind of a basic knowledge about body size. Kind of an understanding."
Female in her 20's

1133 "I know I don't care . . . about body image now [as much as] I did 20 years ago. When I was in college, I spent all summer without a shirt on, and [body image] was definitely something that I was concerned with. . . . Now [my appearance] . . . drives my wife nuts: . . .'Do your hair.' And I'm like, 'No.' I go for anything that takes less time, so I don't care what it looks like. I just don't want to be messing with [appearance]." *Male, 30's to 40's*

1134 "I can tell that I am getting a little bit heavier, not drastic, but just enough that [I notice]. It's funny how we as humans kind of go at this thing: 'Well, [my extra weight] is not that bad yet. Maybe I don't have to worry about it yet.' It's funny how we do that. . . . I'm a little self-conscious about gaining weight. If [you're] going to put on a swimsuit and jump in the pool, you don't want to have your sides hanging over your swimsuit." *Male in his 30's*

1135 "When I was in the military, I took a lot of pride in my physical appearance, with pressed clothing and everything was always sharp and highly shined shoes, and I liked to look decent. . . . And I work in a public office, . . . and so I deal with people on a daily basis, and so it's nice to present a good image." *Male, mid 50's*

1136 "I was really quite a skinny girl with a potbelly when I was in elementary school. . . . I really can't complain about my health because I have been healthy my entire life, which has been a bonus." *Female in her 20's*

Memorable vignette

1137 "I'm a really big guy, but I'm not aware of it until I see a picture of it. . . . I'm unique looking. Every time people see me, babies cry. You know, the great big huge guy with all this hair. So, you don't see a lot of people that look like me. . . . [Being fat] is one of the most unattractive things in our culture. . . . I read a story in [the] *New Yorker* about . . . [a] prostitute's worst nightmare was a fat guy. . . . I was never beautiful by any stretch of the imagination. I'm just a fat guy. . . . I never was able to make any friends. . . . I don't know if it was because I was heavier or what, but . . . I became a loner. Then the overweight thing got worse and the weight problem became worse. . . . But I don't consider myself unhappy. And I don't remember ever being unhappy. It was just the way it was . . . . Just sitting home watching TV, that's how I spent most of my adolescent years. . . . I was just living in my own little fantasy world. That hasn't changed, now that I think about it. . . . I look at people who just have enormous energy . . . and even fat people have it. Jackie Gleason, . . . he's a huge fat guy . . . but he just had this incredible energy, which I never had. . . . Some people can just go and go and go and go. . . . It's amazing to me to see it. . . . My mother's kind of like that. She's a Type A personality . . . . I'm a Type Z with a series of Zs after it. But I'm not sure it has anything to do with weight. . . . We don't find [fat] attractive [in our culture]. It isn't attractive, at least to me. I don't want to see it, but then again I'm not really aware of it in my own case. . . . I just don't think about [being fat] really very much at all. I know it's unattractive, but I don't care very much. . . . I don't think about body image really at all that I can recall, except when I see myself in a videotape or something and . . . it reminds me [I'm fat]."
Male, late 30's

155

1138 "I think I'm overweight. I know I'm overweight, no question about it. . . . I'm conscious about it, but I don't think about it much during the day. . . . I like the fact that I'm strong, that I'm muscular, and I know that's going to be a part of my weight. That if I were to be a lot smaller, I wouldn't have the strength I do to do some of the things I like." *Female, 40ish*

1139 "When I was really thin, I was too thin. . . . Then between the ages of 15 and 45 or so, I felt pretty good about the way I looked. I was in pretty dang good shape. And now I don't have any real qualms, except that I'm a little bit bigger in the stomach than what I'd like to be, but I think it dropped from the top down." *Male, 60ish*

1140 "[I don't like] my stomach, my little belly hanging over. I've always been too short. But that's who you are, so I don't worry about it too much. I can't change it." *Male, almost 50*

1141 "I have trouble . . . keeping my weight down because I like to eat. . . . So now I've tried to ration myself. . . . I don't lose any weight. I slowly go the other direction. . . . I used to have a 32 waistline. I have a 36 now. . . . I'd like to be 32 again. . . . When I try to lose [weight], it never seems to come off of there. I get more wrinkles than I had before. [I'm] getting to look like a rhinoceros with all this extra skin and nothing under it. . . . I tell you what really gets me is when I get enough [stomach] that my belt starts to slip down under and I can't keep my pants up. . . . Then I think, 'Oh geez, I've got to do something,' and I usually do." *Male, early 80's*

1142 "I wished I would have been a little taller. . . . But it's fine. . . . When you were shorter, you always got kind of kidded about it, but it didn't bother me that much." *Male, mid 50's*

1143 "[My body's] nothing special. . . . I'm no skinny one." *Female, late 70's*

Humorous sidenote
1144 "[My husband and I] have a bird dog, so we were toodling around, going walking . . . . Well, up comes a pheasant and lands right on my head. He's parked on my head, the dog is on my backside. Believe me, you don't need to go to a beauty salon to have a hairdo like that." *Female, late 40's*

1145 "I know you have to eat right and do the exercise, but it was too much to think of at once, so I'm kind of just taking it in pieces. I know I have to get my weight down again so that I can put my sweatpants on and fit into my T-shirt . . . so that I am comfortable even just walking down the block, with the cars driving by. . . . But it's a little scary when you're that heavy. . . . I let my weight get so out of hand that it's kept me from a lot of things, and it's got to change."

Female in her 30's

1146 "With my size, . . . I don't go to the movies as much because the theater seats are tight. . . . There are things that I don't do because I know I have to either weave through a crowd or be uncomfortable for two hours. . . . I don't like that uncomfortable feeling, so I avoid it. And that's too bad, because then I miss out on something that I probably would have enjoyed. But they don't accommodate for all sizes." *Female in her 30's*

1147 "On a personal note, and I don't know how to say anything except for being bold, [but] . . . intimacy, sex, whatever, the good stuff, can be difficult, too, when you're heavy. There's just sometimes that you don't feel like you're pretty and your husband is touching you in places, and it's like, 'Don't do that. . . . I don't feel like I'm pretty, and I'm . . . big [and] fat." *Female, early 30's*

1148 "I can remember being in the supermarket and not wanting to see anybody I knew. I'm sure . . . my weight was up. . . . I was not feeling that good about myself right then. . . . I got nervous and I couldn't be in a store. . . . There was a certain limit of time that my brain could handle [being in the store]. And I can remember I felt bad about leaving the cart. . . . This happened a couple of times. I could not stay there any longer. I didn't buy anything. I walked out. I had to go home." *Female, early 60's*

1149 "My husband's family is really an active family and they like to play ball and I'm hindered because of my weight. And it kind of makes me mad that my weight is stopping me from having fun. . . . It's hard to jump on the tramp 'cause I have two bodies." *Female, mid 40's*

1150 "There's certain things I can't do because of my weight. Obviously, I'm not going to go running for miles. I have a rough time . . . getting up on roofs and doing things like that too. So my [kids] have kind of helped me out with some of those things, which makes me feel bad too. [It] makes you feel handicapped, and I don't want to feel that way." *Male in his 40's*

1151 "[My body] is ugly, and it's uncomfortable. I've gotten to the point that it's starting to limit what I feel I can accomplish, physically." *Female, early 40's*

1152 "I always claim that when you become heavy you become invisible. You go in a room and you want to be social with people, [but] . . . you can't because of [your] size. . . . You totally become invisible. People don't recognize you. They don't know who you are . . . . There's a lot of people that even if they do know you, [they] don't want to know you because . . . it's not sociably accepted to hang out with people that are . . . obese." *Male in his 40's*

1153 "I . . . remember . . . [relatives saying], 'Boy you're getting heavy.' [I'd say,] 'Ah, more of me to love.' [Or they'd say,] 'Your hair's going white, what's wrong?' I used to kid them: 'Well, with the silver in my hair, gold in my teeth, and the lead in my butt, you ought to scrap me out. I'd be worth more maybe.' "
Male in his 50's

1154 "I got lots of compliments on my shape, and I wasn't even doing anything to get that shape. It was just how I was born." *Female, mid 30's*

1155 "My sisters and my mother are heavier set and they'll say comments like, 'Oh, you wouldn't go to *our* store where we get *our* clothes because you're thin.' So I almost get ridiculed . . . because I'm thin." *Female, late 20's*

1156 "Try going in the kids' section [to shop for clothes]. . . . Try having a [grade-school child] that's as tall as you and you go to school and they're like, 'Where's your mother?' " *Female, early 30's*

1157 "When I went to school, we went on an outing and there was a picture. . . . The teacher was at one end and I was at the other end and all the other students [were] in the middle. Then when I saw the picture, somebody asked, 'Is that the teacher?' [but] that was me. Of course, I was so big. And that, I think, was what influenced me, because . . . I'm still thinking that [I'm too big]."
Female in her 70's

1158 "I find myself too busy worrying about what other people think about me when I put on [clothes]. Like, I have to tuck my shirt in at work. I hate tucking in my shirt 'cause it's like, I've got this butt, I've got this belly, I look stupid. . . . You hate shopping for clothes, especially ones that button up, because you have this gap thing [*gestures to front of blouse*] and it's frustrating. You hate it. And you spend your whole day thinking, . . . "How do I look to other people?' I am so tired of thinking, 'How do I look to other people?' " *Female in her 40's*

1159 "[It] makes you feel bad that you've got to be out of the norm, and when you're out of the norm, people treat you differently. . . . And to be honest with you, we're still the same person, we're just a little bigger." *Male in his 40's*

1160 "Right now, I don't care about compliments . . . . All I want to do is survive until the end of the day. And so I figure if I get that far, I don't care what anybody else thinks." *Male in his 60's (suffers from arthritis)*

1161 "Your whole life, your self-image is primarily in how you think others view you. I remember a time when this person was attracted to me and I couldn't figure out what he was attracted to . . . . I couldn't see myself how he saw me. I couldn't go beyond the physical to see my personality. He was attractive physically. Women were cruel. [They would say,] 'What could he be interested in her for? She's fat.' " *Female, early 40's*

1162 "I'm from a bigger city, . . . [and] nobody cares what anybody else does in the bigger cities. . . . In a smaller town, . . . they just have these ideas of . . . 'He's supposed to be with her and they're just *perfect*' . . . and it's all about the way that you look. . . . I just come in . . . with these crazy ideas that I don't really care what other people think." *Female, mid 20's*

1163 "I never thought of myself as necessarily small until my mother-in-law mentioned to a relative that her future daughter-in-law was rather petite. And I thought, '*I am?*' So my own perception, obviously, was different."

Female, late 40's

1164 "I hated PE because you got to go take a communal shower and take all your clothes off, and all these people are making fun of you. . . . I mean, to me, that's cruel." *Female, early 40's*

1165 "[I'm] always being told, . . . 'You have such a cute face, but you could lose a few pounds.' I'm sorry . . . . It pisses me off." *Female in her 40's*

1166 "When our [kids] got to be teenagers, that was when I was more aware of how I should look. . . . I've asked . . . them, 'How did you feel because I was overweight?' And they said, 'Mother, we never even thought about it because we had too much fun and our friends' mothers were the same as you. We didn't ever think that you were overweight and . . . that didn't ever bother us.' . . . And I said, 'Were you ever ashamed of me?' and they said . . . they didn't think about it." *Female, mid 60's*

1167 "I'm overweight. . . . I mean, facewise, I think I look okay. And thank God I have a husband who doesn't mind. . . . With [your] kids you think, well, they're going to get married and [their spouses] are going to go 'My mother-in-law is overweight.' And you think about that sort of thing. And, how do people perceive you when they look at you? Are they looking at you? Are they looking at the body? So those things go through my mind all the time." *Female, late 40's*

1168 "I can remember a guy . . . that said, 'You're pretty in the face. If you'd lose weight, I'd go out with you.' I lost all that weight. He asked me out. And I just told him, 'When you become a man, come back and ask me.' And that's just the way I deal with things, because if you don't like me the way I am now, then don't bother." *Female, early 40's*

1169 "[While I was furniture shopping, I was helped by an employee who went to high school with me, and he] happened to throw something in about how much weight I'd gained. And that's probably the first time in my life . . . I became aware of this trouble." *Male, early 30's*

1170 "On the back of my one leg, I have a birthmark. . . . The [other] kids would make fun of me and, shoot, I could never see it. . . . I got a little self-conscious of it. . . . I was kind of upset the first time, but after you think about it and you see other people with worse problems than that, you say, 'Well, . . . I can deal with it.' " *Male in his 50's*

1171 "I can remember when I was in PTA, . . . my daughter would say, 'Now, what are you going to wear today to the PTA meeting? Let me help you.' [My kids] thought I looked a little frumpy." *Female, early 60's*

1172 "I'm [over 60] years old and I'm still in pretty good shape. People say, 'I can't believe that you're 60.' I think being active . . . keeps your body and your mind young." *Male, early 60's*

1173 "I don't take compliments very well. People say, 'You have a nice figure,' and I'll say, 'Well I can't get fat up front because I have this [curvature of the spine] thing.' I should just say thank you." *Female, mid 30's*

1174 "It's what's inside that really counts. . . . When people look at you, they're not necessarily looking at how heavy you are. That's our image of ourselves and it's just something that we need to get over." *Female, mid 40's*

1175 "A lot of [body image] has to do with what you think you get from others. . . . And I hate to think that your confidence or esteem is developed because of what someone else thinks, but quite often you let that happen." *Male, early 40's*

Memorable quotation

1176 "Sometimes I feel that I'm the recipient of *that look*. That's all it ever is. It's just a look. People are far too polite to say, 'Hey, can you go drop some pounds, fatso?' . . . That is a pretty painful look to get . . . , especially having dealt it out." *Male, mid 30's*

1177 "One time . . . my [daughter] said something about that I was the fattest lady in our [church], and I thought no way and then I thought, 'Let's see, who is fatter than me?' And there weren't very many possibilities. And that kind of downed me a little." *Female, mid 40's*

1178 "I can remember . . . we had . . . neighbors . . . [and] the whole family was overweight, terribly overweight. . . . I'm sure I probably got some negative [opinions about obesity] from that relationship with that family living that close. . . . I certainly didn't want to be like that." *Male, mid 50's*

1179 "Weight is a very personal thing. To me, it's right up there with religion. So, when you're unconsciously measuring yourself against others, . . . that voice isn't quieted in your mind." *Female, early 40's*

1180 "Every time you see somebody, you have some kind of a mental battle with yourself. . . . We're always passing judgment in our minds, whether we share it or not. But anytime you see somebody, there's good or bad thoughts that go on." *Male, early 40's*

1181 "When I stand next to my daughter-in-law, I feel like a giant. When I stand next to my son-in-law, . . . I feel like a midget." *Male in his 50's*

1182 "Girls are horrible . . . . They say things like, 'She's the one with the *huge butt*,' or whatever. I think it makes you more aware of others and yourself . . . when you talk about other people's bodies that way." *Female, early 20's*

1183 "I have to admit, I do notice bodies. But I think as heavy as I am, I notice people that are heavier than me and I think it's because it puts the fear in me of where I could be. I know I'm over the edge now, but this isn't as big as I can stretch." *Female in her 30's*

1184 "It's very important to me the way I look. . . . I see the shapes and sizes [of other people] and I think, 'I don't want to look like that.' " *Male, early 50's*

1185 "There was this huge lady, . . . [when] she sat down, her hips kind of went between the arms of the chairs and, oh, I just thought, she can't be healthy. . . . I'm getting to the point where I fill out my chair pretty good. So, I look at people like that and it kind of gives me more incentive to lose the weight that I need to lose, because I don't want kids [to] point." *Female in her 30's*

1186 "I think all of us tend to look at ourselves at an . . . ideal—based on what we see in others—and sometimes that comparison is looking at the negative side of what we don't want to look like." *Male in his 50's*

1187 "[My dad] was quite a beer drinker and he was quite round and had quite a hangover on his stomach. . . . So, he was one of the examples that I've seen that I didn't want to be like." *Male, early 50's*

1188 "I go to an all-you-can-eat buffet, and I enjoy that, . . . but I look around and notice that it's usually big people that are eating at those. And that always makes me think, . . . 'Am I like that? . . . I'm eating as much as they are. Am I going to be large like this ten years down the road?' " *Male in his 20's*

1189 "When I was younger, I would see people in the military who drank a lot of beer but did very little activity, and they were way overweight, and I thought to myself then I never want to look that way." *Male, early 50's*

1190 "I think I know that everybody is different and no matter what you do you can never look like somebody else because everyone is unique in their own way." *Male, early 30's*

1191 "There are a lot of people [at the gym] that are in tip-top condition, and it kinda makes you feel like maybe you don't belong . . . 'cause you're not in that condition." *Female, early 20's*

1192 "In junior high, you kind of compare yourself with other kids. 'This person's bigger and more muscular or taller than me.'. . . You judge who you are by your peers. . . . I remember there being some competition, . . . just comparing whose bicep was bigger." *Male in his 30's*

1193 "You look at the slimmer, nice-figured young ladies and say, 'Wow! Wouldn't it be nice to look like that!' But in reality, you learn to accept yourself for what you are." *Female, late 60's*

Humorous sidenote

1194 "If you watch TV, . . . you see certain fashions that look good on those people, but boy, when you go try it on, you look like . . . the Pillsbury Doughboy. . . . Well, that's not very flattering. . . . Also, I've played a lot of basketball against [this bigger, stronger guy] and he beat me up my share. . . . I'd like to have that kind of strength, that kind of height, but . . . that's not what I'd like to have all the time because I can get into a Volkswagen a lot easier than he can."

Male in his 50's

1195 "After seeing my friend who was fat go through teasing, I was sure glad that I didn't have any extra padding on me. . . . My friend got skinny. It was just like night and day that people started talking to her, and guys wanted to date her. . . . It's like, okay, I guess if you are thin you do get a lot more attention, which is a sad way to have life be." *Female, mid 30's*

1196 "Somebody that's skinnier seems more attractive than somebody that's heavier. Even when you're heavy, you realize [those] things." *Male in his 40's*

1197 "My little sister . . . is really tall and skinny, and the boys never wanted to dance with her because she was taller than them. And the boys thought she was an Ethiopian because she was so skinny, and I'd never really thought of how hard it must be to be skinny. I mean, everyone knows that it's pretty hard to be larger, but I'd never really thought about how hard it was to be skinny."

Female, early 20's

1198 "[My daughter] eats regular meals and she is called anorexic to her face, . . . very, very painful for her. . . . It's the same for her being called skinny as it is for fat people who take it to heart being called fat. The same with her dad. . . . He is very offended by people calling him skinny, but people who are doing that . . . usually . . . think it's a compliment. . . . That is the biggest eye-opener I've had because of always being on the other side of the fence. These people would like to gain weight as much as I would like to lose it." *Female, 40ish*

1199 "My husband is . . . really, really skinny, but I love him anyway and I wish he would gain weight along with me, but it's kind of nice he hasn't so that he doesn't have to suffer [the hardships of being overweight]." *Female, mid 40's*

1200 "My best friend [has] always been slender, the type of person that has to eat to maintain any kind of body weight. . . . I don't just see [other slender people] now as, 'They are so skinny.' . . . I think of them as that's just the way they are and their metabolism keeps them that way. . . . [And I] look for the underlying fact. Do they smoke all the time and not eat, or what? Things like that. My mother-in-law . . . never eats and she smokes all the time."

Female, late 20's

1201 "Underweight [people], I guess they make me jealous, maybe. I just think they think they have it so easy. . . . I mean, I'm sure if you're in their shoes, it's something that they probably struggle with, too." *Female in her 40's*

1202 "I think something I look at with other people is slim people who are not in shape. . . . I just hate saggy butts on slim people. . . . I think, 'Come on! You're *slim*, what's the deal here? Get in shape.' " *Female, 30's to 40's*

163

1203 "My mother was always slender. . . . My mother was very sick and I don't think she could gain weight." *Female in her 60's*

1204 "I seem to be really comfortable around heavier people or people that are obese, maybe because my family is that way. . . . I tend to be more trusting of people that are . . . what I perceive as my own weight-type status than I am of say the more popular skinny, cheerleading-type girls. I don't tend to get along with those people very well." *Female in her 20's*

1205 "One of my friends has a thyroid disorder and has to keep medicine in herself. . . . [It] just kind of makes you appreciate the fact that skinny is not beautiful [for everyone]." *Female, late 20's*

1206 "I'm always looking at thin people. . . . I just wish I could be like that."
Female in her 60's

1207 "I was always looking for the most appropriate-shaped woman . . . when I was younger. . . . Besides personality first and attitude, I guess I always wanted to make sure that they were trim and slim and nice looking." *Male in his 20's*

1208 "The only thing I was envious of my mother was her size because she could put on a dress and it didn't have to be altered. . . . I wasn't envious of [my mother], only in the fact that she was thin. I'm not envious of her. My mother was, to be blunt, a mean old lady." *Female, 70ish*

1209 "I get tired of hearing these women that are [skinny] telling me how fat they are and how they need to lose weight. That's very frustrating, and I sometimes think it's a slap in the face. And then I stop and think that they're probably wrapped up in themselves. But it's very frustrating to hear that."
Female, early 40's

Exchange from focus group

1210 "All of us in here as women have felt a sort of discrimination, reverse discrimination [if you're thin]. We get told constantly, 'You make me sick, you're skinny.' And other women who feel that they're overweight may get the opposite, and I think that we all can connect on that alone." *Female, late 40's*

1211 "I'm really sorry if I've said anything that offended anybody, I really am. I never looked at things from that perspective [of being thin] and I apologize. . . . I have to re-evaluate my thinking." *Female, late 20's*
[Earlier in discussion, this person made a reference to "skinny broads."]

1212 "Well, I'm an American and . . . I realize that some people are very nice looking, and they're usually not fat people. They're almost always not fat people. So, that's just the way it is . . . . When you see a fat person, your first impression is they're just kind of an unattractive loser. . . . When I see a fat person, I look down my fat nose at him or her." *Male, late 30's*

1213 "I have a stepdaughter that's fairly heavy for her age. . . . If I see her laying around the house and her room's a mess, I go, 'She's lazy.' I know she's no different than fit kids with messy rooms, but I automatically say, 'She's just lazy.' I'm pretty blunt because that's what happens. But I see the struggles she goes through with the image of being fat." *Male, early 40's*

1214 "I always claim that when you become heavy you become invisible. . . . It's not sociably accepted to hang out with people that are . . . obese."

Male in his 40's

1215 "Size has no determination as to [people's] attitude and their inner feelings or inner self. Therefore, size is not relevant to me. A woman can be appealing no matter what her physical stature. It depends on attitude, attitude, and attitude. You know, you hear beauty is skin deep. That may not apply when you're a teenager . . . , but when a male matures . . . [he understands] you can marry a beauty and she can be a real hellcat as far as making life miserable, or you can marry someone that's 400 pounds and she can make life real enjoyable. Which would you rather be married to?" *Male in his 60's*

1216 "I know that bodies do make a difference . . . [with] how people accept you. . . . An extra heavy person . . . [tries] to do something and you can see it by the look in people's eyes or their body language that they sometimes just don't listen to that person. [Heavy individuals] don't have as much influence. [Body size] does make a difference." *Female, late 60's*

1217 "I see real heavy people as lazy. . . . But I know that I am no different . . . , [and] even though I know that in my head, I can't seem to transfer that out . . . and I really have to work . . . not to judge exceptionally overweight people."

Female, 40ish

1218 "I hate to say this, [but] there was a lady [in the store] who was way overweight with a pair of spandex pants on—talk about saddlebags. . . . I wanted to go over and say, 'Let's go to the store and see if we can redress you here.' . . . But watching her around the store, . . . she was proud of who she was. . . . She was just plumb comfortable with herself. Well I thought, 'Hey, that's pretty neat.' Who in the heck gives a rat's behiney what other people think?"

Female, late 40's

1219 "The first thing you notice about a person when you meet them is the size and the shape of their body. . . . Whether it makes any difference, you just notice it. I do. I notice people that are overweight and obese." *Male, almost 60*

1220 "I kind of think I am open-minded, but you stereotype certain things. [If I see a heavy person, I] assume that they're lazy, . . . and that's quite often not the case. But it's just . . . the appearance: 'Man, they're that heavy, . . . they must sit around and eat all day.' You [think] they're lazy and quite often that's not the case or there's other reasons involved. But when you see some people, that's what you think." *Male, early 40's*

1221 "I've had three . . . friends that had gastric bypasses because they were big. . . . It makes me sad that they would do those things, because I also see how sick they get. But . . . they talk to me about how incredibly frustrated they are and we've tried everything and it just doesn't work. Then they do the gastric bypasses and all of them lost truly a lot of weight—like 180 pounds, . . . of course they nearly die to do it. One of them had to go to treatment for alcoholism and another one is having problems with repeated boyfriends . . . that are beating her up. . . . I think about all the issues that must be underlying the reasons [they overeat]." *Female, mid 30's*

1222 "Being big has no benefits at all. . . . I don't remember [being fat] really bothering me. I know it's unattractive though. I look at fat people and I think, 'God they're ugly.' It's not an attractive thing at all, but I . . . don't really think about appearance that much in my case. . . . It's certainly not attractive. It's one of the most unattractive things in our culture." *Male, late 30's*

1223 "[My heavier set friend] is beautiful [and so is] her personality. But you know what? Guys won't see that. I set her up with one of my friends, and he's like, 'Goll', . . . she's bigger than me.' [And I said,] 'Yeah, you want to go out with those little Barbie dolls and they're not going out with you,' because he is a heavier set guy, but he wants the Barbie doll. And I thought, 'Well, usually the Barbie dolls want Ken.' . . . I truly admire my friend because she takes pride in herself no matter what her weight. And it's her actions, her mannerisms, her everything. She just glows. She looks beautiful. And I just wish men would appreciate [her]. . . . I wrote back, 'Your loss, too bad.' " *Female, late 20's*

1224 "I have a friend. . . . She's a really, really big person, but she's also about the nicest person there is. . . . I don't think of her in a negative way even though she is really large. I've even hired her to do some work . . . because she's so good. I might look at another big person and instead of having negative feelings, which is [my] first impulse, . . . [I'll] look at them and say, 'Maybe they're like [my friend], who has some real talents.' " *Male in his 20's*

166

1225 "There's a friend I have, . . . she's really heavy, maybe 350 pounds, but she's really active too and she moves her weight well, and I think a lot of people shy away from her just 'cause she's so big. But she's really fun, and . . . I try not to let [body size] be a hindrance at all of my friendship." *Female, mid 40's*

1226 "I have a brother . . . . He's [over] . . . 300 pounds . . . and I remember always wondering, 'How did he get that big and I didn't?'. . . And to this day he's still huge. . . . I think he has a lot of other issues that probably led to low self-esteem that maybe led to his overweightness." *Female, mid 30's*

1227 "I have a friend of mine . . . that is very, very large, and sometimes the body odors that I associate with that (because I know that she can't always get clean) . . . it's the image that I get when I see someone that heavy. . . . I always think [being that large] is an indication of a lot more deeper problems. . . . To me their physical health is a reflection of their mental health and I worry about her for her mental health state." *Female in her 30's*

1228 "I worked for a guy that weighed probably 400, 500 pounds. A big man. And I found that I didn't respect him probably as much as I maybe should have done. Of course, he didn't respect me either." *Male, mid 50's*

1229 "There was a lady that I met recently . . . and she is quite a large lady and I've really, really come to enjoy her personality. And I think at first I probably judged her a little bit on her size . . . , [thinking] probably that she wouldn't be happy, which is a funny thing to say." *Female in her 20's*

1230 "Obese people don't bother me. Some of them have a problem that they cannot or don't try to control. I'm not offended by it." *Male in his 70's*

1231 "My mother was always heavy . . . . She was always large, and that bothered me when I was in school and she would come to school. It was embarrassing." *Female, late 60's to early 70's*

Exchange from focus group

1232 "My brother always says he wants a fat wife just because if she's skinny it means he's not providing." *Female, mid 20's*

"There's a lot of guys out there who do love full-figured women."
Female, 40ish

1233 "[I'm 5'11" and] my husband . . . was about 5'5". We did not realize the difference in height until someone called our attention to it. . . . It never occurred to us . . . . It never was an issue." *Female, mid to late 60's*

1234 "For some reason, everybody I date seems to be shorter than I am. . . . It doesn't bother me. I do think I've known some men that I think have complexes because they're too short. So I suppose that's their issue; rather than the weight, it's the height." *Female, mid 30's*

1235 "I wouldn't want to be married to somebody who is shorter than me. I would want my kids to have some height, although I did marry somebody who doesn't have height in his genes. I think that's why he married me. Well, not the whole reason. But I think when you are younger you always picture this tall, dark, handsome guy." *Female in her 20's*

1236 "I forget how short I am until somebody reminds me." *Male, 30ish*

1237 "My husband is the tallest in his family, and he's just two inches taller than me, and . . . his family is very petite and short. . . . When we go to [my husband's] family reunions, I look around and [think], 'Wow, how did I get married into this family?' . . . For some people, it might be an issue, and sometimes it is, but sometimes I just laugh about it. I think it's funny."

Female in her 20's

1238 "I just didn't prefer to date [girls] if they were short. I didn't care if they were tall and a little larger, . . . but the short girls, they were hard to dance with and some of them were pretty petite. . . . If they're closer to six foot, I like them. And it's funny. My wife's 5'9" and she's had this complex her whole life because she thinks she's too tall." *Male in his 60's*

1239 "I never had the kind of comments that my [daughter] came home with about being short. . . . It's just, you know, 'Hey, shorty,' and [she has] frustration with finding clothes at that age when she's fully developed physically but stuff isn't small enough." *Female, late 40's*

Memorable quotation
1240 How do you feel about your body size or shape? "I don't like it."

Is there any particular part of your body you do like? "No, uh-huh."

The whole thing, okay. Can you think of anything about your body you do like? "My ears!" *Female in her 60's*

1241 "I find that once you know a person, it doesn't matter if they're skinny or tall or short or what, you still like them for themselves. You don't even think about [their body size] too much." *Female, mid 70's*

1242 "*Pretty in Pink* was this movie in the 80's, . . . and I remember the girl saying, 'Dad, if I don't accept him because he's *rich*, it's like him not accepting me because I'm *poor*.' And the same thing goes with . . . our body image. If I can't accept [people] because they're big, then it's just like them not accepting me . . . because of being thin." *Female, late 20's*

1243 "I was blessed with good parents [who] taught me the fundamentals of how to treat people and how not to treat people. . . . You learn at an early age when you play games whether someone was fair . . . or they were a bully. . . . I have [known] people that were absolutely beautiful that I really didn't want to associate with . . . and other people, a little on the heavy side, [who were] genuinely true sincere people. So, I mean the quality of their character meant more to me than their physical appearance." *Male in his 50's*

1244 "Don't hate somebody because they are thin and don't be disgusted with a person because they are heavy. . . . People inside are not fat or thin or any of those things." *Female, mid to late 40's*

1245 "I really don't have time to judge people. I have too much to do. . . . My former boss would shoot his mouth off on stuff like [someone's body size or shape] and that's just rude. . . . I just wasn't raised that way and I don't like it."
Male, almost 50

1246 "Three quarters of the battle is what you think about yourself. . . . If you're comfortable with [your body], there you go. You know, it doesn't matter what you look like. . . . It's what's inside that counts. If you're happy with yourself, you're happy with the world. . . . If you have like maybe ten earrings in each ear, and one in your nose, and one in your lip, and your eyebrows and stuff . . . , well, [I] hope you had fun at the jewelry store. . . . If you see somebody and go, 'Wow, look at that cow,' . . . did you ever think that maybe it has something to do with medical problems or something you don't even know about? Don't make a judgment on people before you know the story. Just don't do that. That's one of my pet peeves." *Female, late 40's*

1247 "You can see a very attractive person that's a nice shape, but if you talk to them, you may find out that they're very unhappy with the shape of their body. I just have the attitude that [says] live each day as best you can, as happy as you can, and try to be as healthy as you can, and let each and every person do the same thing." *Female in her 60's*

1248 "[All women] seemed to have felt the discrimination of how we look physically, and it's not fair, but when you're at peace with who you are, and if you can find that, you'll let go of [the pain]." *Female late 40's*

1249 "I hire quite a few people every year. . . . I get a wide variety and I have every shape and size of employee working for me. . . . But can they still do the job? Sure. And are they still good people? Sure." *Male, 30's to 40's*

1250 "I was always taught that it didn't matter what you looked like and it was what was inside, and so I guess I never paid attention to whether [people] were tall and skinny or fat [or] really thin. But getting out into the working world and you hear people talking about, 'Well, that person thinks she's gorgeous,' and I'd meet them and wouldn't see that at all. . . . If you're comfortable with yourself, you don't look at [others] and [think], 'Well, . . . she's stuck up because of what she looks like.' " *Female, 40ish*

1251 "I've definitely matured from being a kid as far as body types. I think I'm a lot more accepting of how people are . . . . Some people, their body type is what God gives them. They are heavier because that is how they were designed. And that person may work out and be physically active and not [over]eat, but they're not going to change." *Male in his 30's*

1252 "How you look is your idea. How I look is mine. And I couldn't tell you anything about you, and you couldn't force me to get a different attitude either. Your body is your own personal thing. . . . It's none of your business what I'm like, and it's none of my business what you're like. I don't think you should tell other people how to [look]." *Female, 70ish*

1253 "Getting to know people and seeing who they truly are, . . . you kind of overlook what their body looks like. You just see them for who they are."
Male in his 30's

1254 "I don't think that anybody should be judged [on their body size or shape]. . . . If you carry yourself positive and you seem happy with yourself, I think that other people [will] find you just as beautiful, maybe even more so, than Britney Spears." *Female, mid 20's*

1255 "Like yourself for who you are and don't try to be somebody else that you may not be able to obtain, because it may cause you more grief and stress than you need to have." *Male, mid 50's*

1256 "Friends who are larger than me, I pray for their health and to protect them from the comments and the stares." *Female, early 40's*

1257 "I feel for those people that struggle and struggle with [obesity] . . . . For me, I've never had that problem. . . . And I wish there was a magic answer to [obesity], or for the people that are so thin [that] if you stand them out in the daylight you could see right through them. And you kind of feel for them too. . . . I'm not a good one to be talking because I like a cigarette and I like my beer, so I'm not the [best] authority on this type of stuff." *Female, late 40's*

1258 "I've never been teased a whole lot because of my weight, but the times that I have, it has hurt me so bad that I feel like I am on a mission from God to stand up for people that get picked on. . . . I [won't let] people get picked on. I won't! I'll punch your ass out for picking on somebody, I will. . . . See, look at me, I'm even shaking now just talking about it. I'm getting angry. I [have] this ferocious temper and I stand up for people that get picked on. I can't stand racism, I can't stand prejudice because of religion or because somebody's fat or because somebody's ugly. . . . And, oh, see I'm mad! It affected me so bad when I was a kid." *Female, late 20's*

1259 "And I don't like to hear people say, 'Well, you could lose the weight if you want to,' to anybody, because people can't." *Female in her 60's*

1260 "I guess I have compassion for the real skinny and the real fat. The rest of us, in the middle, you got that bell-shaped curved thing. . . . But when you get people who are pencil thin or hay-stack large, I kind of wonder if it's bothering them just a little bit. . . . If it bothers them, I feel for them. If it doesn't, well, they're as hardheaded as I am, so they deserve themselves." *Male, 70ish*

1261 "I see a lot of overweight people. It doesn't bother me, . . . but I kind of feel for them. If you're that heavy, it's pretty hard for you to get around. . . . But I believe in letting everybody have their space in life. If they want to be that way, that's fine. It's none of my business." *Male, 70ish*

1262 "I had a friend in elementary school who had a glass eye, and there was one time when the rest of my friends did not want to play with her, and . . . I was glad because I didn't go along with them and I stuck with her. And so, I think I've always been sensitive, but I still think that little thoughts creep into your mind. . . . You have to get over all the stereotypes of whatever you thought in the past. . . . I always find I'm wrong when I do the stereotype on somebody. Every time. I don't think there has ever been a time where I've been right, but I keep forgetting." *Female in her 20's*

1263 "I just feel sorry that people have too much [weight] to where they're not happy. They're not capable of doing a lot and it just makes me sad. . . . I love people of all sizes. My best friend . . . has got to be 400 pounds and I feel so bad for her. . . . I don't look down on people, but I just feel sad. And I think that [but] for the grace of God go I." *Female, early 60's*

1264 "I guess I always feel sorry for those that are extremely heavy. Some of them can't help it. It's a disease . . . . You look at them because you can't help [looking]. It's just in you to look. . . . Or you can look at the one that's so skinny that you can't imagine them being out in the windstorm." *Female, 70ish*

1265 "I used to have a girlfriend they called Bones when I was a kid. Kicked a kid's ass over that one night. . . . I had had enough of it . . . . That's the way I am. Don't pick on the one that's getting picked on. . . . I don't believe in . . . picking on people. I'm that way." *Male, 70ish*

1266 "I worry a lot about the kids and the body shape and then . . . the peer pressure that they get. You know the heavy kids get teased and the skinny kids get picked on. . . . Some kids it doesn't bother at all and some kids it just ruins them. . . . I think it bothers every child when somebody teases them or pokes fun at them, . . . even though they wouldn't tell you." *Male, 30's to 40's*

1267 "I'll see [my friends], . . . and I don't mean to . . . think bad about them, . . . but I think, 'Why are they letting themselves go so bad?'. . . Maybe it's worrying about how I look. Maybe that's the catch in it there. I just don't want to get that way. . . . You see friends that have gained weight real bad, . . . [and] you think, 'I hope they're not going to be sick over this.' . . . Just maybe worried about them. I guess I better quit the cookies." *Male, mid 50's*

1268 "My mother struggled with her body weight, and my youngest daughter has struggled with hers. So I have a lot of compassion. I know I struggle to stay where I'm at. I just have compassion for people that aren't the size they want to be, . . . whether it's overweight or underweight. I think one problem is just as hard on that person as the other." *Female, 50ish*

1269 "As an adult, I have had friends that struggle [because] they were excessively overweight. . . . I have had experiences with people who were anorexic. . . . So maybe [I feel] just compassion." *Female, late 40's*

1270 "I do not approve of [being very] overweight. . . . However, some of those poor souls, I think it's beyond their control. Well, I think some people . . . become obese without half trying." *Male, early 80's*

172

1271 "I never really put together why body fat bothers me, but it does. That is just honest. [My body fat] or anybody else's, it just kind of disgusts me. I don't know why." *Male, early 40's*

1272 "There's this highly accepted paradigm that some people can eat and eat and never gain, and some people could starve and starve and never lose. I think that's less true than we like to make it. . . . I accept, as a scientific principle, that we have different metabolic rates, but I think that there's more excuse in high body weights than we probably ought to allow ourselves." *Male in his 50's*

1273 "Most good-looking girls are evil and downright rude. So I really don't care to look for a good-looking female. . . . I really don't find myself looking for the hottest chick in town . . . because a lot of them are just downright mean and not very nice people to know or . . . to be around." *Male, early 20's*

1274 "I don't like to see a fat man. . . . I don't think [fat bodies] are attractive. I don't think a fat body is attractive, no matter who it is on." *Female in her 60's*

1275 "I don't like short guys . . . [and] I'm not attracted to huge guys . . . [but] I do like guys with a lot of muscle, just well built. Gosh I'm picky! I'm sitting here being so picky about them, but then I get angry when [guys] say I have a gut." *Female, early 20's*

1276 "I'm . . . not too empathetic with people who let themselves go. . . . I know there's biological things that happen to people where they can't not be obese, but to just let yourself go there, I can't say I really understand that too well."
Male, early 40's

1277 "I have two . . . friends that are heavier than I am, and they constantly talk about their weight. . . . [I] catch myself with a two-edged sword, knowing I am not taking care of myself as good as I can but wondering why they are complaining about their weight and still eating the chocolate bar. . . . I've seen people that have just completely grossed me out because they are just so big, and . . . they are not taking care of themselves." *Female, late 20's*

1278 "Because I value physical fitness quite highly, I guess I have almost a built-in bias in what I think about others who are not [physically fit]. That's probably not fair. . . . So anyone who's not [physically fit] is kind of not an ideal person in my mind, I guess. It doesn't mean they're not smart, . . . [and it doesn't mean they are of] lower value." *Male in his 50's*

1279 "This girl in high school, she was always kind of chubby, . . . and a lot of people made fun of her. . . . So then she comes back for a five-year reunion deal, and she just looks stunning, just great. . . . All the guys that made fun of her, now she could pretty much just say, 'To heck with you guys. Look at me now. Wish you had been nice then, huh?' " *Male, mid 20's*

1280 "I hate fat . . . . Obesity . . . to me is calories in and calories out. . . . I don't understand . . . how [people] can let themselves get . . . so grossly overweight. I just do not understand it. . . . Very unsightly. Very, very offensive. . . . If you don't burn off more than you eat, you gain weight. . . . When you see a person walking down the street that's wider than they are tall, it's like, whoa! There's something wrong here." *Male, mid 50's*

1281 "I see real heavy people as lazy. . . . In my own mind, I've got this scale [*holds hands apart*] of you can be [between] this weight or this weight and you're probably normal. And if you're outside those areas, there's some major problems." *Female, 40ish*

1282 "[Heavy people] kind of turn me off if they're really, really obese. . . . I don't want to know them. I don't want to know who they are or anything about them." *Female, late 70's*

1283 "[My husband's family] just want [me to be] the perfect Barbie doll image, even though they look *nothing* like a Barbie doll themselves." *Female, mid 20's*

1284 "I find people who are like, 'Oh, so and so is just so fat,' and they talk like that all the time. . . . And those are the people that I don't want to be around. I don't want to be around somebody who's so negative and who's going to judge another person like that." *Female, mid 20's*

1285 "Some people can't help [being fat]. And others that I see are sitting there just shoveling food in. I think . . . something must be very radically wrong in your life that you're using food as a pacifier." *Female in her 60's*

1286 "Every now and then you hear of somebody on the news. Here's some 500- or 700-pound guy that's been living in an apartment for so many years that he can't get through the door. So the EMTs got to chainsaw the door so they can get him on a gurney to get him to the hospital when something goes wrong. And those are the ones that you wonder about. How can they sit in an apartment and keep shoveling the calories in and get that big?" *Male, 40's to 50's*

1287 "I get embarrassed by seeing people who are very misshaped in bathing suits. . . . [I'm] embarrassed for them. There's no way I'd put on a bikini, and yet I've seen people do it. Men and women." *Female in her 60's*

1288 "I just see some kids out there that I think their parents should be embarrassed to have kids that are just huge, and I feel so sorry for them."
Female, late 20's to early 30's

1289 "My grandma was overweight and sassy and ornery, and so that probably related some [to why I dislike fat]." *Male, mid 50's*

1290 "Short skirts are made for pretty legs, and when you see one leg that's three feet around hanging out of a short skirt, that's definitely a turnoff to me."
Male, mid 50's

1291 "I look at fat people and I think, 'God they're ugly.' It's not an attractive thing at all." *Male, late 30's*

1292 "[I] wonder if people realize the health risks that they're at when they allow their bodies to become overweight. And the underweight, I guess they make me jealous maybe. I just think they think they have it so easy."
Female in her 40's

1293 "I remember driving down the road with [my grandma] one day and there was a fairly large guy walking along and she says, 'Well he hasn't missed too many meals.' . . . She made a lot of those types of comments, especially the older she got." *Female in her 30's*

Overweight and job searching

1294 "I'm currently interviewing people, . . . and I had a gal who came in who is significantly overweight, a lot heavier than I am. And she had a good resume. And my reaction was that I didn't want her, . . . and that wasn't a very fair thing to feel. And I was surprised that I felt that way. It was a shock to me. And she called later and said that she wasn't interested in the job. And I was relieved because it wasn't a good reason to not hire somebody. It was a really bad reason." *Female, early 40's*

1295 "One thing that does bother me when I'm around people who are larger is when they talk about their weight, and they do, they knock it. . . . That really bothers me because I don't know how to respond to that, 'cause I want to say to them, 'Yeah, that's no fun to be overweight, but maybe you could do something about it; maybe you couldn't, but don't worry about it.' . . . It puts me on the spot. Am I supposed to say, 'No, you look wonderful, you look thin,' when it's not the truth? And I have to admit that I do that too. I do that to other people and they probably get annoyed too." *Female in her 30's*

1296 "My mother was always heavy. . . , and that bothered me when I was in school and she would come to school. It was embarrassing. . . . I can still see my mother coming to school in a brown tweed coat and a turban on her head. It's like it was so embarrassing. . . . Gosh! And I mean, to this day I try to take care of myself." *Female, late 60's to early 70's*

1297 "I have this friend that's heavier set, but she is absolutely gorgeous, absolutely beautiful hair, beautiful makeup, beautiful nails. And I always look like an orphan child. You know, we're just the opposites. But I truly admire people who are heavier who still take care of themselves instead of putting on that, 'Oh, I'm big so I'm just going to look frumpy.' . . . I think we [should] all just appreciate what we do have and just better ourselves. I remember someone giving a talk one day and he said, 'You know what? Get out there and paint your barns. Some of your barns need a little fixing up.' And I always loved that. You know, put a fresh coat of paint on them. Fix up the little things that are missing or that are loose and strengthen yourself." *Female, late 20's*

1298 "I think a person, . . . no matter what the size they are, . . . can look beautiful by the way they portray themselves. And if they portray themselves as a very confident person, and you can see that they're happy with [themselves], I think it makes you view them in a different light versus if they are constantly, 'Well, I'm fat. I'm ugly.' . . . If they're always negative I'll probably think, 'Maybe they should do something if they're that unhappy.' " *Female, mid 20's*

1299 "If there's somebody who's grossly overweight and . . . it seems to be part of their lifestyle, that bothers me. . . . Not doing anything. Sitting on the couch watching TV. If they're out doing things [and] the weight doesn't seem to affect how they perform and how they are, then I have no problem. It's how they deal with who they are, maybe." *Male in his 20's*

1300 "If you look nice, even though you're on the heavier side, you still feel better about yourself." *Female, late 40's*

1301 "Like I told you, my world is black and white. . . . I read people really well and I'm almost always right. It's not an ego. It's just a lot of practice. I could think of one person here in town who is really heavy, but it's his attitude that stinks. I know some other people that I guess people classify as heavy. They're wonderful people. . . . There're just two kinds of people in the world. There's givers and takers. There's nobody in between." *Male, late 50's*

1302 "I think even if you are completely obese, . . . don't walk around and keep your head down and shuffle and [act] like you're a disgrace to your body. Projecting yourself on people has a big impact on how everybody views you, how well you're accepted. I've met obese people that were totally down in the dumps. And then I've had other obese people . . . that [were] very chipper. They were happy people. They were great friends. They tried their best to live life." *Female in her 20's*

1303 "I admire people that are real overweight [and active]. Just like today, I had a mechanic . . . that I know. Hell, he's huge, but . . . he's a mechanic, holds down a full-time job, . . . and he did a good job. . . . So I admire people that [are overweight] and still [do] not let that be a deterrent for them to be a productive citizen and live a good life." *Male, 40's to 50's*

1304 "If you feel good about yourself, you will do things. If you don't feel good about yourself, you just kind of sit back and [think], 'This might not work anyway, so why even worry about it.' " *Male in his 40's*

1305 "As long as you feel good about yourself and the way you look, I don't think it matters if you weigh 200 to 300 pounds. . . . If you carry yourself positive and you seem happy with yourself, I think that other people [will] find you . . . beautiful." *Female, mid 20's*

1306 "When you walk up to somebody and they smell, that's a big turnoff. But it's not any more of a turnoff because they were skinny or fatty either one. Just let me get upwind while holding my breath." *Male, late 50's*

Overweight and physical appearance

1307 "I see some people that sometimes have let themselves go to the point . . . [that] they don't care about [their physical appearance]. You see people that are overweight and they . . . [let] other things go down. They don't keep their hair nice and they don't care how they dress. [They] go to public places . . . in sweatpants and their gut's hanging out under a shirt that's six inches too short. . . . It kind of repulses me a little bit." *Male, mid 50's*

1308 "I've worked with . . . kids who all through their life were teased about being the fat kid, and the impact that's had on them . . . is amazing. . . . So I hope I try to be more sensitive, . . . but there's still opinions and judgments and assumptions that people make. I think if somebody is overweight, [people] just assume automatically they're lazy or they don't care. . . . Maybe it's arthritis or maybe it's genetics or maybe it's a lot of different things. So I try to be sensitive. . . . But I'll be honest with you, sometimes in certain groups of people . . . comments are made about somebody's weight, . . . and I try to be sensitive, but I don't know that I always am. . . . So, I think I try to be sensitive to it, but there's still maybe a stereotype to a degree." *Male, 30ish*

1309 "I still think that little thoughts creep into your mind, so it's a constant thing to get over when you meet somebody new. You have to get over all the stereotypes of whatever you thought in the past. . . . You grow up with these thoughts, and I always find I'm wrong when I do the stereotype on somebody. Every time. I don't think there has ever been a time where I've been right, but I keep forgetting. . . . There was a girl who moved into our neighborhood, and I don't remember exactly . . . the stereotype I put on her, but she was a little bit heavier, and for some reason I just did not think we could be friends, . . . but then I found out later that we were actually really good friends."

Female in her 20's

1310 "People would immediately stereotype [my large friend and large brother], and they wouldn't get to know them, and I always thought that was so rude."

Female, mid 30's

1311 "There was a lady that I met recently, . . . and she is quite a large lady. . . . And I think at first I probably judged her a little bit on her size. . . . [Now] I'm glad that we're friends." *Female in her 20's*

1312 "I don't remember in junior high even thinking about weight, . . . but it seems like high school was when the whole issue came up that people could stereotype you by your body shape." *Female, mid 30's*

1313 "I know a teacher that lost a lot of weight and she said the best evaluation she's ever gotten was when she was [thinner], because she gained the weight back. . . . And that makes you wonder. [She] didn't change the teaching; she'd been a teacher for years. The only thing that really changed was the size of her body, but she got the best evaluation she's ever gotten [when she was thin]. So you can't tell me that [size] doesn't matter, because it does. And that's just one little example. I really feel that as much as we want to say equal rights and everything should be the same across the board, I still think [body size] influences." *Female in her 30's*

1314 "I think [fat acceptance is] harder in White communities because we feel like we have to look more like the supermodels and the actresses that are all skinny and on TV. Because I was watching one movie, . . . and there was a big Black lady there, and . . . she knew that she was really sexy even though she was fat and big. And I thought, 'What's our problem?' 'Cause all of us, if we're big, we feel like we're not sexy . . . . When I'm having intimate times with my husband, my body's kind of not how I want it to look, and I think, 'Well why can't we feel sexy when we're big?' [Large Black women] just know they're sexy, and I thought, 'Well we need to be like that too.' And so just watching that movie made me think I can still be [sexy]." *Female, mid 40's*

1315 "The White, U.S. world has a real problem trying to accept their fatness because of all the media that you see." *Female, mid 40's*

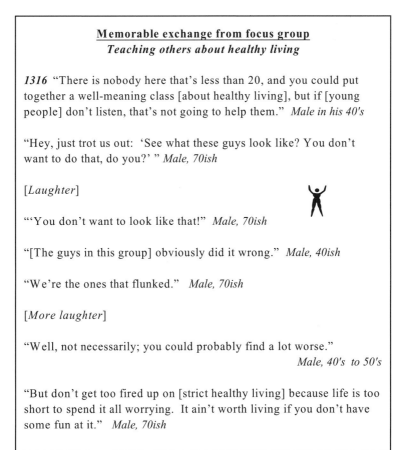

Memorable exchange from focus group
Teaching others about healthy living

1316 "There is nobody here that's less than 20, and you could put together a well-meaning class [about healthy living], but if [young people] don't listen, that's not going to help them." *Male in his 40's*

"Hey, just trot us out: 'See what these guys look like? You don't want to do that, do you?' " *Male, 70ish*

[*Laughter*]

"'You don't want to look like that!' *Male, 70ish*

"[The guys in this group] obviously did it wrong." *Male, 40ish*

"We're the ones that flunked." *Male, 70ish*

[*More laughter*]

"Well, not necessarily; you could probably find a lot worse."
Male, 40's to 50's

"But don't get too fired up on [strict healthy living] because life is too short to spend it all worrying. It ain't worth living if you don't have some fun at it." *Male, 70ish*

1317 "It seems to me the more I think about [losing weight], the more I gain."

Female, mid 70's

1318 "I *hate* being overweight. Absolutely hate it. I don't like it when my pants are tight. . . . And it drives me nuts . . . . I think about it every day. I think about it constantly. And my wife says, 'Don't worry about it.' [But] I do worry about it." *Male, 30's to 40's*

1319 "I think different bodies react differently, but mine is not comfortable being so overweight, and it was screaming at me to do something."

Female in her 30's

1320 "You know, you have that particular weight where you feel good, and if you get heavier than that, you don't feel good." *Female in her 40's*

1321 "At this point in my life, I'm fighting three diseases now, and just to get up out of the bed in the morning is an awful lot of pain. . . . I put on 100 pounds laying in a bed the last two and a half years . . . . And I was a big guy anyway, but now I've got so many problems, I can't seem to do anything to get [the weight] off." *Male in his 60's*

1322 "I can tell by my jean size [that] I've gained a little weight this winter. . . . I think it's because of not exercising. I'm sure it is. . . . Too much . . . watching TV instead. . . . I have watched TV from six 'til ten o'clock." *Male, mid 50's*

1323 "[My husband and I] noticed that we had gained a lot of weight. When I look back at pictures now, I think, 'Oh Lord, I *did* gain a lot of weight.' "

Female, mid 20's

1324 "I don't think necessarily [my mom] was trying to hurt my feelings, but she would always [say], 'Well, you look like you've lost weight,' or 'You look like you've gained weight.'. . . It's always been a real issue in [my mom's] family to be slender, and . . . I came to the point where I just got tired of hearing that." *Female, mid 20's*

1325 "I want [the extra weight] to be off in six months. . . . It sure went on pretty quick. I bet it didn't take six months to go on. It takes a lot longer to get it off, though." *Female, mid 30's*

1326 "I had a pretty severe [car] accident in [the late '80s]. . . , and since then, it's pretty much slowed me down. . . . I was a little heavy before then, but I probably gained 125 pounds since then." *Male in his 40's*

1327 "I try to monitor myself . . . . I keep the scales close at hand there so you kind of, 'Hey, I've put on five, I'd better get rid of it.'. . . I'm not one who really puts [weight] on fast, and if I take it off, I have to work it off." *Male, early 40's*

1328 "I'm a pretty big-boned kind of person who's always been a pretty good size. But if I really worked at it, I could lose weight. . . . It's just a matter of putting in the time to do it." *Male in his 50's*

1329 "Now I [weigh myself] all the time because it's positive, because it's been going down, and that's a good thing. If I should get into the thing where I'm not [losing weight], then I just ignore the scale, and I just don't look at it and it goes away after a while." *Female in her 30's*

1330 "I'd like to be thinner than what I am. I'm packing a little extra fat than I probably should be . . . . I think if I could just get back down to where [I was in high school], it would be my ideal." *Male, early 30's*

1331 "[After dieting], I was glad to be at my goal weight, but then my weight crept back on. I'm probably at the highest [weight] I've ever been in my life. Even pregnant I don't think I weighed anywhere near this." *Female, early 60's*

1332 "My metabolism has been where it's fairly easy to lose weight, either by exercising or eating less." *Female in her 30's*

1333 "I think my overall weight that I carry . . . I'm happy with and the fact that I don't have to worry about it very much." *Male in his 30's*

1334 "I'm happy with my size and shape. I like people about six feet tall and thin, not too fat. But I haven't had any problems at all [with my weight]. . . . After I got out of high school, . . . I had four major operations on my stomach, my liver locked up, my pancreas ruptured. I got down to 110 pounds at one time. . . . I usually weigh about 175." *Male, mid 70's*

Humorous sidenotes

1335 "I'm not overweight. I'm just 12 inches too short." *Male, 70ish*

1336 "If there's one thing I'd like to keep, it's my breast size. But when I lose weight, it's not my shoe size that changes."
Female, early 40's

1337 "I wish I weighed a little less so my poor pony didn't have to be scared [of me]." *Male, 70ish*

1338 "When I was in high school, I always felt good about [my body image], . . . and in college, the same thing, until I got a little bit bigger, and . . . from then it was just always a battle. . . . There is a battle there, and it's . . . not won by one or two months of work. . . . It's an everyday battle to stay healthy. . . . Now that I . . . know that I can't keep the weight down, I just have to stay healthy."

Female, late 20's

1339 "I think that I've followed after my mom, which actually frightens me just a little bit because my mom was about my size when she was my age and just gradually got larger and has had a really hard time getting weight off. . . . I think I kinda follow my mom's shape." *Female, early 20's*

1340 "I never liked my body. . . , never been able to get it to where I was happy with it, even when I was young . . . and in really good shape. . . . But even at that, I still didn't like, never have liked, my body. Always felt it was too big. . . . I started dieting when I weighed 250, and I dieted myself up to 350. . . . Every time I got my weight down to about 220, then I would go back up. I would let it get back up, and it would be ten pounds heavier than it was the last time I did it. . . . It's been a real struggle." *Male in his 60's*

1341 "I've probably always been focused on not wanting to gain weight, but sometimes I focus on it less than others. . . . I'm . . . like that guy that I read [about] in *Reader's Digest* that gains weight by listening to dinner music."

Female in her 30's

1342 "Get [weight] under control while you can and try to keep it under control, even if it is a constant struggle. 'Cause when you let down your guard, then it gets way out of control, and then when you're way out of control, it's a lot tougher to bring it back." *Male in his 40's*

1343 "Probably all my life I've struggled with weight . . . and/or gained weight and/or lost it for years. It was probably the yo-yo." *Female, 50ish*

1344 "Don't allow yourself to be more than a couple of pounds over[weight] . . . before you do something about it. That's the secret. . . . Once you get more than five pounds [overweight], you know it gets a little tough to try to lose that again. Anyone who has lost weight and kept it off has never allowed themselves to gain more than five pounds back." *Male in his 30's*

1345 "I think I've always seen myself as obese. I look back, and I see my pictures and I think, 'Wow, I was so thin!' But if I think about what I thought at the time, I thought I was fat." *Female in her 20's*

1346 "People say they're going on this diet and then they'll really be slim. And then next time when you see them, they're all fat again." *Female, late 70's*

1347 "I never liked my body. . . , never been able to get it to where I was happy with it . . . , always felt it was too big. . . . I started dieting when I weighed 250, and I dieted myself up to 350." *Male in his 60's*

1348 "I knew I shouldn't have taken [diet drugs] in the first place, but everyone wants that quick fix." *Female, late 20's*

1349 "I am an addict when it comes to *everything*. Drugs, food, sex, everything. I go all or nothing. When I was on drugs, I got pretty skinny. . . . And then I quit doing drugs, and food became my addiction. . . . I put on a lot of weight. . . . Then I met this girl . . . who used to be really heavy, and she looked *great* and she felt so good and I wanted what she had. So she started me on this [diet] program and *that* became my addiction. . . . And then, . . . I switched one addiction for another again, and I put all the weight back on." *Female, late 20's*

1350 "[At the hospital], we see so many people, especially women, [focused on weight]. . . . We have these young girls in physical therapy [and] they'll say, 'Yes, we've got to lose ten pounds.' Well, you know, they really don't need to." *Female, mid 60's*

1351 "Well, if I have trouble, it's keeping my weight down, because I like to eat. . . . So now I've tried to ration myself. . . . I don't lose any weight. I slowly go the other direction. . . . Well, I used to have a 32 waistline. I have a 36 now. . . . I tell you what really gets me. When I get enough [extra weight] that my belt starts to slip down under [my belly], and I can't keep my pants up. . . . Then I think, 'Oh geez, I've got to do something.' " *Male, early 80's*

1352 "I . . . have some friends who are too heavy, and they always go on these diets, and they look really nice for a little while, and then pretty soon they go off of them, and they gain [weight]. I think they gain more weight after they go off of them than they did before." *Female, late 70's*

1353 "My orthopedic doctor kept saying, 'You need to lose weight'—wanted to put me on phen-pen. Well, thank goodness I wasn't on phen-fen. I just thought, I'll lose weight. I will sometime. And that's been two or three years ago. And it always sticks in my mind and I worry about it. . . . I know what I was told —may be in a wheelchair someday—and I thought, 'Oh dear, I don't want that.' So I'm constantly thinking about weight." *Female, late 60's to early 70's*

One man's story on dieting

1354 "Two times in the past I really did focus on losing [weight]. One time was my last semester in high school, . . . and it was actually starting to work. And I was thinking, 'Gee, if I can take this [healthy living] course about three more times, I might have a life habit.' Because it's a matter of getting into the habit. And I was right on the threshold of being [there], and then I finished school and we moved, . . . so it was a setback in the sense that I had to focus my attention on other things. And then three years ago, my boss said, 'If you could lose 100 pounds, I'll just give you $100 dollars.' I said, well heck, that's not really a bet, it was more of a challenge. . . . For about two months I was doing it and it was starting to work. It was actually working. And I have no idea what it was, but I remember that something happened between me and my wife. . . . It's like those two times I was right there and then something happened. And [I'm] not blaming anything other than my own self for not continuing it, in spite of whatever was challenging [me] at the time." *Male, early 30's*

1355 "[My friend] is the same age I am. She smokes like a chimney . . . because she's so afraid of gaining weight. I keep trying to get her to quit smoking. [She says], 'I would rather be dying of lung cancer and be skinny. . . . My mom and dad—they don't have anything wrong with them. They've been smoking forever'—blah, blah, blah. And I said, 'It doesn't mean that's not going to happen to you.'. . . I mean, all the patients that I take care of are on oxygen. . . . And I said, ' I want you to be around.' And she says, ' I will gain weight and I can't do it.' She just said, 'I will not [be heavy] again.' And it petrifies her. I mean I can really see it. It petrifies her . . . . I have quite a few friends that are heavier and it's just like, 'You're wonderful people just like you are. I want you to be healthy.' " *Female, mid 30's*

1356 "I smoked for 35 years. My doctor forced me to quit ten years ago due to my health problems. After I quit smoking, I gained a lot of weight. When I was smoking, I would grab a cigarette and get some coffee, but I could avoid snacks. Now it seems like I grab for food instead of a cigarette." *Female in her 60's*

1357 "[When I see a slender person, I] look for the underlying fact. Do they smoke all the time and not eat, or what? Things like that. [My mother-in-law] never eats and she smokes all the time." *Female, late 20's*

1358 "I see a lot of people who I think are smoking because they think it's going to keep their weight down. And most of these are females." *Male, early 80's*

The challenge to quit smoking vs. lose weight

1359 "We have a coffee group. There's a waitress there who is a smoker. She's quite attractive, thin, nice build, small gal. She wanted to quit smoking . . . [and] one of the fellows is overweight, so they made a bet that he was going to lose weight and she was going to quit smoking. They each put money in to see who could do it and the rest of us added to the pot. The thing that really set me back was as bad as she wanted to quit smoking, that if she started to gain weight, she'd rather smoke than gain weight. I think why on earth—I'd rather be a little heavy than be a smoker. Anyway, she's still smoking and he didn't lose his weight."

Male, almost 60

1360 "My mom has always been on my case about how I eat, and that's always [been], I guess, just a little evil reminder that I was fat." *Female, late 20's*

1361 "My daughter was teased an awful lot about her weight because she was big. When you sit there and hold your little girl and she's crying because people have said things, and you know what you went through in school, you just ughh! . . . I try to let [my daughter] know that I love her no matter what, that her body size isn't the only thing in the world, but . . . when you're going to school and kids are teasing you, it *is* the only thing in the world." *Female, 50ish*

1362 "[My daughter] eats regular meals and she is called anorexic to her face [and it's] very, very painful for her. . . . It's the same for her being called skinny as it is for fat people who take it to heart being called fat." *Female, 40ish*

1363 "Isn't it amazing how there are times in your life as well as everybody else's that someone will make what is called a flippant remark, and it will stick with you forever, as long as you're alive? . . . 'You're too fat.' " *Male, late 50's*

1364 "I know that when I first started swimming with [my] kids . . . I walked out on deck. . . . I was dressed for swimming. I had a cap on and goggles and the whole nine yards. Sixteen-year-old girls are sorta cruel. I didn't like them when I was 16 and I still don't like them. And I walked on deck, and this girl looked at me, and she turned to her friend and said, 'Is *she* swimming?' And her friend said, 'Well, let's see, she has on a swimsuit, she has on a cap, and she's got goggles. Yeah, I'd say she's swimming.' And even though I'm [over 40 and] I have an advanced education, it was very demeaning, and it hurt my feelings."
Female, early 40's

1365 "I guess I probably always thought I was bigger than most kids, most girls, because I was. How about truth? . . . My self-image was really not wrapped up in my weight or my body size. I always had a very supportive family, very excellent siblings, friends that were wonderful friends, and of course there were kids that made fun of me. I can't say there weren't. . . . [The teasing was] just the typical fatty-fatty, two by four, . . . stuff like that. . . . I personally just thought, 'Boy, that was mean.'. . . And I think it probably only made me realize, 'Yeah I guess I am. I am heavier.' And I was. That was absolutely true, yeah."
Female, 40ish

1366 "When I was growing up, I was a little bitty kid. . . . I didn't really start to grow 'til I was a senior in high school. As a result, in any confrontation, I had to hit and run like hell. . . . So that's the only thing I remember from youth, was being able to outrun everybody." *Male in his 60's*

186

1367 "I remember being in middle school, . . . and I remember a boy making a comment that I had a gut. And I know that I've been self-conscious probably since that very day . . . about my stomach because a little boy, who probably didn't know that it would ever affect me, said that I had a gut." *Female, early 20's*

1368 "I remember when I was real young, I was called string bean 'cause I was so darn skinny. And then as I got older, I got lots of compliments on my shape. . . . And I just couldn't understand why people were even saying it to me, 'cause I didn't work hard to do it, it's just how I was born." *Female, mid 30's*

1369 "I grew up in a family where most of us were overweight. . . . My grandmother was particularly always giving me a bad time. . . . I remember one time she said, 'Sixty pounds, you haven't weighed that since the day you were born.'. . . And the teasing just became more of a fact of life. . . . There's . . . a picture of myself and my . . . siblings . . . and [my sister's] husband says, 'That's her ton-of-fun picture.' " *Female in her 30's*

1370 "I have a younger brother. . . . He would eat five times the amount of food that I did. . . . , and he's still not heavy. . . . I remember going to a church meeting one day when I was a kid and the . . . lady turned around and looked at my mother . . . and said, 'What do you do, starve one and feed the other one?' "
Male in his 60's

1371 "I was picked on a lot. I still have a rude brother who likes to harp on me about my weight. He thinks it will get me going to lose it, but it doesn't. . . . You'll be walking through the store and you'll hear a little kid say, 'Now that guy is pretty fat.' . . . And that can affect your self-esteem. . . . I mean, they're not meaning to do harm, they're just little kids. . . . But being teased about it would force me to go home and have some ice cream or something. Kind of kill the pain with food. Being teased is not a good thing for me." *Male, early 20's*

1372 "My boyfriend, . . . who is now my husband, . . . is very vocal on how I look. . . . He has no problem saying, 'Do you need that?' or 'Your pants are getting too big or too tight,' things like that." *Female, late 20's*

1373 "After I was married and had the kids . . . one lady I hadn't seen for quite awhile . . . came up to me on the street and says, 'My! You've gotten fat!'. . . I was so shocked!" *Female, mid 70's*

1374 "[When] we were kids, we'd tease some kid because he was overweight, . . . call him 'fatty' or something. Kids tend to be really cruel and they say and do things to each other that you and I would never do." *Male, early 50's*

1375 "I got teased a lot. . . . They'd call me string bean and bean pole and stuff. . . . When I would get on the school bus . . . the boys would really tease me. I went through that awkward stage where I was just legs and arms and neck and nose. . . . They used to call me turkey, and they would gobble when I would get on the bus. But you know what? It really didn't matter. . . . I *would* get a little fed up with nose jokes." *Female, mid to late 40's*

1376 "Sometimes . . . [my wife] is a little obnoxious, like telling me I look like I'm pregnant, . . . and [it] just gets to the point where it's just an incessant type of situation." *Male, mid 50's*

1377 "[A friend I had when I was growing up] was really very obese, and he was much bigger than I was. And [the other kids] said things to him and it . . . really ticked me off. . . . I had a Black friend . . . and he actually had some trouble with kids taunting him. And it was the same feeling I got. . . . It's the same thing as being attacked because he's fat. Because it never made any difference to me that he was fat. . . . I haven't seen him in 25 years. . . . I've been to his stage for a long time now." *Male, late 30's*

1378 "I was teased as a child. And the funny thing—I wasn't heavy as a child, but I always thought I was . . . because . . . my girlfriends [were] smaller than I was. . . . I was . . . called "Big Red," . . . and I hated that! . . . I've never viewed my body as quite thin enough, and yet I know that a couple of times that I was."
Female in her 60's

1379 "I grew up . . . being teased, and it sticks with you. And it's still with me. I still have to fight it once in a while. I worry about what people think and how I look, and how I look to other people. As I get older, I'm kinda getting the idea, well, hey, as old as I am, this is me, take me as I am. I'm the same person inside no matter how large or small I am on the outside." *Female in her 60's*

1380 "There was a boy once who said to me that I have a large nose. And you know, that stuck with me for the rest of my life. . . . When I was in elementary school, . . . a boy ran into me and I held my ground. I didn't fall over. And they called me 'brick wall' for like a week or something because I was able to not let him push me over, and I thought, 'Oh, little girls aren't supposed to be brick walls.' " *Female in her 20's*

1381 "My first husband . . . used to put me down and tell me how horrible [I was]. An example, 'You're good -looking enough to be in anyone's front office, but you're too stupid.' So I decided right then and there, I'm showing you. I lost the weight and got a good job. . . . I divorced him." *Female in her 40's*

1382 "When I was about six years old, I remember my mother signing me up for tap dance lessons. After about three months, I remember so clearly, the dance teacher came over to my mother and she said, 'You've wasted *my* time and *your* money long enough. She is so clumsy you might as well not bring her back.' . . . And it became an absolute conscious effort to avoid physical activity situations."
Female, 60ish

1383 "In seventh grade, . . . 36-24-36 [were] my body measurements. . . . That might be great for an 18-year-old, but [not a seventh grader]. . . . And I had an older brother who said, 'You shouldn't hang around that other girl. You look like an elephant by the side of her.' . . . He didn't mean to hurt me, . . . [but] it hurt." *Female, 40ish*

1384 "Being fat turned me into a bitch. I was the nicest kid that you'll ever meet in your life, *I was*. I was happy-go-lucky. I loved everybody and didn't have a problem. I started putting on weight, and I started getting teased, and that teasing stopped quick because I found out I was a slugger. I was! I was taking dudes out and stuff, and I didn't care. Really, if you tease me you're going to get knocked out. . . . [Teasing] turned me mean." *Female, late 20's*

1385 "My body image allowed me to really develop the . . . power to let things blow off. . . . I'm really friends with a lot of the bullies that bullied me back in grade school. . . . And I think that the way I look has kind of made me the person I am today. . . . I don't really like the fact that they teased me, but I've accepted it and gotten over it. It's fine with me." *Male, early 20's*

1386 "My mother was a very small woman. And she was the only person who ever said anything particularly to me about my size. And when it finally reached a point where my mother went to the doctor one time, he told her she was ten pounds overweight. . . . That's when she finally didn't think it was funny anymore. She realized how painful that had been. But she had her own problems." *Female in her 60's*

1387 "I was just as guilty [of teasing others] as any kid. When we were kids, if somebody was really heavy, . . . a lot of times they would be made fun of. Kids are brutally honest. They are punishing, especially with their peers. And there was one kid in particular that I grew up with. It wasn't so much that he was really fat, he was just big. He was a huge kid. I mean, he had a big head and he was just a very large kid and a lot of kids teased him. They called him a whale. . . . I look back at junior high, and . . . there was kind of a popular group. Most of them weren't real heavy . . . . As far as fitting into that group, a lot of times the little short fat kid would be the one that would kind of be on the out."
Male in his 30's

1388 "It's a little scary when you're . . . heavy. 'Cause I notice people riding their bike and it's like, 'Where *is* that bicycle seat?' I don't want to be the person who the people are looking at saying, 'Hmmm.' " *Female in her 30's*

1389 "I definitely do not like having a large bosom. . . . I have always envied flat-chested people. It's just easier to buy clothes and everything else. . . . I was always teased about my bustline. Always." *Female in her 60's*

1390 "I hate to admit [this]. There's probably those [I] made bad comments to, and . . . that's probably shook their world to this day. . . . If [I could] go and undo that stuff [I] would." *Male, early 40's*

1391 "I've had . . . people say, 'Man, you've got yourself quite a gut there,' and that irritates me. Okay, you don't have to call attention to it. I know I've got it."
Male in his 70's

1392 "When I was growing up, one kid on the bus was pretty overweight and they used to make fun of him. . . . I guess I always was sensitive to that . . . because I was picked on for being short." *Male in his 30's*

1393 "I was a late bloomer. For one thing, I was teased a lot because I hadn't matured yet." *Female in her 30's*

1394 "Because I was so tall, I had big feet. . . . But I just kind of had an attitude that [the teasing was] people's opinion and it never really bothered me. It's kind of water off the duck's back. . . . [Worrying about teasing] is a waste of time."
Female in her 30's

1395 "My little sister got pointed at when she was younger, and she really wasn't big. She was just a kid, and kids have all different body sizes. And she grew up to be a beautiful woman now. I feel bad that kids would tease her, 'cause it really affected her self-esteem." *Female in her 20's*

1396 "Nowadays, I don't care if somebody calls me fat. [It] don't bother me. But as a kid, it was a traumatic experience . . . . I've been teased about my size my whole life. [People] used to ask me if I got my suits at . . . Tent and Awning." *Male in his 60's*

1397 "When I was in junior high, . . . a lot of people made fun of [this one kid]. And probably in the last 15 to 20 years, I've thought of him quite often because I hurt him quite bad as a kid. . . . Being one of the group, or trying to be popular, I hurt this young man. I always wonder, where is he? How's he doing? . . . Would I have the courage to say I'm sorry for what I did?" *Male, early 50's*

1398 "My mother . . . just thought we were all wonderfully beautiful, big people. So I always grew up with a pretty good self-image of just how I am. . . . I think basically [my parents] gave us a good healthy image. I think that was a real blessing." *Female in her 50's*

1399 "My folks were real supportive of me as I was growing up and I felt pretty good [about my body image]. . . . Then being married to my first husband was a real negative experience on my self-image. . . . Falling back on the things that I had learned as a child . . . allowed me to recognize that what was happening to me during the time of my first marriage was not true. This wasn't truth that was being spoken to me. . . . Also, knowing that I was worth being treated better."

Female, 40ish

1400 "[My husband] is a *miracle*. He is so wonderful to me. And the first time he told me that I was beautiful I was like, 'Yeah, right.' And I said, 'I'm not, . . . how can you say that?' And he goes, 'To me you *are* beautiful, and I love you, and I hope someday you will learn, because you love *me*, to trust what I say.'. . . I know he loves me, and . . . he treats me with respect." *Female, 40ish*

1401 "I would say things to my husband like, . . . 'I am only in my 20's, . . . and I shouldn't just look like this.' And he . . . would always use positive reinforcement and say, 'But I like you the way you are.' . . . I remember when I . . . had my bathing suit on and I was like, . . . 'I feel embarrassed and I won't take my tank top off.' And he said, 'You know what? You're beautiful to me.' . . . He was such a positive person, he made me feel so good about myself. My attitude finally started to change." *Female, mid 20's*

1402 "We're tall Germans in my family. . . . I was the tallest person in junior high school [and] . . . there were a lot of kids. But I had the support of family members and I was told . . . , 'Stand straight and be proud of it,' and that was pounded into me. I mean it was, 'Listen, stand straight and be proud of it. God made us the way we are.'. . . I like being tall. I thoroughly enjoy it."

Female, mid to late 60's

1403 "[My husband and I were exercising regularly] and of course the scale isn't saying anything. . . . And so I said something to my husband: 'The scale is not going down.' He goes, 'Well, your butt's getting smaller.' And I mean, that's what he said, but it's like, 'Well, that's the nicest thing you ever said to me.' " *Female, late 40's*

1404 "They say I got a nice butt. . . . Oh yeah. Yeah. Some of the women. It's funny. It's always the *married* women who always say that." *Male in his 30's*

1405 "When I was in high school, . . . [a lady] made the comment to my mother how impressed she was that I had two friends with me and neither one of them went past my shoulders and I didn't slouch. . . . And so that always made me feel good, and it made me pay more attention to my posture." *Female in her 30's*

1406 "I've had men say how nice I looked, and so then that made me feel better. I felt like maybe I wasn't as heavy to other people as I felt I was, and that really helped. . . . And when [my son and I went] to church one Sunday . . . one man . . . said, 'You look too young to be his mother.'. . . And . . . that made me feel better. And I think that other people can help you. Just a compliment from somebody else." *Female, mid 60's*

1407 "My mother never made me feel like I was big. She never did [*shaky voice, starting of tears*], 'Oh dear.' . . . I was a big girl, but I never knew it. . . . So, I always thought I was okay because of [my mother]." *Female, late 70's*

1408 "Your whole life, your self-image is primarily in how you think others view you. . . . [You need the] support of family and friends." *Female, early 40's*

1409 "I feel like a big, fat blimp. Sometimes I get frustrated with myself, and I say, 'Well, come on, fatso,' and it makes my husband mad when I make comments . . . like that. He doesn't like me to call [myself] like lard ass. Sometimes I feel so ugly." *Female, early 30's*

1410 "[My husband] compliments me, and that goes a long way. I've got a good guy. I tell him all the time, 'You make me feel young and beautiful.' And he does." *Female, early 60's*

1411 "My husband—I have to give him credit—is very accepting. He has never said word one about how I look or anything, which is nice. He just accepts what I look like." *Female, early 40's*

Finding peace with the help of a friend

1412 "I've always hated myself. . . . Oh, damn it! I hate it when I cry. I've always hated myself, and . . . [the person beside me] is the best friend that I have ever had. She has made me feel at peace with my spirit, . . . and she makes me feel beautiful and funny. She's just unconditional. She doesn't care that I'm fat. She doesn't care. She's always riding my ass about, 'Quit being hard on yourself.' I couldn't come up with the peace. I had to get it from somebody else."

Female, late 20's

1413 "My grandmother was probably two feet taller than my grandfather, . . . but it was like they were meant to be together. So, when I see something like that, I just kind of chuckle 'cause I think about them." *Female in her 30's*

1414 "I definitely am the body type of my dad's side of the family. . . . We all favor each other. . . . I think it's pretty cool. It kind of gives you a connection. I didn't grow up around my [dad's] family. . . . Instead of going into a room filled with people that don't look anything alike, . . . I go into a room filled with people that look a lot like me, but I don't know them. It kind of increases the comfort range a little bit." *Female in her 20's*

1415 "We've always been able to talk to our kids . . . that being small has its advantages. We can get in places that bigger people can't. Yes, you can always stand on something, but you can't shrink." *Female, late 40's*

1416 "[My wife's] had [several] kids, so she attributes her size and weight to having . . . kids. But I know a lady that's similar to her that's had [even more] kids. [She] doesn't look like that because she does something with her body. . . . I've tried to get [my wife] to cut down [on portion sizes] and she says, 'You leave me alone,' and '[Eating] is the only thing I enjoy in life. It's the only thing I can do. . . .' So I've just backed off and let her be. But lately, she's gotten to the point where she realizes that she needs to do something about her weight."
Male, early 50's

1417 "My mom was always dieting, and I'm probably about the same size or maybe a little bigger than she was at her biggest. And since she was dieting, it makes me feel like I'm too big because she felt like she was too big."
Female, mid 40's

1418 "I don't want to be like my mom. I cannot remember the last time my mother wore a pair of pants. I mean, she's that large of a woman. . . . And I just have that in my head. I'm thinking, 'I never want to get that big to where I feel like jeans are not comfortable.' And I think how your parents are, what they say as you're growing up, really shapes how you feel about your body and what you do or don't want to do when you grow up." *Female, late 20's to early 30's*

1419 "Our daughter is really overweight. And as a mother, you can't say things like you can to other people. . . . She puts up a barrier . . . . [If I say anything,] I think she drinks five times *more* pop and eats *more* junk food. . . . [The people at work] are helping her more than I can help her as a mother." *Female, mid 60's*

1420 "I guess I got to where it didn't make a difference what I ate. I've always felt like I came from that kind of background and that kind of family and it was just going to be that way, that I guess maybe I didn't have a lot of control over it. And the teasing just became more of a fact of life." *Female in her 30's*

1421 "I think the women in my family have affected the way that I think about myself. . . . They have never been happy with their bodies and so I'm constantly confused. What is wrong with my body? And so I look at myself in the mirror in the morning, and I feel like I should change this . . . or I should change that."
Female, early 20's

1422 "My dad's side of the family is all obese. So when I saw them, . . . I thought, 'Wow! They're very severely obese.' " *Female in her 20's*

1423 "I have a brother . . . . He's [over] . . . 300 pounds, . . . and I remember always wondering, 'How did he get that big and I didn't?' " *Female, mid 30's*

1424 "I thought . . . that I had to look like my sister and I had to look like my mom and I had to be super, super tiny." *Female, mid 20's*

1425 "I would want my daughter to be friends with everybody. So in a way, I guess I'd like to set the example. . . . My thinking has changed to how would I want my daughter and my children to react to people of all sorts of disabilities or weights or sizes. . . . I wouldn't want her to be the one pointing the finger."
Female in her 20's

Are children embarrassed by their overweight parents?

1426 "One of [my son's] classmates will say, 'Your [mom's] fat.' And I said, 'Does that bother you?' And he said, 'No, because they don't know you.' " *Female, early 40's*

1427 "My mother and father were heavy and that never embarrassed me. I mean, for them being heavy, that never embarrassed me. That was just my parents." *Female, late 40's*

1428 "My mother was a large woman, and I was always embarrassed when I was a teenager. . . . And I can see that I was being a teenager."
Female in her 60's

1429 "I remember my friends would say, 'Well, my mom is so fat and you're lucky your mom's not.' I remember being glad that she was not overweight." *Female, mid 30's*

1430 "One of my best friends is very heavy. She knows she should lose weight, and I know she should lose weight, and we never discuss it." *Female in her 60's*

1431 "Just hanging out with your girlfriends and looking at magazines saying, 'I wish I looked like this,' or 'I wish I looked like that,' that's a little chip to your self-confidence." *Female, early 20's*

1432 "Kids are brutally honest. They are punishing, especially with their peers. And there was one kid in particular that I grew up with. . . . He was a huge kid. . . . They called him a whale. . . . We were all good friends with him, but he did get teased about his body size." *Male in his 30's*

1433 "Girls are horrible. . . . They say things like, 'She's the one with the huge butt,' or whatever. I think it makes you more aware of others and yourself."
Female, early 20's

1434 "In junior high, you kind of compare yourself with other kids. 'This person's bigger and more muscular or taller than me. . . .' You judge who you are by your peers . . . , just comparing whose bicep was bigger." *Male in his 30's*

1435 "My self-image was really not wrapped up in my weight or my body size. I always had a very supportive family, very excellent siblings, [and] friends that were wonderful friends." *Female, 40ish*

1436 "I was never overweight in high school, but I had a friend who was. . . . [My friend] was really obsessed with not ever being fat again. . . . She would talk about it all the time. Even now when I see her, she's like, 'Oh I've gained a few pounds.' And with my other friends, we don't even go there. We don't even talk about weight." *Female, mid 30's*

1437 "[My friend] said, 'I can't believe you ever thought you were fat [in high school].' She said, 'You were so skinny.' . . . And to this day, I actually diet less and worry about that stuff less than she does. And she's very, very into it."
Female, mid 30's

1438 "I had a friend in high school that was a football wanna-be. . . . He knew about [our annual hunting trip], and he heard the stories and wanted to go. It really hurt me to tell him, 'No, you can't go because physically you can't do it.' . . . The next year, . . . he lost a 100 pounds and went on the hunt in my place. . . . I guess I really admire him for that." *Male, almost 60*

1439 "My best girlfriend . . . was tiny, and I wasn't, and it didn't make a bit of difference. . . . We just were friends. . . . I feel sorry for the kids nowadays because there is so much emphasis on being slim." *Female, late 70's*

1440 "My body's fine. At this age, . . . everything's starting to go south. My behind is now in a different spot than it used to be . . . . Everything is just going south, including the face. [I have] the ol' flabby things under the arms. . . . But heck, I've earned it. I don't mind it." *Female, late 40's*

1441 "I'm probably the only postmenopausal woman here, . . . [and] something . . . started maybe about four years ago. My body chemistry changed, my metabolism changed, my appetite changed. Over the last four years, I've gradually . . . shed . . . a pound or two a month. The last time I was on a scale, I was [down] about 75 pounds." *Female, 60ish*

1442 "The older I get, the worse [it is to lose weight]. I mean, it was tough enough the way it was. But the older I get, the worse it is." *Female, late 40's*

1443 "I graduated as a 98-pound senior. . . . Even after I was married for a long time, my wife was frustrated because I wasn't putting on any weight. Once I reached about 38 years old, it's just kind of like she put glue in all the food, because it was sticking to me. And from that time on, I realized I had to be careful what I ate." *Male, early 50's*

1444 "I think I'm shrinking in my height, and I'm staying the same weight. I think I'm getting a tummy. Is that what you do when you get older? I think so, uh-huh, I think so." *Female, late 70's*

1445 "When I married my wife, . . . I weighed 175 and I was thin and trim, looked good. And then I guess you slide into that deal, where you think, 'Well, [I] don't have to worry about being competitive anymore,' and you kind of let yourself get complacent about things. Pretty soon, your complacency is formed around the middle of your pants." *Male, mid 50's*

1446 "I see myself . . . gaining weight the older I get, and it scares me. I know that, because . . . no one wants to get fat. So I am *definitely* headed down the road of filling out. . . . I think that I've followed after my mom, which actually frightens me just a little bit, because my mom was about my size when she was my age and just gradually got larger." *Female, early 20's*

1447 "I look at [school pictures of me] now and think, 'Wow, you looked good, you looked really good.' . . . So, I feel like now I can look back, and I think that was silly that I was so concerned about my weight and didn't think I looked good, 'cause I'm not particularly happy [about my body size] right now. . . . Maybe one year I'll be even heavier than I am now and look back and say, 'Hey, you looked good, what were you thinking?' " *Female in her 20's*

1448 "When I was younger, I could eat anything, anytime, and never be the least bit concerned . . . because I had a 29 or 30 waist. . . . I went to a size 32 waist and then I gradually moved up to a size 36. . . . I have no idea what caused my . . . weight gains. Maybe it's . . . time." *Male in his 60's*

1449 "My husband has this little potbelly, but then his little butt is still little and his legs are still little and he's not considered fat. But I just think women maybe gain [weight] in a different way. . . . [Men] age different than us. . . . He doesn't want to change his pants size. Finally, [he said], 'Oh, maybe I *do* need a 34.' [I said,] 'Yeah maybe you do, hon'.' . . . He doesn't want to admit [he's gained weight]. . . . He still thinks it's muscle." *Female, 30's to 40's*

1450 "I was too thin [when I was young]. . . . Then between the ages of 15 and 45 or so, I felt pretty good about the way I looked. I was in pretty dang good shape. And now I don't have any real qualms except that I'm a little bit bigger in the stomach than what I'd like to be, but I think it dropped from the top down, . . . 'cause I was a lot huskier up at the top than I am now. So I think it's just due to age." *Male, 60ish*

1451 "My mom always says after you have kids and the older you get you need to be very careful because the weight creeps up on you. And you know what? This is the first year in my life I will admit she's right. [I'm in my 30's] and it just seems like now the weight is not staying off like it used to." *Female, mid 30's*

1452 "All those times that I dieted, I had a very young image of myself. . . . But this time, I'm having a really hard time getting [weight] off. I'm [over 60] now. . . . I'm not young anymore. I always took it right off." *Female in her 60's*

1453 "My brother . . . could eat and eat and eat and never gain a pound. [Now] he's bigger than me. And he came home one time, and . . . he said, 'It's muscle, it's not fat.' I said, 'Where did you get *this* muscle?' [*points to stomach*] And he said, 'It's not fair. It's not fair.' And I said, 'Well, I wasn't the one who could eat 20 pounds of prime rib in a weekend. You know it's going to catch up eventually.' And it finally did with my brother." *Female, early 40's*

1454 "My dad was taking me for a ride on the four-wheeler. I put my arms around him and I couldn't touch, and I thought, 'Dad, are you this fat?' But it seems . . . guys as they get older, they just kind of get a paunch and get a little bigger." *Female, mid 40's*

1455 "When our [children] got to be teenagers was when I was more aware of how I should look because . . . my weight was harder to get off and wrinkles came." *Female, mid 60's*

1456 "[My] hind end and stomach . . . have too much fat in there, but I don't let it stop me from going swimming. . . , especially now that I'm a grandmother. Well, I'm supposed [to look like this]—blue veins and fat." *Female, early 60's*

1457 "I'm not afraid to age. . . . I look forward to being all gray."

Female, early 40's

1458 "If you're a man that thinks that your spouse. . . [is] always going to have this real perfect body . . . you're going to have a rude awakening. . . . Your wife's body is going to change. . . . You need to understand that."

Male in his 30's

1459 "I . . . look back and realize how thin I really was and how good I looked, and now I'm old and [I] don't have that shape anymore." *Female in her 30's*

1460 "I don't know what caused me to put [weight on]. I have to blame it on my age, I suppose." *Female, early 60's*

1461 "It seems like you tend to hold onto a little bit more shape as you get a little bit older, but it's not a concern that, like I say, is going to bother me, but I do notice." *Male in his 40's*

1462 "I was probably 21 when it kind of hit me that the actual womanhood took over. The hips went big and all that kind of stuff." *Female, late 20's*

Men discuss growing older

1463 "I notice . . . as I get older, damn, my hair grows in more places than it's supposed to. I think that would be one of my complaints. . . . Just wake up one morning and go, 'Where the hell did that come from?' " *Male, 30ish*

"[Hair] grows everywhere but where you want it." *Male, 40ish*

"Yeah, it's a sad day when your wife pulls a gray hair out of your ear." *Male, mid 30's*

1464 "I think you are finding the normal psychological profile of males. You know, at [age] 63, with a 42 [inch] waist and 38 [inch] chest, a guy can walk down the street with his bald head and think he's looking good. You ask any woman if she gets just a half a pound past a size 6, '*Oh I'm fat, I'm fat!*' I've lived with that . . . [and] that's why I'm single again." *Male, 70ish*

1465 "[Body image] is a powerful dissatisfier in life. . . . That is particularly true for women. I think it's a stronger self-condemning thing for women." *Male in his 50's*

1466 "I'm probably more critical of [overweight] men than I am of [overweight] women. I'm a man myself and I think, 'Well, do something about it.'. . . I can excuse women. . . . They have to go through things which we don't have to deal with. If I'd borne children, . . . what kind of effects would that have on my body? . . . Women have to go through some changes we don't. I can excuse . . . [extra weight] in women more than I can men. I'm pretty critical of men."
Male, early 40's

1467 "For men, what I see with my teenage son is that . . . they are pushed into . . . this attempt to be highly buff. . . . Arnold Schwarzenegger types . . . are really unattainable for most of your average males, even if they lift weights every day." *Female, late 30's*

1468 "My ten-year-old [son] comes in and wants to be a six-pack or an eight-pack . . . and they're supposed to be buff and they're supposed to be this certain height. And he's ten!" *Female, 40ish*

1469 "So many people, especially women, [focus on weight]. . . . And I just think that sometimes we as humans say, 'Oh we need to lose 20 pounds,' and it doesn't matter how much we weigh. . . . [Body weight] is sort of part of our conversation anymore." *Female, mid 60's*

1470 "[My husband has] probably gained more weight than I have since we've been married. But nobody looks at him and sees that he's fat. But he's got a little potbelly. And he's gained a little weight, but it's not the same with a guy. . . . Supposedly it's all right for [men] to get a little potbelly, but for [women] to get a little potbelly, then we're getting fat." *Female, 30's to 40's*

1471 "You . . . tell a woman she's small, . . . that's a good thing for them. They try to say that to me. Well, I don't take it as . . . a . . . compliment."
Male in his 30's

1472 "I don't think that men that are overweight are looked at [negatively] near as much as women are . . . . But honestly, sometimes [men] also seem a lot happier, though. They don't seem to have near the self-image problems that women do. They'll be like, 'Oh yeah I weigh blah, blah, blah, blah, blah.' But they don't care, whereas women are like, 'Oh, I can't look [at the scale].'. . . I do think I've known some men that I think have complexes because they're too short. So I suppose that's their issue: rather than the weight, it's the height."

Female, mid 30's

1473 "I would be more attracted to . . . a female who had a little bit . . . more fat on her. I wouldn't be one to be attracted to someone extremely skinny. . . . I first don't think it's attractive, and second of all, I don't think it's healthy." *Male, early 30's*

1474 "Weight seems to be more of an issue with women than it does with men in most cases. Women don't seem to accept themselves as being overweight maybe as much as men do." *Male, almost 60*

1475 "[My] one son especially . . . has always felt really challenged because he's a little bit smaller. . . . I've kind of watched him and his struggles with it, but I don't think [being short] ever really bothered me. . . . A woman being small is not the same as a man being small." *Female in her 40's*

1476 "Women like me a lot better heavier than they did when I was thin."

Female, mid to late 40's

1477 "I think probably that I react more to women that are heavier than to men. . . . I would say that women are definitely looked at differently than men, more negative, I think." *Female, late 60's*

1478 "I know lots of men that fight with their weight just as much as I do. And the same issues that I fight with, they fight with themselves." *Female, early 40's*

1479 "I look at women that are musclely and I think that's really cool, . . . but [most] women . . . don't want to look like that." *Female, mid 30's*

1480 "I think society is more willing to accept the way men look before they accept the way women look. There's two different standards." *Female, early 40's*

1481 "I didn't realize that the boys are under the same kind of [body image] stress that the girls are, and it's too bad." *Female in her 50's*

1482 "An in-shape, well-built man is intimidating, I think. I feel inferior when I'm around somebody like that. But I also don't like [men] looking like fat slobs either." *Female, early 40's*

1483 "I think society is definitely harder on women. . . . It just seems like that our society is way more picky on how big [women] are." *Female, mid 30's*

1484 "I just feel safer with a guy who's bigger than I am. Maybe it's something that society has just kinda placed with some perfect picture of the protective guy. . . . If I was taller than the guy that I was with, I'd just feel [awkward]. . . . I don't want to seem too powerful." *Female, early 20's*

1485 "I think bulgy muscles everywhere [on women] . . . kind of distracts from their natural beauty." *Male, early 30's*

1486 "I never liked working out in gyms. . . . I'm not a very big guy. I've never liked being around . . . [the] body-builder type. When you're younger too, you're a little more self-conscious about things. I think men are more [self-conscious about a small body type] than women are anyway." *Male in his 30's*

1487 "If you lined up ten guys, from the fittest to the not, I'd pick the not because I couldn't keep up with the fit ones. I couldn't! My husband's got a gut. . . . More for me to love. . . . It's like, 'Hey, you're my electric blanket at night, don't lose it.' But *men.* They need a reality check because they want the Barbie. It's like, *'What?'* They have no brain. I'm sorry." *Female, early 30's*

Gender and body size: Insights from male focus group

1488 "I think what society taught me was that it is a far sadder state for a lady to be looking [heavy] than a man." *Male, mid 30's*

1489 "I would bet nine times out of ten people would say, 'Well, yeah, that's a big guy and that's a really fat gal.' " *Male, 30's to 40's*

1490 "Boys are supposed to get bigger and stronger. And if you have an overweight boy, he's a lineman. Yeah, he's going to be a great football player. You have an overweight girl, it's like, . . . what's she [going to] do when she gets older?" *Male, 30's to 40's*

1491 "And as far as society comparing men and women, it's the same as with gray hair. A man with gray hair is distinguished. A woman with gray hair is an old lady." *Male, 30's to 40's*

1492 "No matter how many ab crunches [I might do], there's no way I'm going to have a six-pack unless I'm drinking it." *Female, early 40's*

1493 "I was looking back at all the pictures of [my mom] and her family, like my great-aunts and great-great [relatives], and I told [my mom], 'You should have showed these to me in high school because I was doomed a long time ago.' There was no way that I was going to be teeny and petite." *Female, mid 30's*

1494 "I'm short. My mom and dad—short. Sister— short. . . . My grandmother on one side of the family was 4'2". So I grew up to be 5'2". I thought, yeah, I've really done something!" *Female, late 40's*

1495 "The fact of life is things aren't even-steven, and I'm a firm believer in genetics and what [role] they play. [Some of my kids are heavy and some aren't, and] they were all raised on the same cooking and everything else, but that's just . . . the ball that life gives you to carry, I guess." *Male in his 60's*

1496 "I have a younger brother. . . . He would eat five times the amount of food that I did. . . . He will eat a whole pie while the rest of the family shares the other one. And he's still not heavy, even though he's in his 50's. I have a daughter-in-law that's . . . skinny as a rail, and she drives me crazy when she comes because she's got to eat five times a day. I can't believe the food she puts down. She'll eat as much in a weekend as I do in a whole week and a half. . . . So that's been my observation, that genetics has got to play somewhat of a role in food and the way it affects your body and your mind . . . because sometimes there's no rhyme or reason how it affects different people." *Male in his 60's*

1497 "I am a product of my genetics and environment. [When] I was younger, I was active, and my environment kept me healthy, . . . [but] as I [got] older and away from my natural environment . . . , genetics took over." *Female, late 20's*

1498 "I am adopted . . . and it seems that the weight runs in the family on my birth mom's side. . . . When I met my birth mom, . . . it was nice to know [where] my genetics had come from." *Female, late 20's*

1499 "My mother-in-law and her . . . sisters are all huge women. So I guess I do feel that heredity has a role in weight. . . . Heavy people do sometimes eat a lot and they get that way. But then sometimes overweight people are given that shape through genes." *Female, mid 30's*

1500 "I'm blessed to have genes so I don't put on weight. . . . I have good friends that I know struggle with weight." *Male, almost 60*

1501 "My dad was one of those who ate anything he wanted at any time he wanted and was very healthy. . . . I am a firm believer that so much of whether we are thin or fat is a genetic thing. I follow somewhat in his footsteps. I've always been able to eat anything that I've wanted and never had any weight trouble." *Male, almost 60*

1502 "I have a sister that's like a beanpole. . . . She's always been smaller than me. And it just irritates me. . . . She cannot gain a pound if her life depended on it. Then there's me. I have to watch what I eat 'cause, man, I can just put [weight] on. . . . It's genetic. It's irritating." *Female, late 20's to early 30's*

1503 "I always wished I had my dad's genes. I mean, he weighed 120 pounds soaking wet. He could eat six candy bars and three dinners and never gain a pound. And I'm a sponge. . . . But that's just the way it is." *Female, early 40's*

1504 "I always wished I was taller. I'd like to lose some weight too, but then I just finally decided that maybe that's me. My grandfather was short and stocky. My mom is short. . . . I just think that's maybe the way we're made. . . . I've kind of maintained the same weight . . . and so I finally said, 'Well, maybe that's what size I'm supposed to be, darn it.' " *Female, 30's to 40's*

1505 "Some of my family members tend to be a little on the heavy side . . . . Maybe that's why I try and watch my weight more, because I know that genetically there is a possibility for [weight gain]." *Female in her 40's*

1506 "My mother's side of the family were all heavy people. . . . My father's side of the family were thin. And I gained more of my mother's genes than I did my dad's. . . . I [also] inherited [my mother's] bat wings." *Female in her 60's*

1507 "I don't have big hips, 'cause I have no hips. That's a pattern passed down from my mom. . . . In fact, when I went to [a family] funeral and my cousin was there, I said, 'Boy, you're built just like me—big top, no hips.' " *Female, mid 40's*

1508 "My husband and my mother could eat a gallon of ice cream and not gain a pound, but I probably could *smell* it and gain a pound. But that's just the way it is. . . . [My mother] weighed 114 pounds her whole life. . . . I think that was genetic, because she ate good." *Female, 70ish*

1509 "[I have a relative who] looks like that pencil. She always . . . eats as much as I do and never bashful about it. . . . Yeah, her metabolism burns it off. Some of us, we gain five pounds by looking at a recipe." *Male, 40's to 50's*

1510 "I just had my last baby and I'm not going to have any more, so I've got to work to get [the weight] off because I don't have an excuse anymore to be fat."

Female in her 30's

1511 "When I got married, my wedding dress was a size 9, . . . but [I] started right in having babies, . . . and that takes its toll on your body." *Female, early 60's*

1512 "My husband is getting a paunch on him. . . . For each pregnancy I have, he gains weight with me. . . . Now we're done having kids and it's time to lose the weight that we've gained." *Female in her 30's*

1513 "I have been currently trying to lose weight. . . . I guess I'm probably more conscientious now ever since I've had children, just because of the general health and the example that I set every day for them." *Female in her 30's*

1514 "I lost 35 pounds being pregnant. I never ate so much food in my entire life. And the doctor was yelling at me. . . . But I am not getting pregnant again to lose weight." *Female, early 40's*

1515 "I've had [multiple pregnancies] and it seems like every child I've had has added pounds on me, and I haven't been able to take them off." *Female, mid 40's*

1516 "With my first child, I gained 55 pounds . . . and, oh, that was awful. And I was fat and a blimp. . . . I gained 15 pounds with [my second child], but it was real easy to get caught back up in the thought that you were fat or gaining weight, and you shouldn't gain that extra pound." *Female, 40ish*

1517 "I have . . . kids. I have stretch marks. Yes, I have a belly. . . . Before I had my kids, I didn't have that belly. I didn't have the flab like I do now."

Female, early 30's

1518 "I was thin until after I had my . . . [children] and then I started gaining weight and I felt so much better. But I just kept gaining. . . . I started gaining weight after having children." *Female, mid 70's*

1519 "After I had each one of my kids, it's always been an issue to get that weight back off . . . : eating more healthy, being more careful." *Female, late 30's*

1520 "I had [several children] and I never lost that extra weight here out front, so it looks like I'm fatter than I am. . . . So I am still carrying [the extra weight]."

Female, mid to late 60's

1521 "Why do we always have the skinny minnies on the commercials? . . . I'm three-quarters of a century old. Why should I worry about 25-year-olds who got their abs? . . . And then they get to the September and October time of their life [and] it's not going to be that way, but that's not in their vision." *Male in his 70's*

1522 "They project images in magazines and . . . on TV that show a guy that's got washboard abs and pecs to die [for], and a woman that's a size . . . 3 with ample breasts and a beautiful body and a beautiful face, and everything is perfect, and so you think, 'Well, this is the way I'm supposed to be. Why do I look the way I do?' I really think that generates a lot of mental unrest in a lot of people trying to get to that level of perfection when they don't realize there's maybe 1 in 10,000 that look like that. . . . We all want to be perfect, but it's not going to be obtainable for some of us common folk." *Male, mid 50's*

1523 "On TV, they're always talking about . . . you have to be physically beautiful. You can be as dumb as a post, but you have to be physically beautiful. But it doesn't bother me. I'm just more amused by it because I know that's superficial." *Male, late 30's*

1524 "I think the body image [promoted by] the media [is] that we should look a certain way, and if we look this way, we will be successful, people will like us, . . . when in fact your health is what you're going to be concerned about [in later years], not whether you can still wear a size 4" *Female, mid to late 40's*

1525 "I went to high school with a girl who . . . has bulimia . . . . I just think that it's so sad that our society is so focused on how our bodies look that people will do anything to have the body that they think they should have."
Female, early 20's

1526 "My ten-year-old [son] comes in and wants to be a six-pack or an eight-pack and you are like, 'What?' . . . They get it off the television and they're supposed to be lifting weights and they're supposed to be buff and they're supposed to be this certain height. And he's ten!" *Female, 40ish*

1527 "I think society and the media just cast out that you have to look this way in order to be somebody. . . . We're supposed to have this certain hair length, and . . . our bodies are supposed to look the same, and . . . you're not supposed to have an inch of fat on your stomach." *Female, mid 20's*

1528 "[The] media . . . does impact the way we think about others . . . [and] the way we think about ourselves. It makes a big difference. That is why they do it. That's why they'll pay a million dollars for an ad in the Super Bowl. You know, it makes a difference." *Female, late 30's*

1529 "I watched a show the other night with my teenage girls and some of their friends. It was talking about how in reality the average size was 14 but how most of the models are all anorexic. . . . The kids were like going, . . . 'Everybody is supposed to look like that,' and 'We're just fat.' And it's like, you know, this show is telling you what they weigh and how . . . they're starving themselves." *Female, 40ish*

1530 "You look at the magazines, and the girls are so pretty and fit, and I worry about my daughter, . . . and she's just two. . . . My first thought is they . . . fix up the picture. . . . It's a fake perception of a real woman." *Female in her 20's*

1531 "The media today, it seems like they try to scare people into anything and everything. I mean, everything from food, how you live, what you do—it's all scare. . . . It's like gossip. You hear a little bit of gossip, and [then] it's the gospel truth." *Female, 70ish*

1532 "I definitely look at magazines all the time and I go, 'Gosh, I wish I had that flat of a stomach'. . . and I invest a lot of money into [magazines], too. . . . I definitely . . . look at magazines and wish that I looked like the girls in the magazine." *Female, early 20's*

1533 "The Victoria's Secret models . . . *starve* themselves. . . . That's where you see every hipbone. . . . These hips [*points to her own*] will never be that much smaller 'cause that's where my bones are." *Female, early 40's*

1534 "This society, there's no question that it distorts . . . women. . . . They show models on TV and it gives people the perception that . . . you've got to look like that. Beautiful. And that is a sad thing in our society that women are portrayed that way. You don't have to be heavily breasted and able to fit in your bikini well to be beautiful." *Male in his 30's*

1535 "It's not sociably accepted to hang out with people that are . . . obese."
Male in his 40's

1536 "The media I think portrays all these skinny ladies. They need to have real-life people." *Female, mid 40's*

1537 "There are some societies who do like overweight bodies and some who like the slim ones." *Male in his 50's*

1538 "People say . . . , 'You're fat because you choose to be fat.' Excuse me. . . . Every day you can't get away from body image. Society doesn't make it easy." *Female in her 40's*

Cosmetic surgery
1539 "I have a [female relative by marriage]. She is a trophy. She's gorgeous. And she's had lots of things done. She's half my age and she's had things put back in place, . . . and she is gorgeous. But to talk to her, I cannot hardly carry a conversation with her. . . . It's just so *about her*." *Female in her 30's*

Income
1540 "We've always been kind of more poor or on a lower income side, . . . and when I was between second and third grade, my dad decided he would go off to [find work in another state] and when he left I guess . . . I didn't do a lot. I missed my dad. So I kind of gained a little bit of weight there and kind of held it ever since." *Male, early 30's*

1541 "Why don't I have more problems with my [short] height? . . . I suppose part of it is that I grew up in a family that was relatively well-to-do. I didn't have problems that way. [Friends] were always in my yard playing. If we took the .22 and went up to [shoot] targets or something, it was my gun, my shells. . . . In other words, I had advantages." *Male, early 80's*

1542 "Let's face it. I'm here today not because of anything I did, but when I was born, my parents happened to be White mid-America, so I'm a White mid-American. I could be an Afghan and be over there hiding in a cave if I had been born over there." *Male, almost 60*

1543 "I think of the clothes that I have now [compared to when I was a kid]. [Growing up], we were lucky if we had one good pair of shoes and one good dress to wear to church. And boy, you changed your clothes the second you came home from school." *Female, late 60's*

"Freshman 15"
1544 "They say your freshman year you gain 15 pounds, basically because you're sedentary. You do your homework and that's about all you have time for. It's pretty true. I think . . . in three years [of college] I gained almost 30 pounds." *Female in her 20's*

1545 "I know my freshman year in college I gained a lot of weight, and they always say you get that Freshman 15. . . . [I was] away from home maybe for the first time and had that freedom to go to a candy machine." *Female, mid 30's*

Community
1546 "There's a pecking order in a community based on how long you've been there. You could . . . become a different person in a different community. . . . It can be hard for someone who has lived in the same place all their life."

Female, late 40's

Chairs

1547 "I have this big friend and I [think] how does she fit in chairs at places like theaters . . . and airlines? . . . And I thought, . . . we are being wheelchair adaptable, maybe we need to be fat adaptable and have things more accessible."

Female, mid 40's

1548 "I have a friend of mine . . . that is very, very large. When you walk into a room with her, she couldn't sit in a lot of chairs. She's told me my bathrooms are too small and they're actually quite large. . . . She hasn't been to a movie in years and years 'cause she can't get to the seats." *Female in her 30's*

1549 "Just looking around the room, you'll look for more sturdy chairs, because how embarrassing that would be to be in a huge group and have the chair collapse? . . . It's probably goofy, but that would just be horrifying to me. So I avoid things that I shouldn't." *Female in her 30's*

Clothes

1550 "[We need] exercises that adapt to fatter people. And it's hard to find clothes to fit. . . . I can't find bras to fit at all, even through the Internet."

Female, mid 40's

1551 "[My daughter and I] went into [a store] to try and find some clothes for her for school. I mean, there just was almost nothing. There just wasn't anything we could even find, as I recall, at that point, let alone have choices in style, unless she went over into the ladies—her quote—'the old ladies' department.' She wasn't ready for that." *Female, 50ish*

1552 "A lot of people get this midriff . . . at our age. . . . And the last size that you can really buy is 43, 44 size of pants. And I'm glad when [I'm] down to 43. When I can get down to 40, then I can go [to] about any store. But you get over the 44, and you have a hard time finding pants. I know." *Male, 70ish*

1553 "I probably have to go into . . . Big and Tall or some fat store to get something off of the rack. . . . I don't like shopping [for clothes]. You can't go into the [local store] 'cause there is nothing for me there." *Female, early 30's*

1554 "When I gained all the weight, there was no place to find clothes. But now there's getting more and more catalogs and magazines [where large people] can find decent clothes." *Female, late 40's*

1555 "I still have all [my] skinny clothes because I'm going to get back into them." *Female, early 40's*

1556 "I've been going more toward Eastern medicine from Western, how the body works, . . . meditation, . . . natural way of dealing [with your body], learning how to breathe right. [With my other doctor, I walked] out of the doctor's office with a prescription pad." *Female, early 40's*

1557 "When I hear a doctor say that to me [I need to lose weight], I want to so bad say, 'You're kidding. I have never looked at myself in the mirror. I don't know this.'" *Female, early 40's*

1558 "The height-weight charts say if you're 5'5" you should weigh *this*. Where did we lose the individuality?" *Female, early 40's*

1559 "When I was about 13, those were in the days when doctors still prescribed amphetamines, . . . and the doctor prescribed amphetamines for me and I lost 45 pounds." *Female, 60ish*

1560 "You stop going to the doctor because you know what they are going to say every time you go, and you still gain weight." *Female 30's to 40's*

1561 "My blood pressure is borderline . . . . That's one of the reasons I decided I had better lose a little weight. . . . You go in for that annual physical thing where you check for colon cancer and prostate and stuff and [the doctor] gets a little ugly with you and says, 'I'm going to force you to do this,' and I think to myself, 'I don't know how you can force anyone to do anything unless you lock them in a room and chain them to the wall.'" *Male, mid 50's*

1562 "There is a [physician] up there in the medical community that I can talk to . . . on the phone. Friendly, I mean, we can visit. We can talk. I mean very friendly, very open. We tease each other. Out in public, that physician will not even acknowledge that I'm there. And I think . . . it's because of my weight. Seriously. It irritates the heck out of me. . . . It's like you know you've got to maintain [a healthy weight], but [doctors] also got to explain it . . . appropriately enough in order for [people] to *want* to lose weight. But if you have a physician say, 'You're too heavy, you've got to lose weight,' well, most [people] will probably think, 'I'm going to flip you the bird, and I'm walking out.' . . . A lot of people . . . won't go to the doctor because of the scale. And the scale is an important part of the physician's office, but it shouldn't be the main focus. And there's a lot of physicians where it is the main focus." *Female, late 40's*

1563 "They say [being fat] is a health risk. . . . So not only do we get it from the media and exercise people, we get it from medicine too, that you've got to be skinny. It probably makes it worse. It probably makes us eat more, because it's so hard to lose weight and . . . sometimes you just . . . give up." *Female, mid 40's*

1564 "I was on that Optifast program that they have [at a regional medical center], which turned out to be really bad for a lot of people. A lot of people . . . [from] that class had gallbladder problems, and I think out of 20 people that were in that class that I went to for six months, there was only one that . . . when they got done with the liquid diet was able to maintain their weight."

Male in his 60's

1565 "Obesity. I feel for those people that struggle and struggle and struggle with that . . . . But there's help out there. . . . Find somebody that's compassionate enough to actually listen to them and not judge them. A lot of doctors . . . these days judge a lot, too. That's not good." *Female, late 40's*

1566 "My orthopedic doctor kept saying, 'You need to lose weight'—wanted to put me on phen-fen. Well, thank goodness I wasn't on phen-fen. I just thought I'll lose weight . . . and that's been two or three years ago. And it always sticks in my mind and I worry about it." *Female, late 60's to early 70's*

1567 "I've had three . . . friends that had gastric bypasses. . . . I think about all the issues that must be underlying the reasons [they overeat]: 'I'm going to eat because then I don't have to worry about certain other things.' . . . The one [friend] I think of specifically, she's in for alcohol treatment, but she's so thrilled that she can buy Tommy Hilfiger. . . . I mean, she truly looks amazing. I'm like, 'Is it worth it? I remember how sick you were.' " *Female, mid 30's*

1568 "[My brother] has health problems with his [extra weight]. I don't have any diabetes. I don't have blood pressure problems, and he has all of it—gout, the whole nine yards. And I feel bad for him. But he really has a hard time trying to diet." *Female, early 40's*

Memorable quotation

1569 "Medical professionals can be so insensitive to a person with weight problems. It's like they are saying, 'Why don't you just diet? Why don't you have any self-control?' . . . He wrote 'obesity' in my chart even though I'd lost 40 pounds. These aren't tears of sadness, they're tears of anger. I got a different doctor." *Female, early 40's*

1570 "One thing that has always been fascinating to me is the psychology that takes place when you lose a bunch of weight rapidly. When I was about 13, . . . a doctor prescribed amphetamines for me. And I lost 45 pounds. . . . When I went back to school, there were people who didn't recognize me. . . . You're changing so much at that point in your life anyway. But I found that I got angry at the positive attention that I got, because I thought, 'I'm the same person inside I was before. How come you're being so nice to me and giving me all this positive attention because I have shed some pounds?' And I had a hard time not letting that [anger] control my emotional behavior." *Female, 60ish*

1571 "When I start losing weight and all of a sudden men start flirting with me, or I have attention drawn on me, I am so uncomfortable. It's like, 'Who's this other person that they are looking at or talking to?' . . . Sometimes when I look in the mirror, I still see the woman that was 250 pounds, even though I am much less than that. I still buy my clothes a size too big. . . . And I realize that weight loss is as much of a mental exercise as it is a physical exercise in changing how we feel about ourselves. . . . I feel comfortable inside myself, but if I'm to look in a mirror at the physical outside of myself, . . . that's where the conflict begins. . . . I still see myself as weighing 250 pounds." *Female, early 40's*

1572 "I know of some women that are very heavy, and my sister is one, and her legs and knees are giving out, but yet mentally, she's unable to go on a diet. . . . My sister's always [had] a lot of depression in her life, and I think that has a lot to do with it." *Female in her 60's*

1573 "[Excess weight is] a mental protection . . . , [but there's a] mental war that's going on in me . . . . [I] need to lose weight to have a long . . . [and] productive life . . . . [For] the first time in my life, . . . I'm just content where I am. . . . I would never be the kind of woman that . . . a husband tells me he doesn't like my haircut, so therefore I would grow my hair long. It'd be like, 'Tough Twinkies. You don't have to fix [the hairstyle] every day.' . . . After . . . turning 40, my mouth came out and a few other things came out, too. . . . I think it's a . . . unity and feeling of pride in myself. But in that unity [is] also figuring out what has to change, too, for the goal of . . . being able to go out and do anything and everything I want to do and not having health concerns."
Female, early 40's

1574 "[My advice to others is to] be yourself and learn who that self is. Take down the pretty boxes and deal with them. My therapist [has given me] an image of a beautiful box that is ornately wrapped [but] it masks ugliness, things like envy, greed, and low self-esteem. If someone irritates you, look first at yourself." *Female, early 40's*

211

1575 "[When] I see [large individuals] that are sitting there just shoveling food in, I think . . . , 'Something must be very radically wrong in your life that you're using food as a pacifier.' " *Female in her 60's*

1576 "[My daughter] had really low self-esteem. But you know the thing I have seen is the losing of the weight has really helped her self-esteem, too. I mean, they just have seem to gone together somehow. More than I wished they did."

Female, 50ish

1577 "I always wanted to appear tough and in control. . . . Once you feel at an early age that you're kind of somewhat dominant, . . . you maintain that degree of persona throughout your life. I know it's important how you feel about yourself because that carries over in how you carry your day-to-day thinking. . . . A lot of [body image] has to do with what you think you get from others. . . . And I hate to think that your confidence or esteem is developed because of what someone else thinks, but quite often you let that happen." *Male, early 40's*

1578 "If you're not secure in yourself, which I was not, it can really make a difference in how you view how others look at you and then how you view yourself, because oftentimes, I'm sure I had a very distorted view of [myself]. At 103 pounds, I did not think I was thin. Emotional things really do play a very strong role [in how you view yourself]." *Female, mid to late 40's*

1579 "[My son's] a big boy and he gets teased because he's a big boy. . . . But he feels bad. He has a really low image of himself, and I have to say it started in third grade, because when he hit that 100-pound mark he was devastated. . . . 'I'm fat.' . . . And I'm starting to wonder if there's too much focus at that 100-pound mark, because there shouldn't be. . . . But for the last couple of years, he is really down on himself because of his size. And he's stout, there's no doubt about it." *Female, early 40's*

1580 "I'm just looking forward to the casket and getting some rest."

Male in his 60's (suffers from arthritis)

1581 "Body image is tough because it goes beyond just how [you] look; it goes into how [you] feel." *Male, early 40's*

Memorable quotation

1582 "I hate the word 'obese.' It just absolutely puts me over the edge. You feel like you're anonymous in some respects." *Female, early 40's*

1583 "I've had three . . . friends that had gastric bypasses. . . . One of them had to go to treatment for alcoholism and another one is having problems with repeated boyfriends . . . that are beating her up . . . . I think about all the issues that must be underlying the reasons [they overeat]: 'I'm going to eat because then I don't have to worry about certain other things.' . . . And they're so thrilled. I mean, they're truly happy, [even though they suffer with] alcoholism or their boyfriend's beating them up. . . . Now they seem so much happier because it's, like, 'I can fit into a size 10.' " *Female, mid 30's*

1584 "[My sister is] so skinny and she's still not happy with herself. Why am I even trying? I will never be that thin. . . . She's so skinny, and she's popular. . . . And come to find out, . . . she was actually anorexic and almost died. . . . So I tied being thin and being skinny with self-fulfillment and that you'll be popular and . . . the world's . . . laying at your feet just because you're skinny. [People are] trying to kill themselves to be thin. Thin doesn't equal happiness."
Female, early 40's

1585 "My mother-in-law is . . . fairly overweight, but . . . I just don't think that it matters what size she is because she seems like she's happy. . . . If [large individuals] carry themselves confident and they portray themselves as happy with themselves, then I'll probably think that . . . [and] have that same attitude about them. . . . I think when somebody is so unhappy with [themselves] and they voice it all the time that you kind of get the opinion, 'Yeah, probably you should do something different if you're that unhappy.' " *Female, mid 20's*

1586 "I had an aunt . . . who was severely obese. . . . And my aunt was the coolest. I mean, she had a great sense of humor and she was a wonderful, wonderful person. But I'll be honest. I see how much [being overweight] must hurt [people] and how they struggle . . . , because I have yet to meet any people that are really overweight that . . . are happy. . . . [My aunt] probably actually was [happier] than any [overweight person] I ever knew." *Female, mid 30's*

1587 "I just think that it's so sad that our society is so focused on how our bodies look that people will do anything to have the body that they think they should have. . . . I mean, everyone's guilty of it, including myself. . . . Be happy with the way you are, if you're healthy. . . . And I know the root of it is not to please yourself, but to please others. . . . I just think it's really sad that body image has that much an influence on your everyday life." *Female, early 20's*

1588 "I've got pictures of [me at] all sizes and I did look better when I was slimmer, [but] I can't say that I was a happier person." *Female, early 60's*

213

1589 "At 25, would I look at somebody who was my size with disgust? You bet. At 35 plus, that view is much different. Now I can look at somebody and say, 'Damn, you got a lot of crap going on in your life.' . . . Being on the receiving end of the big-guy story, I see things much differently now." *Male, mid 30's*

1590 "My sister is . . . maybe twice as big as what I am. But it's the normal size inside that's coming out. And we teased her a lot when she was growing up and I don't know when it changed. It was probably when I got into high school that I realized that [there] really wasn't anything that she could do about [her body type], and I changed my attitude towards [her]." *Female in her 30's*

1591 "As I've gotten older, [striving for a perfect body] kind of seems irrelevant anymore. It's not my goal to be Mr. Universe. I don't care as much. . . . My wife and my kids are what are important. I don't really focus on me as much, I guess. . . . Kids are very self-centered. When I was a kid I was self-centered and kind of indestructible, I guess. . . . Teenage boys, at least a lot of them, go through that phase where they think they're ten feet tall and bulletproof in a way. And I was like that when I was a kid and the world kind of revolves around you and your friends. . . . [As you age], you become a lot less judgmental about people. . . . So I think that you just learn that the world is a lot different than what it was when you were a kid. And that's definitely been a factor in my life that I've changed a lot." *Male in his 30's*

1592 "I wasn't always overweight. . . . As a teenager, . . . I would look at people and go, 'Uh, *she's* overweight.' But as I got older, it's like it doesn't make any difference to me. . . . But I will truly admit that when I was younger, yeah, I mean it was *very* important, this body." *Female, late 40's*

1593 "Before I was married . . . [when I was with other] guys, . . . it was always who could get the best beach muscles, the biceps, the six-pack. And since I've been married, I haven't been too worried about that as much anymore. . . . It just seems less important now that I'm not worried about chasing after girls. . . . I'm not as worried about [muscularity]." *Male in his 20's*

1594 "I'm happy with a higher goal weight than I would have been 20 years ago. I mean, I'm more realistic and my body is telling me, 'You don't need to be down there [that thin].' " *Female, early 60's*

1595 "When I was a kid, there were two real, real heavy ladies in our community and I know we all just . . . laughed about it, . . . but then when I got older, . . . [I] realized they didn't want to be that way." *Female, mid 70's*

1596 "I can tell that I am getting a little bit heavier, not drastic, but just enough that [I notice]. It's funny how we as humans kind of go at this thing: 'Well, [my extra weight] is not that bad yet. Maybe I don't have to worry about it yet.' . . . I'm a little self-conscious about gaining weight. If [you're] going to put on a swimsuit and jump in the pool, you don't want to have your sides hanging over your swimsuit. But I was in the swimming pool this winter with my daughter, and I really didn't think much about it. . . . When I was in high school, I know that it was very important to be in good shape. You wanted to be muscular. . . . But as far as now, I think I probably worry a lot less [about how I look] than I did when I was in high school." *Male in his 30's*

1597 "I'm okay with where I am [with my weight] because I can do the things I want to do, and for me, at this point in my life, that's a victory. I decided that maybe I'm not going to get down to the weight I was before I had [several] kids. I'm definitely not going to." *Female, 60ish*

Military training and body image
One woman's experience

1598 "I'd love to look like Cindy Crawford. It is not going to happen. . . . Basic training [for the military] was a huge thing for me because I think before I always thought I can lose more weight. I can lose more weight. And I was very, very physically active . . . and I came out of [basic] weighing like 180 pounds. . . . I'm in really, really good shape and my body fat percentage was down pretty low and I thought, 'Okay . . . , I'm just not going to be a real tiny petite person.' . . . And so, that was huge . . . . When I look at the charts, I'm overweight right now . . . but I don't think badly of myself. But like I said, basic training was a huge eye-opener. . . . I was in really good shape and felt really good and I was way heavier than I thought I was supposed to be. . . . [My mother] says if [my sister and I] would have been in a different time period, [men] would have really went after us because we're good at having babies and all that stuff and I'm like, yeah, yeah, yeah—I'd still rather look like Cindy Crawford." *Female, mid 30's*

215

1599 "When I start losing weight, and all of a sudden men start flirting with me, or I have attention drawn on me, I am so uncomfortable. It's like, 'Who's this other person that they are looking at or talking to?'. . . And sometimes the weight is comfortable. It's a good shield to have between yourself and other people. . . . [In terms of this shield], I'm single [and] I have a hard time if someone's attracted to me. I want them to be attracted to my personality, not to what I physically look like. And so I feel like having that weight, he can't possibly be attracted to me physically, so it *has* to be my personality or my humor or something else that he's attracted to or not attracted to. . . . [Extra body weight] is a mental protection." *Female, early 40's*

1600 "I think sometimes there's some protective mechanism in there [when people overeat]. 'I'm going to eat because then I don't have to worry about certain other things.' " *Female, mid 30's*

1601 "[Excess weight is] a mental protection . . . [but there's a] mental war that's going on in me . . . . [I] need to lose weight to have a long . . . [and] productive life. . . . For the first time in my life . . . I'm just content where I am. I think it's . . . a unity and feeling of pride in myself. But in that unity [is] also figuring out what has to change, too, for the goal of . . . being able to go out and do anything and everything I want to do and not having health concerns."

Female, early 40's

1602 "I have known people who have been heavy and then they've lost weight and they kind of go off the deep end, so to speak. I mean, they don't know how to handle that maybe. Sometimes it becomes a stressful thing in their marriage because all of a sudden they are feeling a little more physically attractive and so maybe they become a little more flirtatious. And there's a difference; a fat woman can flirt —using that term very loosely—and a thin woman can flirt, and it would be considered entirely differently, at least from my experience. . . . When I was thin, I was, for the lack of a better term, hit on a lot . . . . I wasn't any great goddess . . . . I've been a pretty open person and . . . perhaps this was misinterpreted. . . . I think I thought what I need to do is make myself less attractive, [so I started gaining weight]." *Female, mid to late 40's*

1603 "My second husband . . . didn't handle heaviness at all. . . . [My] being pregnant was very unappealing to him and he was very offish with me for a good five years. And I think that also played a point . . . when I began to gain weight. . . . I didn't care if I was less desirable to him. . . . I think I wanted to punish him in some ways. . . . It was kind of like it was a snowball and it gained momentum and just got bigger, and so did I." *Female, mid to late 40's*

1604 "I tried . . . [a computer] singles line for a month. And one of my friends, she tried it. And she gets like 185 hits a day, but she's like a Barbie doll. . . . Well, I tried it and I had no picture on there, and . . . these guys . . . said, 'Hey, you sound really interesting. Send me a picture.'. . . I sent it and do you think any of those guys wrote back? [*voice quivers*] Talk about not feeling good about yourself [*starts to cry*]. . . . It's hard. I give thanks for the fact that I get the rewards from [my work], . . . and I'm achieving, . . . but I [don't] have a boyfriend or the husband who appreciates me. . . . So when people think, 'Well, I'm big, I'm never going to get somebody,' you know what? I'm thin and I'm not getting anyone either. And it's hard." *Female, late 20's*

1605 "If you're a short guy, it's a little odd trying to find women to date sometimes. Most women generally want somebody tall, dark, and handsome. . . . I think that's an evolutionary thing, too. . . . Women are, from a reproductive standpoint, attracted to power resources, security, somebody [that] can protect them [and their] offspring. . . . I hear the same things from women that are really tall. Obviously, most men aren't comfortable with that. . . . Having a woman that is bigger than you could be threatening." *Male in his 30's*

1606 "I'm probably in the best shape I've been . . . since I was a teenager. . . . I'm getting old, and I'm not married. It's one of those deals where you try to stay in the best shape you can because opportunities are dwindling." *Male in his 30's*

1607 "I always wanted to marry somebody taller than me. . . . I would want my kids to have some height. . . . But I think when you are younger, you always picture this tall, dark, handsome guy." *Female in her 20's*

1608 "In high school, there was this one girl that really liked me. . . . We were good friends and she wanted more than that. And she was quite heavy set, and heavy-set people just have never really excited me. I mean, I can be friends with them . . . but when I was looking for someone to spend my life with, I shied away from overweight people." *Male, early 50's*

1609 "I was [older] when I got married and so I had the chance to go from 'I just want a guy that's good looking' to 'I just want a guy.'" *Female, mid 40's*

1610 "As I looked for a mate, . . . body shape and composition was very important to me. And that's just brutally honest." *Male, almost 50*

1611 "When I was in high school, I always felt good about [my body image]. I know that's one of the reasons I have my husband." *Female, late 20's*

1612 "When you get on the scales [and] you see what you weigh, . . . you know you shouldn't be that heavy. You can see me, I'm quite a bit overweight. I know I need to do something. I want to be around to see my grandkids."

Male in his 40's

1613 "I have a brother-in-law that I just love to death [and] he's fairly heavy. . . . I really wish [he] could lose the weight because I realize the health risks involved, and that scares me. When you see people that are heavy like that, you know that their incidence of heart attack and stroke and everything increases so much, and so, just for their well-being, you wish that they could somehow reduce [their weight]." *Female in her 40's*

1614 "I've always known that my mother's weight was a factor in what I would allow myself to become. And not because I didn't love my mother, because I did, but just because of the difficulties I saw her go through." *Female in her 40's*

1615 "I was really starting to feel the weight. It wasn't so much feeling uncomfortable with myself as the way I felt. The shortness of breath, some of the warning signs of possible diabetes and some different things that, you think like, 'If I don't get a hold of this thing now, it's going to be too late. And I'm really going to pay the price.' And I think different bodies react differently. But mine is not comfortable being so overweight. And it was screaming at me to do something." *Female in her 30's*

1616 "[My mother] was heavy from the time I can remember. . . . It made physical activity very, very difficult, and I don't want to be in that situation. . . . [She struggled with] different things. Diabetes for one thing . . . . And I've got a sister that has adult-onset diabetes and, again, she's heavy. And so to me, that's a really good reason to not let your weight get out of hand . . . . , realizing that [diabetes] is a very good possibility." *Female in her 40's*

1617 "Just because somebody's thin, . . . I don't always think that they look the greatest. I think that somebody that looks healthy and clean and their clothes fit, whether they take a size 6 or the size 14, that doesn't bother me."

Female, mid 60's

1618 "I've never made any attempt to change [my weight], although I tried phen-fen because it seemed easy, but I've never really made any major attempts, because [my extra body weight] doesn't really bother me. I'm more worried about the physical problems down the line." *Male, late 30's*

218

1619 "Sometimes [when I'm battling my weight], I have to say . . . , 'It's not how you look, it's for your health.'. . . [When I was younger], I tied being thin and being skinny with self-fulfillment." *Female, early 40's*

1620 "[When it comes to my body weight], there is a battle there. And it's . . . not won by one or two months of work. . . . It's an everyday battle to stay healthy." *Female, late 20's*

1621 "I have a brother who has rheumatoid arthritis. . . . He's about 200 pounds overweight, . . . and it is very detrimental to his health. And I just swear to myself that I am not going to end up in that place." *Female, early 40's*

1622 "Everybody's not the same size and there's always going to be some flaws in everybody. . . . I just have the attitude that [says] live each day as best you can, as happy as you can, and try to be as healthy as you can, and let each and every person do the same thing." *Female in her 60's*

Humorous sidenote

1623 "I stand erect, and I walk straight, and so I feel good about that. I have to say I get that from my mother. My dad . . . tended to shuffle his feet and she'd say [to him], 'You straighten up and stop that, because you're walking like an old man.' And here he was 90. And we laughed about that." *Female, mid 60's*

Chapter Four

CONNECTIONS

Physical Activity ✳ Food and Eating ✳ Body Image

> *Good health is physical, mental, social and spiritual well-being.*
>
> Definition of good health from Wellness IN the Rockies

1624 "Whenever I had a job [where] I was physically active, . . . [food] was more enjoyable to eat because you were hungry." *Male in his 30's*

1625 "I am really a junkie for sweets, so I justify my exercising. If I go and ride my bike and I go for a walk, then I can eat that hot fudge sundae. And then I have a diet pop so I can eat." *Female in her 50's*

1626 "We've got to keep well fed because if you don't, you're going to get sick and then you won't be able to keep in shape. And then . . . you will look at yourself as being out of shape and that . . . affects you mentally, . . . which can cause you either to overeat or not eat enough. And the cycle just continues. It just goes downhill." *Male, early 50's*

1627 "When you're raised on a farm, I think you eat heavy foods. You eat three heavy meals. You work hard . . . . And when you got to a physical environment that you don't work as hard, . . . three heavy meals with heavy foods isn't as acceptable as it was when you were burning the 6,000 calories a day."

Male in his 50's

1628 "[In the service] as a combatant, it was important to be large and strong, so . . . that was part of the game plan; you worked out, you drank raw eggs for breakfast. . . . And then getting out of the service, physical activity, that tapers off, but you still are on this hunger mode all the time. . . . And I found it was impossible to maintain that activity level in the real world." *Male, mid 30's*

1629 "I've actually been thinking about . . . the secret to life. And it's variety and moderation. Food and fitness, physical activity; everything has to deal with variety and moderation." *Male in his 20's*

1630 "I think that having a program that is livable is important, both with the dieting and with the exercise; . . . if you're not enjoying them, it's pretty tough to stick with it." *Male in his 40's*

1631 "[Playing football], I was lifting weights and training from 12 till six o'clock at night. On that schedule, . . . I was always hungry." *Male in his 20's*

1632 "I wouldn't change a thing about my life. I think all men experience certain challenges that made [them] a better person. The only thing I would do is probably right after I left home . . . was to get into a habit of not only eating healthy but also getting out and doing [physical activity]." *Male, early 30's*

1633 "We were in such a level of physical and mental conditioning [during military basic training], you looked forward to going to the chow hall and you ate everything they gave you." *Male, mid 50's*

1634 "I always struggled to get to the . . . weight that I wanted to be. Like, my [football] playing weight . . . goal was always about 205, and I could never break about 198. . . . I tried like crazy, . . . eating and lifting hard and taking supplements, . . . peanut butter and jelly sandwiches five, six times a day. . . . I just couldn't figure out why it didn't work for me." *Male in his 20's*

1635 "I'm trying to get to where I don't eat as much because I'm not as active as I used to be. That's pretty common sense as far as maintaining weight, that the two things that determine weight is how much you eat and how much you burn off." *Male, almost 60*

1636 "You'd play football and you'd bulk up and you'd then go into wrestling season and you'd literally starve yourself to death." *Male, almost 50*

1637 "There are some foods out there that I really enjoy, and I am a hearty eater. . . . That's why I have to force myself to exercise. I like food so much."

Male in his 30's

1638 "You've got to just decide, . . .'I'm going to the gym and I'm putting that as a priority.' Or, 'I'm going to eat better and that's my priority. . . . I'm not going to skip breakfast.'. . . So [you] have to set a goal." *Female, mid 60's*

1639 "I know for a fact that if I limit what I eat and if I exercise more, it's a definite decrease in weight, and it's also an increase in energy." *Male in his 50's*

1640 "I try to think about everything that I put in [my mouth] . . . , because I figure if I eat more, then I have to exercise more." *Female in her 30's*

1641 "[After high school], I suddenly became a father. I tried to complete school and work at the same time. And it's like I was distracted [from healthy eating and physical activity]. . . . Now I want to get back on track."

Male, early 30's

1642 "Back when I was . . . playing soccer so much, I didn't have to worry about what I ate. . . . Now I really have to watch what I eat or I'll gain a lot of weight."

Male in his 30's

1643 "Weight is a very personal thing. To me, it's right up there with religion. And so when you're unconsciously measuring yourself against others, . . . that voice isn't quieted in your mind. So, I would just rather do the physical exercise on my own." *Female, early 40's*

1644 "I never liked working out in gyms. . . . The chickies . . . were all running around after these bodybuilder guys and you'd just kind of go, 'Well, what am I doing here? I think I'll go have a beer.' " *Male in his 30's*

1645 "By my senior year of high school, . . . I got to the point where I really wasn't interested in [sports]. . . . It wasn't so much *laziness*; it was that I didn't feel good enough about myself. . . . It was . . . being with . . . boyfriends that didn't make you feel good about yourself." *Female, mid 20's*

1646 "When I went to the college gym and I was around all the little hard-body girls who looked like little supermodels out of magazines, . . . I always was comparing myself to them, and I didn't feel as good when I worked out because I didn't see myself looking like them. Little did I know that I don't have to look like them." *Female, mid 20's*

1647 "I've always been pretty proud of my physical development . . . even though I was fairly short. I've always lifted [weights] and been in pretty good shape. . . . I was pretty proud of it and showed it off whenever I could, . . . wearing tank tops, chasing chicks." *Male, almost 50*

1648 "I know I'm overweight, no question about it. . . . I'm conscious about it, but I don't think about it much during the day. . . . I like the fact that I'm strong, that I'm muscular, and I know that's going to be a part of my weight. . . . If I were to be a lot smaller, I wouldn't have the strength I do to do some of the things I like." *Female, 40ish*

1649 "I seem to gain more weight when I exercise hard . . . . When I was running on a track team, I got up . . . [to] the heaviest I've ever [been] and I was *really* in shape at that time." *Male, mid 70's*

1650 "In the process of chemotherapy, it paralyzed my diaphragm so breathing is very difficult for me now and I get real frustrated in the winter because I can't even get outside when it is cold. . . . Cold weather I can't handle, real hot weather I can't handle, wind I can't handle. Trying to walk doesn't work. . . . So I sit at home and eat more and get fatter." *Female, mid to late 60's*

1651 "I have always been able to do things physically as compared to people I've known where it's very difficult. . . . I can imagine that if I were excessively overweight . . . that it would be very frustrating, and I've not had that kind of an experience." *Female, late 40's*

1652 "When I was in junior high, . . . all the other kids thought that because I was heavy that I couldn't participate in these activities, but in PE, . . . I *creamed* all those skinny girls. And it made me feel really good about myself."

Female, late 20's

1653 "[My wife's] had [several] kids, and she's still fighting with her weight. And she is not happy with the way she looks. A lot of it's changing because she's exercising, . . . and she's a lot happier now that she's exercising." *Male in his 30's*

1654 "[Physical activity in my life is] positive in the fact that it's good for me, but it's negative in the fact that I feel like I have to do it to . . . be the ideal shape and size that needs to be." *Female, late 20's*

1655 "I'm a kind of body-image person. . . . If I don't get my exercise, . . . I feel kind of crummy." *Male, early 40's*

1656 "I've been fairly inactive all winter long and so it just seems like the calories kind of pack on and I tend to gain a little bit of extra weight."

Female in her 40's

1657 "As far as my body image, because . . . I was athletic, . . . I was good at sports . . . . So that definitely influenced the way I perceive myself. And I felt good about my body image." *Male in his 30's*

1658 "I never got involved in weight lifting . . . because of my size. I'm not very big, so it doesn't take too many jokes [to make me quit]." *Male in his 30's*

1659 "I've been inactive, and I guess I enjoy more being active. . . . Your work isn't quite as hard after you get in shape. . . . I try to . . . keep my weight to a level where I feel comfortable. . . . It's hard to work when you really have a lot of weight on you." *Male, early 60's*

1660 "[When I was about eight, physical activity] generally made me tired, so I didn't do it. . . . But that's when I gained all my weight in a matter of two years." *Male, late 30's*

1661 "I'm at peace with [my weight]. . . . I'm healthy, and . . . I'm at peace with that. It's not a fight with food." *Female, late 40's*

1662 "Show by example that you enjoy life. You enjoy food. You enjoy people of all shapes. And be positive to other people. Be happy. Talk kindly about everybody. Our children are watching us all the time." *Female, early 60's*

1663 "Pouring four or five teaspoons of sugar in . . . coffee when you're overweight is, . . . well, it's nonsense. . . . It's abuse of your body. . . . I mean, they know what causes [obesity]. It's just like smoking. . . . [People] are told it can cause lung cancer and they still do it. So I don't understand it."

Male, early 60's

1664 "One day [my daughter] said, 'Mom, when you grew up, were there heavy girls in school?' and I said no. I could think of one. And I do believe it is [because] we didn't have the pop and the chips and all those kinds of things."

Female in her 50's

1665 "I went through high school . . . and I got teased a lot being so thin. . . . I didn't worry about what I ate because it . . . didn't have any effect on me as to gaining weight. I guess I could say that I could eat all the ice cream in the world." *Male, 60ish*

1666 "Once you get fat, it's nearly impossible to get rid of it. . . . Once it's there, it doesn't go away . . . . And some [of my weight gain came from] bad eating habits, certainly." *Male, late 30's*

1667 "I thought that I needed to stay super, super skinny to [please] the person I was dating. . . . I wasn't eating healthy. . . . And I think now . . . I . . . realize what healthy eating is and what you can do to stay healthy. . . . I guess it's getting older and getting wiser." *Female, mid 20's*

1668 "I think once I stopped worrying about how much I weighed and whether or not I was a hard body and just looked like all the models in the magazines, I think I was able to enjoy what I ate more, versus when I was so consumed about that." *Female, mid 20's*

1669 "We are bombarded that we have to look a certain way, and when I gave up thinking [like that], . . . I let go of the anorexia, I let go of the bulimia. And it's like an alcoholic. I was addicted to that thought of food. I needed to have it. I needed [the control over food] to make me feel good." *Female, late 40's*

1670 "The White, U.S. world has a real problem trying to accept their fatness because of all the media that you see. . . . And in fact, I think . . . [the media's focus on body image] makes us fatter because we get more nervous and eat more." *Female, mid 40's*

1671 "I remember when I was in junior high when I was growing up . . . I could eat like a horse and . . . never ever gain anything. And I remember my grandma would come through and say, 'Well, you can't eat like that when you get older or you'll be fat.' " *Female, mid 20's*

1672 "[Sometimes] you see obese people and they just sit down and eat and eat and eat. . . . People that are . . . overweight . . . say they get tired easy. They wear out because they're carrying all that extra weight." *Male, early 60's*

1673 "I was probably 21 when it kind of hit me that the actual womanhood took over, . . . the realization that food wasn't something you could consume at your own pace, that it . . . needed to be monitored." *Female, late 20's*

Love-hate relationship with food

1674 "It's a love-hate relationship [with food]. . . . I love food, but I hate how it makes me look." *Female in her 40's*

1675 "You are what you eat. Your [physical] activities definitely have a factor on you. How you think of yourself definitely matters, too. And how you look at other people matters. It's just one of those things that's intertwined with you." *Male in his 40's*

1676 "I should be healthier, but I think that a lot of times I don't diet or exercise . . . for myself but for others. And I think that it would make me feel a lot better about myself in so many ways if I would do it for myself and not other people."

Female, early 20's

1677 "As I've gotten older, I've been more aware of physical activity and the way I eat and the way I look . . . because . . . I don't want to be in a nursing home. So it's made me really, really aware of trying to do things so that I don't just sit and then . . . my bones crumble." *Female, mid 60's*

1678 "I think a lot of people misunderstand that just because you may look healthy doesn't mean that you *are* healthy. . . . If somebody's body weight is heavy, then [people] think that person must overeat. Well, that's not always the case. . . . I'm still built about the same . . . [as] I was when I was really physically in good shape. But I don't eat the way people probably think I do. I eat whatever I want. . . . I like to go to McDonald's . . . . Probably my weakness is I like sweets and salty things." *Male in his 30's*

1679 "Everybody is different, and what works for some doesn't work for everybody. And maybe it will take each one of us to give our own testimony of what we need to do to maintain [good health]. And it's just going to be a self-commitment thing, [because] a lot of the answers are already there."

Male in his 50's

1680 "I'm probably the only postmenopausal woman here. . . . Something . . . started [to change] maybe about four years ago. My body chemistry changed; my metabolism changed; my appetite changed. . . . And I'm at a point now where I can look at the hill above my house and [say], 'I can go there.' . . . That barrier [of] . . . I've gotta avoid [physical activity] . . . has left me. . . . I look for small meals that I can get at the restaurant. I can go into just about any store and buy something off of the rack 'cause most of the places have 1X or 2X or 3X, but [I'm] not looking for those impossible sizes that go beyond that. Those changes make it a lot easier to live with myself. . . . I don't want to do the paper bag on my head thing [when I] look in the mirror." *Female, 60ish*

1681 "[One person I know] is in that situation where she sits down and eats because she worries about her health and her kids and not doing enough exercise. And [she is] scared to go out in public. . . . It keeps going around in a circle. Her health goes downhill, her self-image goes downhill, and then it affects her mentally. . . . But it can go the other way, too. If . . . you've kept yourself well fed with the proper nutrition, you exercise enough, your self-image is good, which in turn feeds your body image. You feel good about yourself and then you're more alert and attentive and on the ball."

Male, early 50's

1682 "There are so many heavy people now . . . . They just come home and sit in front of the TV or play TV games. . . . They're couch potatoes and they're very, very inactive. And not only that, the fast food business is doing a great business. . . . I think this is where it has changed, because you didn't see as many heavy people back in the 1930s, '40s, and '50s." *Female in her 60's*

1683 "Usually when I am walking or bicycling or doing those things, I'm trying to diet [and lose weight]. And so, I guess I would say maybe that puts a negative light on [physical activity]. . . . I'm doing it because I have to." *Female, mid 40's*

1684 "The media says you need to be skinny, and then exercise people come and say you need to exercise, and so it's kind of like this guilt trip on you. . . . They say [being fat] is a health risk, too. . . . It probably makes it worse. It probably makes us eat more because it's so hard to lose weight and so hard to exercise. Sometimes you just . . . give up." *Female, mid 40's*

1685 "I think I know that everybody is different and no matter what you do you can never look like somebody else because everyone is unique in their own way. . . . You'll never achieve the image of yourself that you're trying to get without eating correctly or having some kind of fitness." *Male, early 30's*

1686 "Being in sports and being physically active, . . . you've seen how you can feel, . . . and you've always kind of strived to be that way. . . . Then . . . it's so easy . . . not to do anything and become heavy. . . . It takes work to keep your body healthy. I mean, it's nice to sit down and read papers and eat all day long. . . . I mean, it's easy to sit there . . . and not do anything." *Male, early 60's*

1687 "This is going to be your body and you want it to be healthy. So the eating and the physical activity should be to make you feel better. It shouldn't be to make you fit into a size 8 or a size 6. If you feel good and you can do all the things that you want to do, then that's what you're supposed to be doing it for."

Female, mid 30's

1688 "I have a stepdaughter that's fairly heavy for her age. I see her struggles. . . . I can't say, 'You're not going to eat this' and 'We're going to go run now,' and know sooner or later it will click. With a good physical activity regimen and diet control, her extra weight would be gone. But right now, she's dealing with all those problems of being overweight. And there is a solution, but you can't force [her] into that solution." *Male, early 40's*

1689 "[When I was training for a marathon], physically I was very active. I looked really good. I felt really good. I could do what I wanted. I could eat what I wanted. . . . That's when I think I was at my peak physically. But I don't know if I'd say emotionally, 'cause I was also dating someone, and you go through that roller coaster [ride]." *Female in her 20's*

1690 "I'm one of the guys that [has] no physical control relative to eating things. So I have to fill in the other side of the equation, which is I just have to get enough exercise so I stay in weight and feel good about myself." *Male in his 50's*

1691 "If you live healthy and you exercise, you should be happy with who you are because everybody is different. . . . With exercise, there's many things that it can help overcome physically, emotionally, and mentally. It's a good tool to use to balance your life. . . . And then the body image, . . . if that's healthy, then you're going to be happier. . . . I think [exercise and healthy eating] elevate your self-worth . . . . Someone can withstand the challenges they face, and [they] may not have the illnesses they would otherwise have if they didn't take better care of themselves." *Female in her 30's*

1692 "I really do try to eat most of the time things that are more nutritious, and I do try to get exercise because I think that's the only way you're going to stay healthy. And I think we have to be responsible for our own health. . . . [Physical activity, food and eating, and body image] are kind of a good part of who I am. . . . I just think we have to always work hard to stay healthy. I think that's an ongoing thing. It's something we need to always work at. Anything worth having is worth working at." *Female, 50ish*

Memorable quotation

1693 "I think a lot of people misunderstand that just because you may look healthy doesn't mean that you *are* healthy." *Male in his 30's*

1694 "One thing that I have always said [is], 'If you don't have your health, you don't have nothing.'. . . And if you got your health, you can face life and go on and do a lot of things. . . . So we really need to as a nation [put a priority on health] education, . . . so everybody has a good chance to have a good healthful life." *Male, 70ish*

1695 "I went to [college] and [the nutrition class] and college algebra had the two highest levels of failure. . . . So I got a pretty good knowledge of what's all involved with [nutrition]. The [foods] which are recommended for your body intake are real because your body has certain needs and demands for either building or maintaining . . . . We know about them, but quite often we don't [follow good nutrition principles]. Well, today I'll do this, and then tomorrow, I'll start doing [something better]." *Male, early 40's*

1696 "People say, 'Oh, we can't eat bananas because they're fattening.' And I say, 'Yes, but look at it this way: a half a banana, then you're getting the potassium that you need.' . . . And they don't know that. . . . They just look at a magazine, and it says, 'I lost 20 pounds in six weeks.' They're looking at that and they don't look at what that's going to do down the road for them. . . . I just think that we need to be more educated in the nutritional things."

Female, mid 60's

1697 "My goal now is to help my kids develop a healthy lifestyle. I'm going to influence that, but they are going to make . . . the choices themselves. . . . And I definitely see myself influencing my kids with food . . . [and] trying to guide them in the things that they eat and how much they eat. . . . There's a lot of good and bad choices that we make as humans. And certainly food and physical activity tie into two of them. And perception of others or your own body, if you perceive yourself as having a bad body type, that can be hard on your self-image. So, I think that's something that I will pass on to my kids, to make sure that they're confident in who they are no matter what their body type is . . . . The same with physical activity. I think it's important that we teach kids the importance of exercise . . . because it will help their health in the future. There are a lot of kids that are so-called couch potatoes that aren't physically active."

Male in his 30's

1698 "As an adult, I have had friends that struggle [because] they were excessively overweight. . . . I have had experiences with people who were anorexic. So I've seen both sides. . . . I . . . think [it's] . . . important . . . [to] recognize . . . the family structures that you as an individual are going to have to deal with. . . . High blood pressure has not been an issue [in my family], and yet, in my husband's family, that is very much a pattern." *Female, late 40's*

1699 "A lot of what you read and hear influences the way you feel about food."
Male in his 50's

1700 "I worry about my [kids] .... I wonder in our schools and our communities how good a job we do teaching ... people how to eat.... They sure as heck didn't do it with me when I was growing up.... In this little town alone, we have more fast food restaurants than I've ever seen in a small community, and that's what we eat. That's what our kids eat." *Male, 30's to 40's*

1701 "I took this course in wellness [in high school]. It [was a] very well-rounded approach, not just to eating, but to physical activity. And I had a mind-set then [that] I was doing the activities and it was actually starting to work. And I was thinking, 'Gee, if I can take this course about three more times, I might have a life habit.' " *Male, early 30's*

1702 "If ... younger people can ... realize what's in store for them, maybe they can learn by our mistakes.... When you're 18, you think you're invincible.... You don't give a darn about what's happening when you're 40 or 50. You don't. Maybe some of those kids could look a little further down the road and have a little anticipation of what problems could arise." *Male, 40's to 50's*

1703 "Let's get people educated.... I think once you start to educate yourself ... [about] feeling good about yourself and feeling good about what you eat and having good nutrition and getting into a good physical activity program, ... I think once people start learning about that, they'll understand stuff so much more and they won't have such negative attitudes." *Female, mid 20's*

1704 "[I] would have given anything when I was a kid to have had more of the physical education on conditioning.... I fumbled through .... Just because of size, I made the football team. And that was a rude awakening to go from just kind of being big to trying to be big and in shape.... [Schools need] physical education teachers rather than coaches who are pretending." *Male, 70ish*

Creating a community attitude

1705 " I just like the idea ... as a community, we [can] create a community attitude. It just really bothers me when parents say there's nothing for kids to do here, and then I'm a parent who can't even sit down and eat dinner with my kids 'cause they're so busy.... [Staying physically active] is a matter of what you choose, and it doesn't matter if you're seven years old or 50 years old."
Male, 30's to 40's

233

1706 "You are what you eat. Your [physical] activities definitely have a factor on you. How you think of yourself definitely matters, too. And how you look at other people matters. It's just one of those things that's intertwined with you. It's kind of like religion, almost. You're intertwined with your religion and how you feel about things. It's the same way with [physical activity, food and eating, and body image]. I mean, it's a part of you." *Male in his 40's*

1707 "Everybody has different strong points and weak points, things we do well and things we do poorly, but we all eat about the same. So, when you sit down and eat with somebody, you're both at the same talent level. One guy isn't better than the other and then you can talk on the same level. . . . Sometimes I think that's kind of the idea in the Bible that . . . [eating is] a place where you can really share." *Male, almost 60*

1708 "What we are really talking about here is health in general, and there's a spiritual aspect to health we haven't covered." *Male, almost 60*

1709 "What I think is unpleasant [is] when I get to my car . . . to find out that I don't have my key in my pocket, and I have to walk back to the house, up the steps . . . . You know, sometimes God's orchestration . . . is the perfect timing for what I was supposed to be doing." *Female, mid to late 60's (has limited mobility)*

1710 "To me, food is a gift from God. He blessed us with all these different foods that we can eat, and it's up to us to use judgment on how we eat it."

Male in his 30's

1711 "I love to walk . . . . It's my prayer time." *Female in her 50's*

1712 "Weight is a very personal thing. To me, it's right up there with religion."

Female, early 40's

Spiritual well-being

1713 "[Physical activity, food and eating, and body image] are kind of a good part of who I am. That's the essence of our physical being and well-being. What does that leave? You've got a spiritual well-being on the other side, but you feed that a little different."

Female, 50ish

1714 "Our family . . . socializes around the TV. . . . We like to laugh together and comment together, and . . . we use TV to do that, a lot of times more than conversation. . . . TV is on . . . when we come home, and when we go to bed the TV finally goes off. We'll get involved in this show or that show or some movie, and . . . that will take the place of doing other stuff that we should be doing." *Female, 40ish*

1715 "My husband really enjoys TV, . . . especially since he's so physically active all day. So . . . that's kind of where we are if we want to spend time with him. And I'm not going to tell him to turn off the TV, 'cause he's an adult."
Female, 40ish

1716 "I wish they would spend as much time and money advertising good nutrition, exercise, and body image as they do some of the . . . vices they [show] . . . on TV." *Male, early 50's*

1717 "We love to make popcorn and watch a movie, and it's kind of like a family gathering thing. The popcorn is an addition to the warm and fuzzy of everybody getting together." *Female, late 30's*

1718 "I have no concept of being full. I eat until it's gone. But that's improved over the last couple of years. . . . I just liked eating. And it went along with watching TV. They go together, you know." *Male, late 30's*

Growing up in front of the television set

1719 "Get rid of the television if you have kids. . . . The failure rate [for diets] is like 90% for people who lose a lot of weight. People like me. They just get it all back. The failure rate is just staggering. . . . Just keep your kids away from the TV because it's really an insidious influence, and I still watch too much TV. . . . It's easy to plunk [kids] down there in front of the tube. . . . [TV] became such an important part of my life. When you're kind of a loner, it's a bizarre form of human contact. You feel like you're a part of something. You're not, of course, but you feel like you are. So, . . . it's very easy to abuse TV. I still love sitting in front of the tube and having something to eat. . . . I love doing it. . . . I don't even have a kitchen table in my house. Right before I came, . . . I had a sandwich in front of the TV, watching the news. [In front of the TV] is just kind of where I grew up." *Male, late 30's*

235

Conclusion

We hope the quotations you have read from the people whose lives and voices are illuminated on the pages of this book help you better understand yourself, your clients, or even family members and friends. Perhaps some of our impressions may add to what you have already gained.

Body image. After reading and rereading the narrative transcripts many times, we think that if we could share only one message the focus of that message would be the importance of addressing body image when promoting healthy lifestyles related to physical activity and food and eating. Many of the quotations in this book represent ways in which behaviors associated with eating and physical activity are inextricably tied to attitudes about body image. These life stories clearly illustrate why health promotion efforts that focus on healthy eating and active living but ignore respect for body-size diversity will likely fail. A number of our interviewees attributed their reluctance or failure to engage in regular physical activity to stares and rude comments from others. They also described their own feelings of uneasiness and even dread when trying to be active in public places, given our thin-obsessed culture. In addition, we found that most of the stories about losing weight had much more to do with trying to become a smaller dress size and pants size than with trying to live a healthier, more fulfilling life. Furthermore, several individuals, in describing a futile quest to reach an unrealistic body size, discussed their long-standing struggle with food. Rather than seeing food as a precious and nourishing gift to be savored and enjoyed, they viewed it as a fattening enemy with which they were destined to have a lifelong battle.

Another powerful theme related to body image that emerged is the difference between *looking* healthy versus *being* healthy. Within the growing culture of virtual or hyper-reality, where bodies are surgically sculpted and images are air-brushed to perfection, the vast majority of real or natural bodies are seen as flawed and unacceptable at best, objects of disgust and ridicule at worst. Contemporary society and especially the mass media consistently and relentlessly equate thinness with good health, but many of the life stories shared with us belie this stereotype. For example, one woman had lost weight due to her battle with cancer. Another women feared for the health of her friend who smoked cigarettes as a weight-control technique. One man shared his life story of always having been underweight due to constant stomach ailments as a child. Many stories also involved slender individuals being teased and ridiculed. Although this may seem somewhat ironic in a culture that worships thinness, it is consistent with our earlier assertion that real bodies are seen as flawed and unacceptable. In contrast, we view respect for all body types as essential for developing healthy and enjoyable lifestyles.

Dieting. Although the foundational oath in the field of medicine is to do no harm, the multitude of weight-loss diets, schemes, and scams that bombard

Americans every year fail to meet this most basic standard. One man we interviewed said he started dieting when he reached 250 pounds and "dieted my way up to 350 pounds." A woman described becoming so hungry on diets she would binge and "clear out the cupboards and the refrigerator." Another woman described how she viewed food as an enemy for several days prior to weighing in at her group diet meeting, and then after being weighed she would overeat. Some of the most powerful stories shared with us are related to dieting and disordered eating, whether from a food perspective or a body-image perspective. Insights from these quotations can lead the way toward healthy eating where food is enjoyed and eating is not a guilt-ridden experience. For example, one woman who had suffered from an eating disorder identified the turning point in her life: she "let go of worrying what everybody else thought" about how she should look and concluded, "I'm at peace . . . . It's not a fight . . . with food."

Individuality. Another take-home message from the quotations in this book is the importance of recognizing individual differences when it comes to ways of eating and being physically active that are both healthy and pleasurable. A one-size-fits-all approach is no way to effectively promote healthy, enjoyable lifestyles. For some people, an hour at a gym brings great satisfaction, and to others it is a boring waste of time or, as one man described the experience, like "a rat in a cage" and "staring at a wall." Some individuals want to build physical activity into life's everyday tasks (for example, take the stairs, walk the dog, mow the lawn, chop wood, mop the floor) while others see their daily run as personal meditation time. Some people love certain vegetables, which in turn other people can't stand. Some people eat three meals a day while others eat several smaller meals throughout the day. The road to well-being can be wide enough so everyone has the room to develop their own healthy eating and physical activity habits that they truly enjoy. That road also must include genuine respect for diverse body types.

Power of others. Many interviewees shared stories illustrating how other people can have profound and lifelong influences—both positive and negative—on how individuals feel about their own bodies and physical abilities. Instances of such influence extended from childhood memories right up to the present and include an array of people, from family members and close friends to acquaintances and even strangers. This power of other people to shape an individual's identity and affect her or his self-esteem can be seen clearly in terms of how interviewees' feelings of self-worth and competence, both essential aspects of self-esteem, have been influenced by the words and actions of those around them.

Values. As principles, standards, or qualities considered worthwhile or desirable, values have emerged as a salient theme. A person's values reflect what that individual considers important or significant. The Protestant ethic is one example of a value system that permeates much of American culture. Two components of this value system, productivity and frugality (or avoiding wastefulness), have prominent places in experiences shared by a number of participants. For example, some individuals said they felt physical activity was a waste of time unless the effort was productive, for instance, chopping wood, cleaning floors, raking leaves, walking to do errands, etc. Frugality in relation to food was exemplified best by the "clean-plate" approach to eating. Many individuals, from young adults to seniors, related stories of the importance of eating everything on their plates. One male said that when he was growing up there was some sense of honor in his household associated with finishing all the food on his plate.

The journey forward. We believe interventions to promote healthy and enjoyable lifestyles are more likely to be successful if they address the previously described themes and other noteworthy patterns. Many of the materials developed through the WIN the Rockies project have incorporated or been inspired by what our interviewees have told us. To access these materials, go to www.uwyo.edu/wintherockies. If you would like to share your experiences or your reactions to this book, please send an e-mail to voices-be-heard@uwyo.edu or a letter to Voices Be Heard, University of Wyoming, Family & Consumer Sciences, Dept. 3354, 1000 E. University Ave., Laramie, WY 82071. Feel free to send comments anonymously, but you can also include your name and contact information if you would like to do so. (We would not circulate or publish any communication from an identified source without first securing written permission.)

We welcome any thoughts you would like to send. Let *your* voice be heard.

Betty Holmes
Suzanne Pelican
Fred Vanden Heede

Appendix

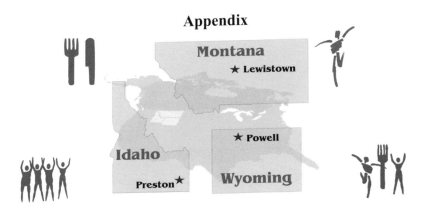

Let their voices be heard
Categories for organizing quotations

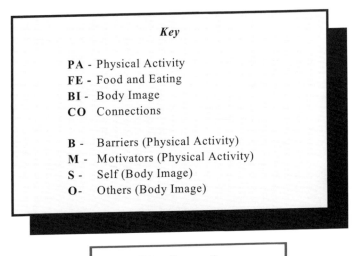

Key

PA - Physical Activity
FE - Food and Eating
BI - Body Image
CO   Connections

B -   Barriers (Physical Activity)
M -   Motivators (Physical Activity)
S -   Self (Body Image)
O-   Others (Body Image)

CO - Connections

Physical activity and food/eating
Physical activity and body image
Food/eating and body image
Physical activity, food/eating, and body image
Education - how educational experiences impacted a person's life or
                references to desired educational information
Spiritual - references to faith, spirituality, the Bible, sacredness of
                the body, etc.
Television - impact of television on lifestyle

PA - Definition

PA - Definition

PA - Type/Routine

PA - Barriers

PAB - Weather/Seasons

PAB - Time

PAB - Illness/Injury/Disability

PAB - Pain/Discomfort
includes pregnancy

PAB - Tired/Fatigued
includes physical inability due to weight, getting out of breath, and mental fatigue

PAB - Fear of Injury/Safety

PAB - Lack of Skills
includes loss of skills/abilities

PAB - Teasing/Criticism

PAB - Self-consciousness

PAB - Boring/Not Enjoyable

PAB - No Results

PAB - No Support

PAB - Vehicles

PAB - Depression/Mental health

PA - Motivators

PAM - Friends/Others
includes dogs and farm animals

PAM - Teamwork/Unity

PAM - Enjoyment
includes play and no pain; also includes references to runner's high

PAM - Energy
includes mental energy/alertness

PAM - Sweat

PAM - Strength/Fitness
includes toned, getting in shape

PAM - Skills/Physical Abilities

PAM - Productive/Accomplishment

PAM - Health/Prevention

PAM - Anti-aging

PA - Motivators (continued)

PAM - Mental Health/Emotions
includes relieving stress, sleeping better

PAM - Self-confidence/Self-esteem
includes earning the respect/acceptance of others

PAM - Appearance

PAM - Weight Control

PAM - Outdoors
includes hunting

PAM - Feel Better After
descriptions of PA helping person to feel better after activity, but not during activity

PAM - Solitude/Time for Self
includes time to think and doing something for self

PA - Individual

Individual traits/experiences/ views associated with physical activity

PA - Attitudes
attitudes toward physical activity, including attitude shifts and feelings of guilt for taking time for self

PA - Discipline/Motivation

PA - Priority/Balance
includes need to rest/relax

PA - Experiences from Youth
includes school and coaches; also includes college PE and athletics

PA - Sore Muscles

PA - Extreme
physical activity that controls a person's life; extreme sports

PA - Lingering Effects

Factors that impact or are related to a person's activity level or abilities

PA - Family

PA - Personality
how personality affects physical activity

PA - Competition

PA - Age
age-associated factors and life-stage changes/factors that influence PA (e.g., marriage); also includes fear of not being able to be physically active

PA - Gender

PA - Strenuous
references to strenuous nature of PA

PA - Facilities/Equipment

PA - Media

PA - Smoking

PA - Work/Occupation
includes housework

PA - Medical
includes doctor's advice to increase PA and medical problems not acted on

PA - Other Environmental
includes changes in society, availability of stairs, etc.

FE - Food and Eating Codes

FE - Enjoyment of eating and comfort foods

FE - Enjoyment

FE - Comfort
includes fighting boredom

FE - Dysfunctional eating

FE - Dieting
experiences with dieting to lose weight, relates to the "how"

FE - Undereating
undereating not tied to dieting

FE - Overeating
references to overeating and binge eating, includes buffets

FE - Clean Plate
ideas associated with finishing everything on your plate

FE - Impulsive Eating

FE - Food Pushers
references to individuals, organizations, military, etc., that push food on a person

FE - Eating Disorders

FE - Personal experiences with eating

FE - Childhood Experiences

FE - Relationship with Food

FE - Ethnic Influences

FE - Self-control/Hunger Cues
includes lack of control over eating

FE - Emotions/Feelings
includes guilt associated with eating

FE - Illness/Medical Disorders

FE - Food Preferences

FE - Strategies
strategies for eating

FE - New Foods
attitudes toward trying new foods

FE - Negative
negative experiences associated with food

FE - Eating to Gain Weight

FE - Gives Energy

FE - Reward

FE - Factors/beliefs associated with eating and food choices

FE - Health/Nutrition
includes eating a variety of foods and health problems from poor eating habits

FE - Ideals/Goals
includes goal of eating healthier sometime in the future

FE - Lack of Time/Energy

FE - Work/Occupation

FE - Cost
issues related to cost of food

FE - Cooking

FE - Portion Size/Who Portions

FE - Doesn't Care/Waste of Time

FE - Gardening
impact of gardening on eating

FE - Atmosphere/Setting

FE - Other Environmental
includes seasonal variations in eating patterns and larger societal influences

FE - Age
includes fear about not being able to eat in the future as one does now, how the body handles food differently with age, and changes in caloric needs

FE - Smoking

FE - Factors/beliefs associated with eating and food choices (cont.)

FE - Medical
changes in eating as result of advice from doctor

FE - Eating patterns

FE - Meals
size, frequency, timing, etc.

FE - Snacking

FE - Beverages

FE - Fast Foods

FE - Restaurants

FE - Speed
quickness or slowness of eating

FE - Influence of/over others

FE - Eating in Public

FE - Family/Parents

FE - Parenting

FE - Competition for Food

FE - Friends/Peers

FE - Eating Alone
includes hiding when eating

FE - Socializing
eating related to sharing time with others

FE - Rebellion

BI - Body Image Codes

BI - Self

BIS - Satisfaction
includes acceptance of self

BIS - Dissatisfaction

BIS - Struggles

BIS - Perception of Appearance
not satisfaction or dissatisfaction

BIS - Hinders Activities
includes intimacy

BIS - How Viewed by Others

BI - Self (continued)

BIS - Comparison to Others
includes fear of becoming like others; also includes being envious of others

BI - Others

BIO - Thin

BIO - Heavy

BIO - Short/Tall

BI - Others (continued)

BIO - Acceptance

BIO - Pity/Sympathy/Compassion
includes fighting/sticking up for others and concerns for others' health

BIO - Nonacceptance
includes observing people not accepting others

BIO - How Others Present Self

BIO - Stereotypes
includes size discrimination

BIO - Race/Ethnicity

BI - Weight/size/shape

BI - Weight/Size/Shape

BI - Battle to Control Weight

BI - Dieting
relates to the "why"

BI - Smoking

BI - Other factors

BI - Teasing/Criticism

BI - Praise/Verbal Support

BI - Family/Parents

BI - Peers/Friends

BI - Age
includes changes in body shape over time, including maturation

BI - Gender

BI - Other factors (continued)

BI - Genetics

BI - Having Children

BI - Media/Society

BI - Other Environmental
examples: chairs are too small, differences between big city vs. small town, financial well-being, and problems finding clothes that fit

BI - Medical

BI - Psychological

BI - Mental Health/Emotions/ Feelings
includes thoughts about body image being "all consuming"

BI - Happiness
beliefs about body size and impact on happiness

BI - Changes in Perception
changes in body image perceptions over time, including the process

BI - Weight as a Shield

BI - Search for a Mate

BI - Health

BI - Health/Wellness

Index

Boldface type references page numbers. All other numbers reference individual entries.

1615, 1650
Buchanan, David, **viii**
buffets, **81–82,** 826, 837, 874, 978,
1188
bulimia. *see* eating disorders
bullying, 455. *see also* teasing
bustline, 1383, 1389
busyness, 45, 46, 128, 354, 355, 900,
929, 975

C
cabin fever, 256
caffeine, 954
calories, **ii, v**
camping, 517, 723
cancer, 27, 709
candy, 707
carbohydrates, 1040
cardiac therapy, 459, 498
chairs, 1547–1549
challenge, 423, 1354
chemotherapy, 709, 1650
childbearing, **204,** 383, 510, 1416,
1466, 1653
childhood, **48–50, 89–90,** 103, 349,
360, 399, 518, 525, 534, 607,
611, 621, 784, 893, 995, 1030,
1543
children, 11, 82, 243, 278, 289, 343,
344, 355, 397, 400, 403, 410,
411, 437, 445, 619, 622, 765,
800, 1020, 1288, 1361, 1419,
1425, 1591, 1697, 1719
  embarrassed by parents, 598, 1166,
1171, 1231, 1296, 1426–1429
chin-ups, 372
chocolate, 629, 631, 749, 944
choices, 173, 633, 1024, 1027, 1705
cholesterol, 330, 504, 919
chores, household, 17, 507
circuit training, 118, 452
clean plate, **ii, 83–85, 239,** 694, 748,
749, 780, 840, 869, 875, 879,
880, 1025, 1028, 1030

clothes, 271, 273, 1095, 1100, 1106,
1109, 1125, 1389, 1418, 1543,
1550–1555. *see also* shopping,
clothes
clumsiness. *see* coordination
coaches, 361, 368, 1704
coffee, 335, 723, 785
college, 12, 249, 343, 344, 905, 930,
974, 1646. *see also* Freshman 15
(pounds)
comfort, 1078
commitment, 160, 161, 194, 328,
337, 1679
communities, 1546, 1705
companionship, 163
comparing self to others, 113, 115,
161–162, 577, 1084, 1434, 1643,
1646
compassion, **171–172,** 1308, 1392,
1565
competition, 12, 55, **56–57,** 364, 418
for food, **140**
compliments, 1154, 1160, 1173,
1368, 1404, 1406, 1410
computers, 507
conditioning, 367, 368, 482, 820,
1633, 1704
confidence, **37,** 206, 1123, 1175,
1298, 1431, 1577
contentedness, 1125, 1127, 1573,
1601, 1661
convenience foods, 806, 808, 842
cooking, **116–118,** 522, 553, 732,
812, 846, 852, 863, 1019
  men and, 843, 844, 848, 849, 854,
859–862, 865
coordination, 95, 97, 100, 102, 107,
373, 377, 1382
cosmetic surgery, 1539
cost, **114–115,** 466, 468, 473, 977
couch potatoes, 7, 336, 1682
cravings, 546, 696, 730, 731, 949
Crawford, Cindy, 101, 1598
criticism, **15, 186–190,** 1399, 1433,

meat and potatoes, 722, 793

media, **63, 205–206, 237,** 903, 1057, 1060, 1067, 1194,1315, 1563, 1669, 1670, 1684

medical profession, **66,** 502, 921, 922, 1569. *see also* doctors

medication, 719

meditation, 1556

menopause, 695, 1441, 1680

mental health, **20, 35–36, 211–212,** 1227, 1626, 1681

mental strength, 210

mental war, 1127, 1180, 1573, 1601

metabolism, 695, 725, 1200, 1272, 1332, 1441, 1509, 1680

military service, 46, 60, 138, 311, 343, 495–497, 638, 639, 1135, 1189, 1628

  basic training, 212, 820, 1598, 1633

milk, 729, 951

Mills, C. Wright, **ii**

models, 1529, 1533, 1534, 1668

moderation, 747, 749, 755, 788, 1629

money, wasting, 825, 837

mothers. *see* parents

motion, range of, 202

motivators, self/others, 1676

mowing, 222

muscles, 1467–1479, 1485, 1492, 1522, 1593

  soreness, **51**

N

nagging, 1065

narratives, **i, vi–vii**

nervous breakdown, 578

nutrition, **109–110**

nutrition education, **viii, 232–233,** 1695

O

obesity, **ii,** 670, 1057, 1178, 1280, 1565, 1582, 1663

open-mindedness, 144

Optifast, 545, 1564

overeating, **80–82,** 519, 628, 1064, 1221

overexertion, 88, 388, 391, 458

P

packaging, **ii**

pain, **10,** 237, 277, 322, 384, 388, 446, 1321. *see also* discomfort

parenting, **138–139,** 946

parents, **135–137, 193–194,** 411

  influence of, 402, 573, 1697

  single, 248, 259, 343, 344, 833

pastries, 590, 790

peer pressure, 547, 1266

peers, **140, 195,** 1192

perception, changes in, **214–215**

perceptions of others, **158–160**

perfectionism, 99

personality, **55,** 747

  introvert/extrovert, 416

  Type A, 385, 412, 1137

pets, 30, 442, 698

phen-fen, 550, 1353, 1566, 1618

physical activity. *see also* sports

  avoidance of, 76, 95, 107, 1382

  barriers to, **6–20**

  definitions of, **3–4**

  as emotional outlet/release, 249, 253, 259, 304

  enjoyment of, **24–25,** 301, 302, 309

  extreme, **51**

  level of, 47, 99, 339, 340

  and medical conditions, 498–501, 504, 506

  motivation, **44–45,** 369

  motivators, **21–41**

  outdoor, **39**

  seasonal, **6**

  skills, **29**

    lack of, **14,** 107

  strenuous, **61**

  time for, **7**